||||||||||||||||||||||||||||||||||||||||||||||||||||||||||||||

More Than One Goal

||||||||||||||||||||||||||||||||||||||||||||||||||||||||||||||||||

Mark D'Ambrogi

Published by Salt Water Media
29 Broad Street, Suite 104
Berlin, MD 21811
www.saltwatermedia.com

Cover image provided by the author and courtesy of Jay Elliott and background by unsplash.com user marjanblan; overall design by Salt Water Media

Contact the author at morethanonegoal@gmail.com for questions or inquiries.

||||||||||||||||||||||||||||||||||||||||||||||||||||||||||||||||||||||

MORE THAN ONE GOAL

||||||||||||||||||||||||||||||||||||||||||||||||||||||||||||||||||||||||||

To Cleta,
you always knew how to take a human
and shape them into a soul.

|||||||||||||||||||||||||||||||||||||||||||||||||||||||||||||

PROLOGUE

|||||||||||||||||||||||||||||||||||||||||||||||||||||||||||||||||

It is night in Baltimore late July 1982, hot, humid and dark everywhere but under the stadium lights. The game is about to begin and I have to be ready. The United States is about to play Australia for the Lacrosse World Games championship and I am on the end line, ball boy, ready for anything that comes my way. The United States has been crushing everyone in the tournament but this game feels different. During the earlier games against Canada, England, or the Iroquois, the US team has been much looser, smiling more and talking a lot. In this game, everybody has his game face on. Their eyes are narrow and everything they're doing in warm-ups is at full speed. These guys are fast, big and when they miss the goal, shoot it all the way back to the fence at Homewood Field. There are no nets behind the goal, just straight to the fence.

We work during warmups. That's how you earn your keep. The game is a reward for keeping the balls coming back to the shooters. As a ballboy, you make it your duty to get the ball back fast. And tonight, these guys have been firing hard. And a lot. We don't wear helmets, so we have to keep our heads up, making sure we don't get hit. These guys in the red, white and blue look to me like the greatest lacrosse team I have ever seen. I'm thirteen years old.

Up until now, the best lacrosse I've ever seen is the club championships played every year at Homewood Field on the campus of JHU, where we are tonight. Club lacrosse is where former college players play. They are sponsored teams and they just love to play. And in lacrosse, the very best players like to play together. In the club lacrosse championships, it's always either Mt. Washington or Maryland Lacrosse Club from Baltimore against Long Island Hofstra from New York. The games are classics every year with awesome plays the whole game, big physical defensemen flying around and clearing the crease. The score is always something like 20–19 or 23–21. A lot of those players are here tonight on the same team and ready to fire. That team is Team USA. This is going to be cool.

As long as you stand still with your hand over your heart during the national anthem, Dave, the guy in charge of us ball boys, won't bother you the whole game. If Dave comes over, you're done for the day. So I make sure to stand still. I'm sweating like a pig but that makes it even better. There's a game to be played.

Australia is pumped up and yelling. The Aussies sound so funny with all their accents. It's hard to understand exactly what they're saying because they use crazy expressions. It's clear their team is here to win. They yell, "Good on yah!" or "That was a bloody rippah!"and talk about being "stoked" or "buggered." The United States team is stoic and focused. Their precision and skills bring them to an 11–5 halftime lead.

I look to the crowd and the stands are still pretty full. I think they're ready for the second half. Everyone has spent the pre-game tailgating in the International Village partying, having a great time. It looks like the crowd is filling back up and they're getting reloaded. Everyone over eighteen has a drink in hand. It looks like so much fun and I am so far away from anything like that, in my collared shirt and white shoes.

Now I look back at the goal and players are scattered, chasing their misses to the fence and into the corners of the field. I've got room to run and four balls in my stick. The key is to hit your first couple shots, and then you aren't chasing during halftime. Four balls should be all it takes. I drop three at the top of the box in the middle and dodge at my imaginary defender. One full-speed run and roll back and shoot lefty, always boring but safe. I hit the goal. Next, a full speed dodge and bounce shot hits the pipe and bounces out. No goal, but I don't lose a ball as it ricochets up top. I always go for the sidearm crank upper corner on the third ball, and this one actually hits it. I even surprise myself when it hits the corner and I think I hear a noise like "OOH." That was cool, so I try another sidearm crank to the corner and it misses. This time I definitely hear the "OOH." Suddenly I realize they are looking at me and I get nervous. As I dig two balls out of the goal and grab the ball that hit the pipe, I have three balls and this end of the field to myself. I take two high bouncers with all my might and another side arm crank that flies over the goal. By the time I have dug out the last two balls from the goal, three or four ball boys are back and taking some bounce shots. It was nice having the field to myself while it lasted and it felt pretty good. JB, my buddy and my fellow ball boy, says he will feed me if I feed him. JB is a year younger than I am and loves lacrosse just like me. We have hung out at pretty much every game.

JB finds three balls and I pass them to him. He has two nice shots then passes to me twice. We keep going like this for about five more minutes until we see the teams come back on the field. It's time to go, so we roll all of the balls we have to the restraining line and head to the fence to gather the rest. We each get two or three, run them back to the field and give them back to the Team USA players.

Each quarter the teams switch sides, so for the first and third quarters Team USA shoots at our end. Team USA looks fired up, but they are not saying anything loud. They are firing at the goal and talking quietly to each other, moving their hands, moving their heads. It looks like they're talking about plays and don't want to say anything the other side can hear. The eyes of every player look intense, aggressive but controlled. This looks like they're going to go up to another level, you can feel it. The air feels still and warm and everyone is sweating—players, fans, everyone.

The second half starts with Doug Radisson to face off and the US gets the ball. With 6:14 showing on the clock in the third quarter, the US players move the ball and move their feet. Everyone on the field is talking as Vinnie Sombratto gets the ball. He runs across the top of the box and looks like he's ready to rip a shot on the run. Instead he throws a pass to Brooks Sweet, who is coming off a pic. Brooks shoots a laser into the bottom corner and the crowd goes nuts. We all jump around like crazy kids and scream as loud as we can. The sweat, the air, the noise—I'm filled with an adrenaline rush that makes this the coolest sporting event in my life. The third quarter ends with the US up 12–7.

For the fourth quarter, we're on the end of the field with the US defense. Australia gets the ball a few times and manages to score five goals. The only problem for the Australian team is that the US scores five also. As the clock runs down to zero, this is what we all came for. All the boys want the chance to run out on the field, jump up and down and act crazy. Instead, I watch the US team celebrate. What takes over me is the realization that these guys celebrate like men, grown-ups. They're hugging, yelling, grabbing each other with all their strength; they would crush us if they lifted us up and squeezed. These guys look even bigger in celebration than they did during the course of play.

It is electric as officials gather all the players, both championship teams and all the other teams to the field. In a final ceremony teams receive gold, silver and bronze medals. The World Lacrosse Committee recognizes the best players of the world at each position as well as the best player in the world. Doug Radisson is a fitting winner.

Eventually, the US team heads into the locker room while we have to pick up all the equipment, sticks, water jugs and balls. Once we get all of the stuff together, we carry it to the locker room. I am not even thinking about the team as I carry a cooler, three helmets on a stick and a bag of balls until I hear them down the hall. The closer we get, the louder it gets, until we walk in and it is a party. A big, sweaty, equipment-stinking, cleats-smelly, beer-soaked party. They are pouring beer on each other and down each other's throats, and it is spilling everywhere. My shoes are soaked with beer now, in addition to sweat. The group of men in this locker room look like the happiest people on earth and it feels special just to be in here.

JB, Roy, Michael Frederick and I stick together and watch. All the sweet red, white, and blue gloves and sticks lie on the ground. We pick them up, try the gloves, hold a stick, and start messing around with a ball. Brooks Sweet and Norm Engelke come over to Roy and me. Norm says to me, "Hey, kid, you can keep the gloves but you aren't taking my stick."

I say, "I'm sorry, is this your stick?" Duh, of course it is. I hand it to him and punch my hands in the air. "Thanks, sir! Thanks!"

Roy gets the same talk from Brooks Sweet, and just like that, we have two sets of smelly, game-worn red, white and blue sweet STX gloves. Unbelievable!

The floodgates open, every ball boy is asking for swag. Meanwhile, Roy and I hold the gloves by the strings, open the palms and put two beers apiece into each glove. Right out of the cooler. Nobody notices a thing and we are loaded down with beer.

We really don't know what to do with this beer, so we head to the International Village, the pre-and post- game party spot for the adults. As we pass by the ticket booth, a small one, an A-framed wooden box. Since nobody was coming back to it tonight, we figure it's a good place to hide our new loot and figure out what to do with it. We unlatch the door and step inside. Each side has a shelf and we stash them there and head to the village to check in with our parents. We find them already surrounded by friends, drinking and smoking and meeting people from England, Australia and the Iroquois Nation. We show them our new gloves and say hi to some other people we know. Everybody is hanging out under a big tent filled with beer and liquor from the home countries. Australians can really drink beer and the Canadians are really fun too. While our parents are distracted, we tell them we want to get something to eat. Each of our parents gives us a couple dollars for food and tells us to be back by ten o'clock.

We're off, looking for JB and Michael and planning what to do with the beer. We figure they will be near the locker room, so we head back there. Both of them are coming out, walking past the ticket booth, holding their equipment haul. JB has arm pads and Michael has the goalie's chest protector. Michael's brother is a really good goalie in college, so Michael knew he could talk to the USA team's goalie, Tommy Sears. Since Tommy knows Michael's brother, Michael got the chest protector and he has it on, sweaty and all. Our sticks go everywhere with us so we have to look hysterical— four kids all in stained tennis shirts, sweating like crazy, two of us with gloves, one in arm pads and one with an adult chest protector down to his knees.

We get JB and Michael to walk down the street and we tell them about the beers, eight of them, two for each of us. They're psyched so we decide to make a plan. Michael will be the lookout and Roy and I will get the beers and head to the JHU practice field. Nobody will be back there and we can sit on the far bleachers and drink them. Each of us has tasted beer, but this is the first time I will try to drink two by myself in one night. I don't like the taste of beer, but I want to have as much fun as the players, and if drinking beer is what it takes, I'm willing to go for it.

By the time we run to the far side bleachers, we have it all worked out. Roy has bubble gum to mask the smell of beer, a plan to sleep over at Michael's, an escape route from the bleachers if security guards show up. We're ready.

We take the beers out from the gloves and put them on the bleachers. Everybody grabs one, and we laugh and joke as we pop the tabs, as happy as we have ever been in our lives. Beer sprays all over us. These cans have been shaken up for the last 150 yards at full speed. We try to jump out of the way and not drop our beer, but we're all soaked and smell like beer now. We do not have a plan for that, so I make up a story that we can use. "Guys in the locker room were spraying beer all over the place and we got wet," I say, "that should work, don't you think?"

We "cheers" with our half-full beers and start to work on getting drunk. We talk about girls, lacrosse games, school, parents, music, the beach —everything kids in eighth grade talk about. Life is good. Roy and I decide to tell JB and Michael our story about lacrosse camp:

My uncle coaches lacrosse for the University of Maryland, and Roy and I just came back from camp last week. Since Roy and I went for free, we had to run the snack bar for the campers when we were not doing camp sessions. That means Roy and I had to be open from eleven to noon, three to five in the afternoon, and nine to ten at night. We got good at selling candy and drinks, bartering equipment for snacks, and making money for the camp. Every shift, one of the head counselors or my uncle would come by and take the cash out, leaving us with twenty five dollars for change.

I loved the guys from Long Island, they were funny as heck. They would all try to get Roy and me to agree on some crazy offer like one stick for a box of Snickers (no way) but they were funny about it. They wanted six Snickers bars for a string kit, traditional, with brown leathers. I told them I had to show cash, so I could trade Snickers and two Gatorades for two bucks and the string kit. I thought it was a good deal, plus one of the guys from Long Island was good at stringing sticks. I offered to hook him up with a Snickers, Gatorade and a bag of Doritos for stringing my stick. I cut the old strings out and it is now a sweet stick, white Sam Head, new pocket, two new stops on the throat. It is leaning against the bleacher right now with a new wood shaft I picked up from the Maryland locker room after the season one day, taped up just right.

But the real reason we bring up the camp, Roy and I, is to tell the other two the fire alarm story: One day on our way to dinner with two Long Island guys, Roy dared me to pull the fire alarm in the hallway. As soon as he dared me, I felt a rush of adrenaline flood over me. Instead of saying, no I shouldn't, I said, "No, I dare *you*." Roy said, "No, but I double dare *you*." The adrenaline kicked in again as we approached the alarm. "If anyone says anything, I am going to blame you guys," I said to all three .

I put my hand on the red lever and pulled down, and as soon as I did, the sound of the alarm took over the building, louder than any fire alarm I have ever heard. We took off running. We ran down the steps to the first floor and out the exit door and sprinted to the Student Union. Why, I don't know, but I was the fastest and I figured the cops wouldn't be looking for us there. Once there, we sat on some chairs and a sofa and freaked out. I couldn't believe how fast that alarm went off. I couldn't believe we did it. I couldn't believe I did it... *that's right, I did it.* I started to panic. I did it, and I can get in real trouble for this. The two New York guys were talking about getting arrested, going to jail, having a record. One of the guys from Long Island, Lenny, told me that they could dust for fingerprints on the lever and I knew I was done. *I am going to be locked up by the cops and my parents are going to kill me.* I didn't know what I could do to stop either one.

We waited for about twenty more minutes and walked to the cafeteria for dinner, and I was scared the whole time that someone was going to call my name. We ate and went back to the dorm and started to get ready for the night session. There was a buzz in the rooms and the hallways. Suddenly the fire alarm screamed out, and just like that, panic came back, big time.

As we headed out the doors, a fire engine and four firemen loomed into view. I almost threw up when I saw them. One of the firemen yelled at all the campers to line up single file facing the truck, all 231 of us. I knew the camper enrollment number by keeping my ears open around the lacrosse office. I lined up next to

Roy. The two Long Island guys, Lenny and Carlo, were down the line but I looked over at them and their faces were blank. Roy looked at me and I was sure he could see fear. I was scared, fully, head to toe, but I tried not to show it.

The fire chief started walking down the line. "Whoever pulled the fire alarm made a big mistake, he committed a federal offense, he put people's lives in danger, and he is in big trouble." He looked at each one of us, so once I saw him walking towards me, I was ready. I stood as still as I could, but my knees were quaking. I didn't want to drop to my knees but I felt like I might. "If we find out who did this, we are going to come back and string him upside down by his feet and leave him there for everybody to see." I felt a punch in the gut without anyone touching me. He reached the end of the line then turned back our way. "Don't any of you get the idea to do this again. We have lives to save. You have cost the city money, sent us out of our way and possibly screwed up a real fire rescue. We do not, I repeat, do not have time to be messing with kids."

As he finished, one of the coaches yelled, "Everybody to the fields!" and guys grabbed their gear and headed out. I saw my uncle, Dino, in the middle of all the people still standing in front of the dorm. I slowly walked over to the group of coaches and said, "Dino, can I talk to you for a second?"

"Yeah, just hold on for one minute." Once he'd finished telling the coaches what to do for the night session, he came over to me. I'm not sure what he expected me to say, but I don't think he expected this.

As soon as I started to confess, I broke down in sobs. "It was me that pulled the fire alarm, and I am sorry I'm such an idiot, and I don't want to get arrested and I'm so scared." He looked at me with stern eyes and told me that I messed up and it could have been very bad for him and for me. I kept saying sorry between sobs and he put his hand on my shoulder. "I don't want to be sent home, I don't want to get anyone in trouble," I told him.

"Mark, Mark, it's going to be okay, you screwed up, but I'm not going to send you home, I am not going to tell your parents, but you have to quit crying. And—you can never do something like this again." It's not like I felt any better about doing something stupid like pulling the fire alarm, but it did feel better to know I wouldn't get in too much trouble for it. Too bad that I cried like a baby.

My fire alarm story finished, I look around at my three buddies. "Even though I know how, I don't think I'm going to pull any fire alarms for awhile, unless there is a real fire," I tell Roy, JB and Michael. We all laugh and drink. The first beer is down, and I take my time opening the next one. No spill, so I take a huge swig. This one doesn't taste any better. I look around and everybody looks the same, sour-mouthed and unsure. Unsure about how it is going to make us feel, unsure of how drunk one-and-a-half beers will get us, unsure of what is going to happen next. One thing we know, we definitely can not get caught by our parents.

All of us take turns telling more stories, taking big swings, and making bets. Who can hold their breath the longest? Who can hold a one handed push-up the longest? Who can drink on one leg? If this is what it feels like to be an adult, it feels good.

We hang out for I don't know how long, but we know that we have to head back before anybody is looking for us. We take the empty cans to the woods behind the gym, bury them under some leaves, and head back to the International Lacrosse Village. Michael and Roy want to go back to the locker room on the way. We walk in and it's empty. No players, no coaches, equipment and clothes all over the place, empty cans and champagne bottles on the floor, tape bags of ice, everything strewn. The best part of the leftovers was the coolers with a few beers left in each one. All of us check out the hallway and the equipment room and decide to split two beers to make up for the spilled ones. We grab two. I open one and chug the first half. It's cold as ice and it finally tastes good, cold and strong. The burp that follows takes away any good flavor, tastes sour and burns my nose. This must be the taste of Budweiser. I hand the second half to Roy. Michael starts his and JB finishes it off. We look at each other and we all just start yelling "This is awesome!" We echo through the room, take off down the hallway and out the double doors. As we hit the hot, still night air and head to the village, I feel the beer in my muscles. I feel loose now in my head, where I am high, happy and excited.

I've been watching my brothers, my cousins, my friends' older brothers having this kind of fun for a while now and this is my first crack at it. I'm definitely ready for more. We've almost pulled this off. We ask our parents if we can sleep at Michael's house. We can walk to his house from JHU and keep this party going. Chewing our cover-up gum, we walk into the village and notice that the party is still going strong. Australians are chanting and singing their songs, English players and their families are doing the same, and the Canadians are laughing with all of them. The world is united in lacrosse. I realize suddenly that we can stay here, there's no reason to leave. This is a big time party and we can have more fun right here.

A little while later we get the green light for a sleepover at Michael's house and we separate from our parents. On our own, at a big time party, with a buzz on–this feels like total freedom. It has to be at least eleven o'clock and we trade some English kids for their shirts. They take the USA Lacrosse shirts and we get some England Lacrosse shirts, which smell as bad as ours, but we made new friends when we traded with them. The English kids know three Australian kids, so we all hang out at the Australia tent and talk about music, lacrosse, school. The Australian music is The Bee Gees and Abba, the English kids like the Beatles and The Who. We all like The Rolling Stones and The Jackson Five. Their accents make us laugh the whole time. The tent has a keg of beer in it and no adults, so we take turns filling up cups and chugging in the back of the tent. This is cool, a chance to party into the night.

Eventually, and because there are no girls, we say goodbye to our new friends and start home, stumbling, numb and exhausted. We have a half-mile through a neighborhood to Michael's basement. Sticks in hand, two balls, new gloves, a chest protector, new shirts, hats we found, pins we traded for, bumper stickers—we cleaned up with souvenirs. We have scored, big time. Since Michael's parents weren't at the games and it's late, they're asleep when we get there. We take ourselves and our stuff and crash in the basement.

The summer before eighth grade is turning out to be a good one.

III

CHAPTER 01

IIIIIIIIIIIIIIIIIIIIIIIIIIIIIIIIIIIIIIIIIIIIIIIIIIIIIIIIIIIIIIIIII

It's 1983, the spring of my freshman year at St. Xavier High School, where the academics have picked up incredibly. I have at least two hours and sometimes three hours of homework a night. I have gone from being taught by nuns and laywomen to being taught by priests and laymen in all my classes. Mr. Mathias was the only male teacher in grade school and now it is all men all the time—Brother Ron for biology, Father McDonald for history, Father Joseph for Latin, Mr. Stevens for English, Mr. Gerard for math—even the librarians are men. It's way tougher. I am struggling in school, but I am not the only one, everybody seems to be struggling in school. The pace of the school day is intense, and it makes you work. The mantra of the school, the main goal the Jesuit priests strive for is turning the students into "Men for Others." By the time we finish high school, they want us to think of others first and serve those that are less fortunate. And, let me tell you, they beat you down with it, in a good way, in a tough love way. The Jesuits make you think of others, and your impact on others: your classmates, your teammates, your fellow man. All of this and two plus hours of homework each day make me realize that this is not even close to being as easy as the Cathedral School.

My brother Thomas is a freshman at Washington College, so I have my own room while he's away. Thomas didn't tell me about all the homework I was going to have this year.

I'm doing pretty well in lacrosse. I'm one of the only freshmen starting on JV, and our record is 8–1 so far. We lost to Brice Academy in the second game of the year and we're now on a seven-game winning streak. I'm the second leading scorer on the team at this point, but we still have four more games left on the schedule. If we win all of them, we'll play Brice Academy in the finals. I have a couple friends on BL and I know we can beat them, but their goalie is a new kid and he is good. I have never played against him before. He transferred in from Annapolis. As a freshman, I am not a leader on the team or a guy that can tell anybody what to do, but I try to be the best player and teammate on the team. I figure if I try to lead the team in points and ground balls, the coaches will see me as an important piece of the team. I got that advice from my grandfather, Pop, Henry Corrigan.

Pop has told me a lot of things over the years, but it seems different since Thomas went off to college. Now, I'm the only male grandchild in Baltimore, so Pop is always asking me about school and sports. He used to talk to Thomas about these things, but now it seems he wants to know more about me and my teams.

Pop is about the coolest grandfather in the world, in case you didn't know. He is tall, thin, always in a coat and tie, often with an unlit cigar in his mouth. He talks to people wherever we go and he has a good story about everything. He tells me stories about him as a kid, about our uncles, about his friends and his friends' kids. In the last six months since Thomas left, Pop has taken me to the race track to bet on horses, to play golf, to a bar, to church, to a friend's house, to my cousin Hugh's house an hour away, to watch college lacrosse games, all over town. I can tell Pop anything. He gives me advice and he never tells my mom.

Tomorrow, I need to wake up early to get dropped off at school because Mom has things to do. I turn the light off, looking forward to my game against St. John's, against Roy and his school friends.

When the game ends 11–5 St. Xavier, I line up to shake hands with the St. Paul's team. I had two goals and one assist and played pretty well. It helped that Charlie Malone moved up to long stick middie and covered our best freshman middie, Greg. Charlie held Greg scoreless, took the ball away from him a couple of times and generally made Greg's day miserable. I didn't care because we just won 11–5 and I had three points. Roy played well with two goals and his buddy Timmy Shaeffer had the other three goals for St. Paul's.

As I slap Roy five in the handshake line and say "good game," I see Greg kind of palm Charlie's face and push. Charlie rocks back and pushes Greg in the back of his head as both keep moving in opposite directions. Two guys later, as Charlie passes me, he asks, "What is his problem?"

"He acts like a dick sometimes," I say. "Don't worry about him, you played good."

Greg always acts like a baby when he doesn't play well. He is the most obnoxious guy in the world when he plays well but he is a dick when he doesn't, even when we win.

After the huddle with the team, everybody always goes over and talks to his parents and family, friends, whoever came to the game. As soon as I see my mom and dad, I can tell something is wrong. Usually, they're smiling, happy for me and the team, but today, the smiles are fake, I can tell.

Mom says to me, "Great job, honey. I talked to your coach before the game, you aren't riding the bus. You and Mary are coming with me."

"What about Dad?" I ask.

"I'm going to pick up Lauren from practice and I'll meet you," Dad says.

"Where are we going?" I ask.

"We have to go to the hospital to see your grandfather," Mom says.

"What's he doing at the hospital?"

"After I dropped you off at school this morning, I picked your grandfather up at the house and took him to get a procedure done at the hospital," she said. "He's still there and we need to go see him."

By this time, we're getting into Mom's station wagon. Mary has somehow already gotten my book bag and I throw my it and my equipment in the back of the car, get in and close the door.

"Is Pop going to be okay?" I ask.

"Mark, I am not sure," Mom says, and I can tell something is definitely wrong.

I walk into St. Joseph's Hospital in my jersey, eyeblack on my face, dirty white socks and brown school shoes. I took my cleats off in the car and I feel now like everyone is staring at my brown shoes. Mary, Mom and I walk up the steps, down a hall, and into a hospital room, where Pop is lying in a bed with tubes in his nose and in his arm. Cleta is sitting in the chair next to him. She looks up at us as we come in and she doesn't say anything. She just gets up and hugs Mary, who looks scared in her school uniform. Cleta looks at me and puts her arm out, wanting me to come in for a hug, too. I lean in halfway. "I'm stinky," I say, " and I don't want to get you dirty."

"Shhh, I don't care about that right now. I just want your grandfather to be okay. You know he loves you kids, he loves you kids a lot."

"I know he does." Her hug gets harder and I feel a Cleta tear on my face. Lauren and Dad walk into the room and I see the fear in Lauren's eyes. She knows something's wrong, too. I step out of Cleta's hug so Lauren can get in. Mary has not loosened her grip on Cleta's waist and I'm not sure she'll ever let go. I look at Mom and Dad, who look helpless, unsure, at a loss for words.

Dad says, "Here's five dollars, why don't you kids go downstairs and get something to eat?"

Mary immediately says, "I want to stay here with Cleta."

"No," Mom says, "all three of you go downstairs while we talk to your grandmother."

"Okay," we say almost in unison, like we practiced it. Now is not the time to be a pain. I look at Pop in his bed. His eyes are closed, his mouth is open, and every once in a while, he breathes short deep breaths, then quiets again. I look at Cleta and Mom and say, "We'll be in the cafeteria," as I hold Mary's hand and head out of the room.

"Did you know Pop was sick?" Lauren asks.

"No, they didn't even tell me he was going into the hospital," I say. Mary is sniffling but doesn't speak.

"Mom said he's been sick, but now he has pneumonia," Lauren tells me.

"Can you die from pneumonia?" I ask Lauren, but she doesn't answer. She just looks at me with her head tilted, her eyebrows raised and her shoulders shrugged.

When we get to the cafeteria, it's pretty much empty. Two people sit at one table talking quietly, and three nurses are sitting at another table. I order a grilled cheese and get a brownie and an orange juice. Mary and Lauren order food and the total comes to $4.75. Hospital food is the cheapest food anywhere. I hand the cashier a five-dollar bill.

We talk about school, my game, Lauren's practice—anything but Pop. As we're finishing our food and I'm trying to see if we can get anything else for twenty-five cents, Dad walks into the cafeteria and says, "Clean up the table and let's get going. You guys have homework and school tomorrow, so we have to get home." I stick the quarter in my pocket, grab my tray, throw my trash away and slide the tray on top of the trash can lid.

"Where's Mom?" Lauren asks.

"She's staying here with your grandmother, she'll be home later," he says.

We get home and go through our routine: showers, homework, lunches for school tomorrow, clothes ready for school. Everyone seems distracted, even me. I barely think about my game, and that was just this afternoon. It seems like it was a long time ago. The phone rings in the kitchen and Dad says, "I got it." He talks quietly and hangs up.

"Was that Mom?" Mary asks.

"Yes," Dad says, "she won't be home for a while."

By the time I go to bed, Mom still is not home. When I wake up, she's there at the kitchen table with a cup of coffee. She looks tired and is staring off. I say good morning and make a bowl of cereal.

"How's Pop?" I ask.

"Oh, honey, Pop didn't make it through the night," she says.

"Pop died?"

"I'm sorry, honey, he didn't make it," she says again. "Now listen, Mrs. Ruhl is going to pick you kids up for school in about fifteen minutes. I have to go see your grandmother and go back to the hospital. Everything is going to be okay. I want you to go to school today and I'll pick you up after practice. It's going to be okay, do what your grandfather would want you to do." Like I have any idea what that means.

"Do Lauren and Mary know?" I ask.

"Not yet, I haven't told them," Mom says. I put my cereal bowl in the sink and walk out of the kitchen to brush my teeth and grab my school things. I stay upstairs until our ride is here. I can hear Lauren and Mary crying and I don't want to be there.

When Dad calls out, "Mrs Ruhl is here!" I grab my stuff and head out the door. I don't say anything and I get into the car. Mrs. Ruhl looks at me in the rearview mirror. "Good morning, Mark."

"Morning, Mrs. Ruhl," I say, "thanks for the ride to school."

Mary and Lauren are still crying when they get in the car. Mrs. Ruhl begins to console them and my ears go numb. There is only background noise as I think about Pop. I thought I would get a chance to say goodbye. People say you can say goodbye at a funeral but he's already gone. My chance to say goodbye was in the hospital and I missed it. I didn't know that was going to be my last chance but it was. I missed it. I'll never get a chance to see him again.

"Mark, Mark, we're here." Mrs. Ruhl's voice brings me back. We're in the St. Xavier parking lot.

"Sorry, I wasn't paying attention. Thanks for the ride, Mrs. Ruhl," I say as I throw my lacrosse equipment over my right shoulder and grab my book bag with my left hand. "See you guys after school," I say to Lauren and Mary.

Lauren says, "See you later," while Mary blurts out "I love you." It startles me because I don't think she has ever said that to me before. I head to my homeroom.

Somehow the school day and lacrosse happen. Afterwards, Mr. Burt, whose son Tom has been on my lacrosse team since third grade, gives me a ride home. The house is busy with people and phone calls. Mom is on the phone now with one of her brothers or sister.

"Mark, we're having pizza for dinner," she says to me as she covers the bottom of the receiver with her left hand, "now get cleaned up."

"Okay." I understand that when Mom says, "pizza for dinner" it really means you're on your own, get yourself your own food and drinks and clean them up when you finish. That's fine with me because that also means I can stay upstairs in my room and they won't be all over me about my homework.

When I get out of the shower, Mom says, "Mark, Pop's funeral is going to be on Wednesday of next week, okay?"

"Okay," I say as I head upstairs in my towel. I think about it and realize I have a game on Tuesday against St. Stephen's so I won't miss that but I might miss practice on Wednesday, and we play Grayson on Friday. I don't want to lose any playing time for that game because of missing practice.

By the time Tuesday rolls around, all kinds of people are coming to town. Billy and his family from Philly, Doug Radisson and his family from Philly, Brian and his family from Virginia, Hugh and his family from Frederick. Cousins are coming from everywhere.

My parents try to make all of my games, no matter the sport. On this Tuesday, they bring a bunch of my family to watch the game against St. Stephen's. I have felt no pressure at all this season, but today I feel it. When we come out for warmups, I look over at the top row of the bleachers to see if my parents are there, and I see Hugh standing with my dad. Hugh hasn't watched me play in a while, so I'm psyched. I proceed to play my worst half of the year right in front of my three closest cousins, the three guys in the whole world I want to impress the most.

Although I played well in the first quarter, I didn't do shit after that. And in front of Billy, Brian, and Hugh. I felt terrible. They watched me drop passes, get laid out. I didn't score. I sucked and I now feel terrible. After we shake hands with St. Mary's Saints, I keep my head down past our bench, past the bleachers, and up the stairs into our locker room. Everybody is happy, so I fake it, telling T "nice shot," Kevin "great faceoff work," everybody "sorry I played like shit." After Coach talks to the team and we put our cleats away and jerseys in the bin, everybody grabs their backpacks and heads out. I do want to see Brian, Hugh, and Billy, but I am in no hurry. Eventually I head out with Kevin, and as I go by the coaches' office, Coach calls my name. "D'Antoni!"

"Yes, Coach," I say.

"Come in here real quick. I know that you have a funeral to go to tomorrow. Be with your family and we will see you on Thursday," he says.

"Thanks, Coach."

"And, by the way, what was wrong with you out there today? You started well but then, after the first quarter, you didn't look like yourself out there. If you dropped a pass in the fourth quarter, I was taking you out. I don't know if you have a lot on your mind or what, but shake this one off, and be back ready to go. We have a big one on Friday."

"Yes, sir," I say, "I know I have a lot of work to do."

"Believe me, we know you have a lot of work to do."

When I open the locker room door to the late afternoon sky,

I spot the boys on the far side of the parking lot by my parents' station wagon.

As I expect, they each hit me with a smart-ass remark, "How far did you slide when you got hit, that must've been a record," says Brian.

"Dude, you got killed by number 33," says Billy. Same old, same old, I expect nothing less, except this time, they are right, I did suck.

I'm glad they showed up, but man I wish I would have played better. They just saw me at my worst. By the time I can tell them about the first goal of the game, they've all moved on to talk about their own things. Brian and Hugh just finished hoops and Billy is talking about his hockey season, sheer chaos of a different kind. I find myself silent, listening to all the talk and hearing none of it. My thoughts become my own. *The only way to make people know you're great is if you're great every time, it has to be always, every time. I need to practice harder and be better, smarter, faster, smoother.*

When I come out of my stupor, Brian is telling a story about Ralph Sampson taking two quarters off the top of a backboard, and Brian is describing how wide they put the quarters.

"Who's going to give us a ride home?" I interrupt.

Brian says, "Your mom went to pick up Thomas. She had to leave the game at the end of the third quarter and they're going to bring him back here."

Ten minutes later, Thomas gets dropped off and drives us all back to the house. Everybody else is at Pop and Cleta's and we're not going anywhere near there. We settle in for a rare school night off, a Wednesday with no homework and no parents at the house. Domino's Pizza delivers, and in a half-hour or less Thomas, Lee, Brother Bri, Tim, and GT take over the downstairs and the living room. Billy, Brian, Hugh and I roll through the downstairs and outside. The older cousins are all at college and have to come a long way to the funeral, so when they get here, they are ready to do some drinking. The four of us younger guys collect our money and throw it into the pot for beer. By the time Thomas and Brother Bri come back from the liquor store, they have a few cases plus a few bottles of liquor.

Mom has said that she would call to check on us, but she'll be busy with family, so we have the green light for the night. Quarters at the kitchen table, shotgun beers in the backyard, I am assuming this is what a frat party looks like but really, I have no idea. The four of us take a six-pack upstairs and keep drinking. Hugh is talking about a girlfriend, Billy is all about the Flyers, and Brian has been hanging around Charlottesville at the UVA campus all the time. Doug Radisson shows up around nine and heads upstairs to us, six-pack in hand. We clear a night stand and play quarters between the beds, each of us going on a hot streak. The beers taste good and music plays from an alarm clock radio.

The phone rings both upstairs and downstairs and I just let it ring. Finally, it stops as we keep playing quarters, telling jokes, trading stories. A few minutes later, Thomas comes up the steps and tells me to turn the radio down, Mom's on the phone. "Don't say anything stupid," he tells me, "and you guys be quiet when he's on the phone."

I walk in the hallway as I pull the phone line out of the room and pick up.

"Hey, honey, have you had any pizza?" Mom asks.

"Yeah, a lot."

"Okay, don't forget to take a shower. Your sisters are down here, so we'll be home in a little while." It's loud in the background at Pop and Cleta's. I hear Uncle Gregory and Uncle Lee talking.

"Okay, we'll just stay here and we'll see you when you get home. I'll let the guys know they are spending the night," I say.

Smiles abound as we now know that we can hang out and party with the older cousins, a bunch of really cool guys who have done a bunch of really cool things and who are all in college or beyond. They seem so much older–they've driven cross country, they've transferred to different colleges–so that when any one of them takes the time to talk to you, it feels special. Sometimes they give me advice, sometimes they just check on me because they've heard something about me. It is always an honor to be able to hang out with them because they have experience and I am a young buck, real young.

I walk downstairs. "I hung up with Mom, they won't be here for a while," I tell Thomas. Lee hits the stereo button to some Rolling Stones and all the guys go back to partying, telling stories, catching up.

"Make sure you guys stay here and don't go out driving," Thomas says, "We're going to the Crease or the Mt. Washington Tavern in a little while. Make sure you throw all those cans in the trash before Mom and Dad get home. Don't get too fucked up, all right? Eat some pizza."

"All right, I will," I say.

By now, we are all downstairs and I head out to the back porch, a dimly lit red brick patio with iron and wood chairs with pads on them. The older cousins are passing a bottle of liquor around the circle, and when I sit down, apparently I'm in the circle as well. I take the bottle when it comes my way and take a swig. Vodka. It tastes like shit and burns not your skin or your throat but your chest, your heart. I look around and these guys are grown-ups, they shave, they live on their own, they are in a way different league.

A gin bottle makes it around to me. I take another drink, and it hurts worse than the first one. I start to gag, and here it comes. I take off for the bushes and barf about halfway there. I throw up on my tennis shoes, my socks, and I end up on my hands and knees on the side of the house. I just went from hanging with the older guys to being the kid in the bushes, tossing his pizza.

"Nice game today, Mark, I heard you got crushed out of bounds," says somebody. He's laughing.

I feel the muscles in my arms go weak and I hurl again, full of pizza and beer, more beer.

"Uh-oh, it looks like the shots put him on all fours," says someone else.

One thing I know right now is that no one is going to come over and help me. I am on my own and I'm not sure how I'm going to move. I stop hurling and let my arms go. I'm lying in the grass and dirt, inches from the throw-up, so close I can smell it, and I can't move, I can only lie here. Two hours, a game of quarters, two shots and I am on the ground like a bum in the street, unable to move.

I'm not sure how long I'm here, but I hear Thomas, standing over me, "Mark, get your ass up and go upstairs. Make sure you're in bed by the time Mom and Dad get home. We're leaving."

I open one eye and then the other and start to roll over, feel a violent pull in my stomach and throw up on the ground and my hands. It puts me back in the fetal position and I feel sweat on my forehead.

"Come on man, get your ass to bed," Thomas says.

I look over my shoulder. These are Division One lacrosse players, college basketball players, guys I have watched play for national championships. As embarrassment washes over me, I stumble up with my arms out in front of me, and try to get to the stairs as best as I can. I bounce off the walls, get to the bottom of the steps, crawl up on my hands and feet, stumble at the top to my bed, and fall down on my pillow. My breath wreaks, lights are all on, the radio is playing and I close my eyes. My head is pounding, my breath is weak and inconsistent, my stomach feels like it could spasm again. I squint harder, tighten my stomach and pray, not to God, but to not throw up.

I wake in my bed, alive but barely. I feel like shit. I open my eyes and look around. Brian is in Thomas's bed, Hugh and Billy are on the floor. I have to pee so bad I can't stand it. As I get out of bed, I burp and feel sick again. I really feel like shit.

When I come out of the bathroom downstairs, Mom says,

"Don't go back to sleep, you need to take a shower and get ready for the funeral, okay? Good morning." I turn back around and head for the only shower in the house. I didn't take a shower after the game yesterday, so I am crusty. By the time I get out of the shower, dry-heaving two or three times, everyone is awake and moving. My head is pounding and although I'm starving, I cannot eat a thing.

By the time we get to the Cathedral for the funeral, Hugh has told me he threw up last night, and Brian and Billy stuck to beer and got into an epic one-on-one drunken nerf basketball game. I missed it, passed out upstairs. My parents have not said anything to me so far, so I don't think I'm in any trouble with them.

Henry "Pop" Corrigan had six kids. My mom is the youngest. She and my aunts and uncles are all classic Baltimore— Catholic, Irish, athletes and educators—all very social with a wide group of friends and relatives. Our family is the only one that still lives in Baltimore. Jimmy lives in North Carolina; Francis in Charlottesville, Virginia; Gregory in Villanova, Pennsylvania; Lee in Swarthmore, Pennsylvania; and Peggy in Frederick, Maryland. They all have several kids, so I have a bunch of Corrigan cousins. They're all here for Pop, Hank Corrigan, the big guy. The sight of the oldest sons of all of Pop's kids carrying the casket down the aisle at Cathedral is powerful. Jim Jr., Lee and Thomas are on one side, Winn, David and GT on the other. As I look around at all of the cousins, I realize I'm the youngest boy in the family. I have Mary, who is younger, but I am the youngest boy. Damn, I have some growing up to do after last night's performance. I stand in my sport coat, head still pounding, looking up, wishing for wisdom anywhere I can get it.

The inside of the church is huge, the ceiling must be thirty feet in the air. The whole church is made of shiny white cement with stained glass in every window. There must be thirty or forty huge stained glass windows, saints in each one: St .Patrick, St. Luke, St. Sebastian, a whole bunch of saints. There are carvings over big stone arches on both sides of the aisles and there must be thirty arches.

All of the stations of the cross, stories of Jesus and the fishes and loaves of bread, the last supper, all kinds of different tales. Staring at all of them carries me through the service. I think about lacrosse and school and drinking, and I want to do it all. I want to be great at lacrosse, I want to do well in school, and I want to go to parties, meet girls and have fun like older people.

I am snapped out of my daydream by a laugh from the crowd. Uncle Francis is at the podium, talking about Pop. He's telling a story about when he was in college. "I wasn't the best student, and I definitely was not wearing out a path to the library my freshman year. I played lacrosse, I enjoyed the nightlife and I neglected my studies. At the end of my spring semester, classes ended and I stayed on campus for about a week until the ACC tournament was over. I headed home by train to the Baltimore train station, looking for a welcome party, but there was no one at the station waiting for me. From there, I took the bus up York Road to the Senator movie theater and got off the bus and looked again. Still no welcoming party. So I threw my bag over my shoulder, walked through the parking lot, through the gate, across the empty field, and down the block to 1503 Clearspring Road.

"When I walked up the stairs to the porch, I heard Hank say out loud, 'Look who's home, stay right there!' I thought they were getting a cake ready or hiding to surprise me. Instead, just Hank and Cleta came out of the house.. Hank handed me a train ticket, and Cleta gave me an envelope. Hank said, 'Here's a train ticket back to Durham and in the envelope is twenty-five dollars. Your grades made it home before you did and you are not going to stay here this summer. As a matter of a fact, you are not going to stay here tonight. You are going to get back on that train and you are going to go back down to that school and get your grades better, or you are not going to be coming back here at all. You need to make things right. Duke is giving you a chance, and you are going to make the most of that chance.' I looked at Cleta and the first thought that came into my head was 'I guess there's no cake.' So I said, 'Can I come in to use the bathroom?' Hank said, 'Yes, you can, but you can leave your bag out here.' They fed me a meal of pot roast, potatoes and carrots and I hit the road an hour later. No shower, no clean laundry, no dessert.

"That was one of the best things that Hank Corrigan ever did for me. It proved he loved me, he showed me his will and he made me do what is right. I will always love him for the love he showed for me and my brothers and sisters. Henry Corrigan was the best man and father I have ever known," Francis finishes.

People sit, smiling and nodding their heads. A lightness of mood, an uplifting of spirits comes over the church.

My uncle Gregory is the next to speak. Uncle Gregory is a really funny, happy guy. He loves everyone and he's always telling stories. This one, of course, is about Pop. "I want to tell you a story about how Hank helped me get into college. I was an average student and didn't know which college to go to after high school. Truth be told, I didn't have a lot of options. So I went and served my two years in the military right out of St. Xavier High School. When I was done, I was living at home, working at the Senator movie theater. One night before I went to work at the late show, I was upstairs in my room, getting ready. Hank called up, 'Son, come on down here, there is someone who is here to talk to you.'

"When I went downstairs, there was a man, well-dressed in a sport coat, with a University of Maryland pin on his lapel. He says to me, 'I understand you're a pretty good lacrosse player, and we would like you to come to the University of Maryland and play. How does that sound to you?' I looked at this man and I looked over at Hank and he just nodded his head yes. I said, 'I would love to play lacrosse and attend school there.' 'Good, I'll see you next fall.' I thanked the coach and we shook hands. When he was gone, Hank said, 'I think he was here to see your brother Lee, and I didn't want to tell him he was already in the army.'

"I said, 'No, Dad, he saw me play and he wants me.' I was on cloud nine. Well, after the first scrimmage of Fall Ball, where I thought I had played pretty well, had a goal and an assist, I was walking across the field to see Hank and Cleta. The same coach who had come to Clearspring Road and offered yours truly a scholarship said to me, 'Considering you were the leading scorer in the state of Maryland last year in high school, I thought you'd score more goals today.' That's when it hit me. He *did* come to the house to offer Lee a scholarship, not me. When I got to Hank and Cleta I told them so. Hank looked me right in the eye and said, 'Gregory, you looked great out there, they are going to love you here. Plus, when Lee gets home from the army, you guys are going to have a hell of a team. I think you guys are going to beat JHU.'"

Everybody laughs and nods their heads again. People elbow each other in the pews and smile.

"My story is slightly different," is how Uncle Lee starts his talk from the podium. "Hank always came to my games and he would stand down by the corner by the offense and switch sides every quarter. He never told me what I did right or wrong, he just commented about how hard I tried or how many assists I had. He never talked about any of the goals I scored. Well, in the city championship we played Grayson, at Grayson, and as hard as I tried, we could not beat them. I scored six goals but we lost 11–8 and I was mad. As soon as the game was over, I skipped the huddle and the handshake line and went right to the bus. I was sitting there, just me and the bus driver. While I was wiping tears from my eyes and taking off my equipment, l heard the door of the bus open up. I saw Hank nod at the bus driver, the bus driver nod back. Then Hank was looking at me. He said, 'Lee, you are going to get off this bus and you are going to apologize to your coach and Grayson's coach and you are going to congratulate that team on a good game. Now, get your stuff, all of it.' I put my equipment on my stick and grabbed my book bag. Hank walked behind me as I headed towards the field. I walked over to Coach Waibel and told him I was sorry for my behavior. Then I headed towards the Grayson locker room, where they were hooting and hollering about the game. When I started to slow down, Hank said, 'You go in there and you congratulate them, and you better mean it.' I went in that door and into the coaches' office. I said I was sorry for the way I acted. He thanked me for coming in. Then I said, 'Sir, I have to congratulate your team, they played really well.'

"I followed the coach into the locker room and I shook every player's hand. When I came out, Hank was standing there, arms crossed, unlit cigar in his mouth. He said to me, "Carry your things to the car and talk to your mother." When we got to the car, I put my things in the trunk and hugged Cleta. Hank said, 'I want you to walk home from here and think about what you can do to help your team and also what you can do to make sure you don't ever do this again.' We lived about two miles and I started off for home in wet pants, wet shirt and cleats. It was almost dark by the time I got there. When I walked up the steps, Hank said, 'Look who is home, stay right there.' I had heard that before and unlike Francis, I held no hope about a cake being made for me. Hank stepped out on the porch and said, 'When you come through this door, remember that the game is over. I saw what you did out there, I saw how hard you tried. You gave it your all and it did not work out for you today. You have to know that it's going to be like that sometimes. The important part is, you gave it your all. You gave it your best. You can work hard and sometimes you don't win, and a real gentleman uses it for motivation for the next time.' Plus, Francis, I did get to sleep in my own bed that night."

Everyone laughs again.

By the time Lee, GT, Winn, Dave, Jimmy and Thomas have carried Pop's casket out of the church, we begin to feel better. It's now time to go back to Clearspring Road and have a party.

While it is a sad time to be together, we don't waste much of it sitting around and mourning; instead, we head right over to the empty lot on Clearspring Road, split teams, and have a football game that includes every male cousin. The stakes are high, bragging rights are on the line and the competition is fierce. Brothers punch brothers, people bleed and guys limp. There will be a winner and no one wants to be a loser. There is no end in sight from the shit you get for being on the losing side.

Each one of us has ruined, for good, our Sunday church clothes by the time the game ends. Everyone of us is going to get yelled at by our parents and we know it. I don't know what to say to any of the older guys, so I walk and listen. Brother Bry and Big Dave give me a headlock and mess up my hair. I want to be too old for this, but I'm not. It bugs me.

Like I said, my family is the only one left in Baltimore besides Pop and Cleta and now, just Cleta. Everybody is going to be getting into their cars and heading home—too fast—and we don't know when we will be getting back together. Hopefully, at least, at Christmas.

Mom looks at Thomas and me with irritation, but I think she knew we were going to get dirty. She saw me put the football in the car.

Since I'm not one for goodbyes, I say "see you" to everyone and head inside the house. All of the football players take turns running upstairs to use the only bathroom before they hit the road. I go back to the kitchen to see if there is anything left of the Cleta cake. There is, and I am not telling anybody. See, Cleta bakes a cake every day, with homemade icing, in the same rectangular pan, and she never takes it out of the pan. The cake gets cut and served from the pan. Every day, the cake is finished by somebody and today I get to finish it.

I know we're going to be the last family to leave because we live ten minutes away and there's a lot to clean up. There must have been 150 to 200 people here and now they're all gone. I take a seat in Pop's office right next to the kitchen and start to look through his desk drawers. It has the usual envelopes and stationery. I take out a clean sheet of paper and try as well as I can, even though I am not good, to draw. I draw the logo of The Rolling Stones from memory, the lips, the tongue sticking out. No good. I crumple the paper and throw it in the trash can. Since I don't hear anybody around the house, I go out to the living room. As I pass through the dining room, I grab a Schweppes ginger ale. I step into the living room, pull back the tab on the twelve-ounce can, and sit on the couch. As my butt hits the seat, I see Cleta, sitting in the chair in silence, just looking ahead. I'm a little startled and say, "Oh, Cleta, I didn't see you there." She looks over at me and smiles, not saying anything, and looks straight ahead again. I say, "Cleta, I am sorry about Pop."

She says, "Mark, I think I have realized that I will never stop loving your grandfather. I will always love him for the rest of my life." It seems almost too powerful. Cleta will always be Pop's woman, she will always be true to him. I wonder how Cleta can be so strong and have all the answers and always know what to say. But then I realize, she is the one who taught everybody—my parents, my uncles, my aunts, probably even Pop, everybody.

"Come over here and give me a hug." I walk over and she squeezes me and she feels extra soft today, extra warm. While she holds me, she says, "Why don't you go upstairs and put on a clean shirt and come back down here and help me clean up."

She kisses my head and holds my head, and this I don't mind. As I walk up the steps, I ask "Where is everybody?"

"Your mom took your brother and sisters with her to drop off Lee at his car and your Dad went home to let the dog out. Now don't forget to wash your face and hands while you're up there."

"Okay, Cleta," I say and go to do what I am told because with Cleta, you just do what you're told.

III

CHAPTER 02

IIIIIIIIIIIIIIIIIIIIIIIIIIIIIIIIIIIIIIIIIIIIIIIIIIIIIIIIIIIIIIIIIIII

It's July 4th weekend, midsummer. I wake up and leave the house by 10 a.m. to pick up Kevin. He's ready when I get there and we stop by the liquor store and sub shop before meeting Roy and Timmy at Timmy's house. We have a tried and true method of getting beer. Find a young but above-age guy, ask him to buy beer, and offer him ten bucks for himself. This trick has worked for years and the only odd part today is that we're asking a bearded hippie type to buy it before noon. He comes out with two cases of Schaefer, we go buy roast beef subs and put them all on ice. I got a call from Roy last night and we're going water skiing on Timmy's parents' boat. His parents are out of town and the nearly cloudless sky and light breeze promise perfect hours on the water.

The best part of the day is that we all plan on playing summer league tonight, so this will be a nice warm-up and a good way to spend the afternoon. After summer league, we'll all be going to a bonfire in Hunt Valley. It's going to be a full, great day.

When I pull up to Timmy's house, he and Roy are ready to go. They both hop in my dark green, five-speed manual transmission Volkswagen bug with the engine in the rear of the car. Timmy has towels, life jackets and the keys to the boat, so we throw the life jackets under the hood of the car in front and start our twenty-minute drive to Middle River, right off the Chesapeake Bay. I'm excited to see what kind of boat Tim's parents own, because he's pretty wealthy and I have a feeling it will be nice.

When we get to the marina, we park and head down a dock filled with power boats, sailboats and even pontoon boats. We get to slip number 31 and the boat is a 23-foot Boston Whaler dual console. This is the kind of boat that has the steering wheel on the right side behind the glass windshield. The windshield lifts up in the middle and you can sit up front in seats or in the back. It looks pretty new and I notice the motor is a Johnson 150. That means this boat will move pretty well and has plenty of speed to pull us out of the water on one ski. When you ski, it is pretty easy to get up on two skis, because there is more ski on the water and it is smoother getting up. When you get up on one ski, you need a quick pull out of the water because if it takes a while, you really have to keep the ski straight and your knees bent. It's just way easier with a strong motor and I am psyched to see it.

Kevin and Roy have taken the cooler out of the back seat and are carrying it down the dock. My arms are full with four life preservers and towels. Timmy is on the boat already, lowering the motor into the water and priming the gas line. I drop the preservers and towels onto the boat and hop on board. When Roy and Kevin get there, I grab the cooler handles from Kevin and Roy as they lower it into the boat and guide it to the deck. Timmy turns the key and it starts right up. We all look at each other and smile, relieved it has started because we are pumped to get out on the water. Lines are untied and tossed onto the dock as Timmy backs out of the slip and into the marina. Kevin takes his shirt off, I slide off my flip flops and Roy throws on a hat. We're psyched and without saying a word, Kevin opens the cooler and throws each of us a beer. Life is good as we slide slowly through the no wake zone and head towards open water on the horizon. The sky is still clear and blue with only a few light clouds. The air is very light or even still sometimes, the water is flat. This is a picture perfect day for skiing.

While Roy and Kevin sit up front on the boat and bullshit, Timmy tells me to open the glove box on the boat and turn on the radio. I fiddle with it until I find our favorite station, 99.1 WHFS. The Fine Young Cannibals song "She Drives Me Crazy" is on and I crank it so loud that two older people on a sailboat look over and shake their heads. I give them the standard boater's wave and they look away. It's nice to see we can get people upset without even trying.

The next several hours are spent the best way you can spend a summer day. We all take turns skiing, drinking, floating on the bay and jumping off the side of the boat, doing backflips, front flips, belly flops and cannonballs. Timmy knows his way around the bay and he shows us some cool places to anchor and hang out. We eat our subs and put a big dent in our cooler full of beers.

As we start to head home, we ride by a long pier that juts out into Middle River. By now, each of us has had six or so beers and Roy says to me, "Mark, you ever see that bumper sticker that says, 'Ski Naked'? I bet you won't ski naked in front of the pier."

I look at him and, with a straight face, say, "How much do you want to bet?"

"I'll bet you ten bucks you won't do it," he says.

"I'll take that bet," I say and Timmy slows the boat down. I look for the best slalom ski on the boat, a Cypress Garden magic stick, and drop it overboard, jump in after it and grab it with my left hand so it won't float away. With my right hand, I untie my navy blue Birdwell beach britches and ease them off my legs. I throw them back on the boat and feel the water all over my naked body, and it does feel a little different from wearing a bathing suit. I go about putting the ski on and get myself ready. Roy throws me the rope, smiling his ass off, and I yell, "I want my money in one ten-dollar bill, don't be giving me any ones!"

I look into the distance at the pier and see figures walking back and forth, other figures looking out at the water, others leaning over the railings, trying to see fish. I think to myself, "They don't know what is about to happen."

Once I get a good grip on the handle of the tow rope, I yell to

Timmy, "Go ahead, let's do it!"

He guns the motor. I hold tight and pull myself up, swerving slightly because the beer has loosened me up and the earlier ski runs have worn me out a bit. By the time I stand straight up, I look at the boat and Roy, Kevin and Timmy are laughing their asses off. I look down and, damn sure, I am naked and flying in the breeze. We are headed right towards the pier and I hear someone crank up the radio as The Rolling Stones' "Can't Get No Satisfaction" blares through the speakers. Roy has a crazy skill when it comes to whistling and he starts whistling as loud as he can at the pier. By now, we are closing in on the end of the pier and I decide, instead of trying to hide myself at all, I go with the nonchalant skiers' wave, just like what they do at Sea World. I act like I am in a parade and wave to everybody like they are spectators. We are getting close enough to these people that I can see people pointing and laughing. I can see moms putting their hands over kids' faces and I can see other women open-mouthed and aghast. As I wave at the people at the end of the pier, I feel the rope go slack and my stomach drops. Timmy has slowed the engine and the ski is sliding out from under me and my head and shoulders are way out over my feet. I feel panic, fear and embarrassment all at once as I look at the boat and Timmy, Roy and Kevin are laughing their asses off. "Hit the motor!" I yell. I feel the rope tighten as I wobble and sway before straightening back out. As I feel the ski steady under my feet and we ride away, there is no waving or humor, just my naked back and butt heading away from the pier. A minute later I signal that I am dropping the rope and I ease into the water, pulling the ski off as soon as I submerge. As they turn the boat around I yell, "Throw me my shorts!" They're still laughing as I slide the ski towards Kevin and grab my Birdwells. I put them on under the water, grab the ladder and pull myself into the boat. They're still laughing. I am a physical and emotional mix of relief, embarrassment, muscle exhaustion, and drunkenness. "Hold on," Timmy says, "let's get out of here."

He guns the motor as we head back to the marina. As we round the bend into it, a Coast Guard marine safety boat is slowly cruising out. All of us instinctively put our beers under wraps. We sit up in our chairs and look ahead, making a sly wave to the Coast Guard crew. They, in turn, wave back and one of them yells, "Gentlemen, please shut down your motor and remain on the boat, we would like to do a safety check."

None of us answers directly to the call but both Roy and I say "shit" at the same time as we hide the empty beer cans and clean what can be seen on the floor of the boat while the Coast Guard vessel, a 25-foot, orange, decked-out boat makes a U turn. Within two minutes it is behind us and a tall guy, clothed in what looks like a police uniform, with a bullet proof vest, gun, knife and assorted mace cans, throws a rope onto the side of the boat. I grab the rope as he says, "Please tie it tightly to a cleat in the front." He throws another rope towards Kevin and tells him to tie it to a cleat in the rear.

"Gentleman, how are you today?" a different officer says as he emerges out from the portal on their boat. This guy seems to be in charge. The guy who threw the rope suddenly looks young and thin. This one looks older and more intense. His haircut is military and his shoulders are wide. He isn't very tall, but he carries himself like he can fight. His eyes are serious and the tone in his voice is stern. He doesn't look like he laughs a lot.

"We're good, sir," says Timmy, acting as our spokesman, "how are you?"

"I am fine. Thanks for asking," he says. "Do you have your boater's registration card with you?"

"I think it is right here, sir." Timmy flips through the papers in the glove box, the same glove box that holds the radio we just had cranked up to The Who's "Teenage Wasteland." After a few seconds, Timmy hands over a blue card, about the size of a license.

"Is your father John Shaeffer?" he asks.

"Yes, sir, this is his boat," Timmy says.

"Okay gentleman, today I am going to do a safety inspection and I want to see if you have the following items on the boat and available at any moment, in case of emergency. Can I see your life preservers?"

"Here they are, sir," Timmy says as he grabs two wet ones from the back and I hold up the two black ones that have been sitting on the front cushions all day.

"Good, can I see your air horn or whistle?" the coast guard officer asks.

Timmy reaches underneath the steering wheel and shows the man an air horn canister, just like one used to signal the end of a quarter of any lacrosse game I ever played in. This exercise goes on for a few more minutes as we produce our fire extinguisher, radio device and the like. We're all on edge because we know that he's trying to catch us on something, anything so he can take us in.

"I'm glad to see you young men have all of your proper boating supplies, that's good. Now, apparently there were some young men out on the bay water skiing near the pier. Was that you guys?" He asks.

"No, sir," Timmy says. "We were on the Magothy River, coming from my uncle's house." I have never even heard of the Magothy river, but now is not the time to bring that up.

"Have you been there all day?"

"Yes, sir, we left the marina about ten-thirty and have been there all day. We're headed home for dinner now,"

"Are all you boys headed home?" The officer asks as he looks at us.

"Yes, sir," we say almost in unison.

"You want to open that cooler for me?" He says as he looks at me.

"This one right here?" I point, knowing it's the only cooler on the boat and what's in it.

"Yes, that cooler," he says with irritation in his voice.

"Sure," I say as I lift the top on the blue cooler. Under the top are full and empty beer cans, ice, and half-eaten subs from Towson sub shop.

"Are those your beers?" he asks and before he lets anyone say anything, interjects, "You boys don't look old enough to drink beer."

"No sir," Timmy says, "we are bringing the cooler to the marina. My uncle wants us to return it to my dad."

"You can get in trouble transporting alcohol on the bay if you're underage. You know that, don't you?"

"Yes, sir, I apologize, I was just trying to do Uncle Bill a favor," Timmy says. I have no idea if Timmy has an Uncle Bill or not, but this is the story and he is going with it. We are all just nodding our heads each time he says anything.

"Apparently, there were some young men out in the bay water skiing with no clothes on. Do you boys know anything about that?"

We all look at each other with looks of bewilderment. Each of us says, "No, sir" in succession.

"You boys sure you don't know anything about that?"

"No, sir," says Timmy, "but if we see anybody, we will definitely let you know." Timmy's volunteering to help elicits a slight chuckle from Roy and has both Kevin and I smiling under our hats.

"That would be a big help," the officer says in a sarcastic way, letting us know that he isn't buying any of our shit. "You boys travel safely to your slip and make sure you get your uncle to take that beer from the boat. Untie those two ropes and toss them on the bow and stern. You boys be careful and safe boating," he says as he pulls his sunglasses out of his breast pocket and places them on his face.

"Yes, sir," we all say, as Roy throws in a "Safe boating to you as well." We all suppress a laugh and I even snort through my nose. A huge sigh of relief comes over the boat as the two Coast Guard officers pull away and Timmy turns the key.

"Holy shit," I say as we all finally laugh out loud and quietly and slowly head to the slip.

Summer League starts in an hour and a half and we have to get to Seminary Fields for a six o'clock horn.

By the time the game starts, most of my drunk has worn off but my muscles are worn out. Wouldn't you know it, I get two easy chances early that I bury and a one-on-one off the end line gives me three goals in the first quarter. I pick up another one in the second quarter, one in the third and end the game with five goals and a couple of assists. Roy is on my team and he has four goals in the game. It's funny that the two guys who have been drinking and water skiing all day end up with nine of our twelve goals and the team wins 12–9 over Timmy's team.

As planned, we all pile back into my car, sweaty and smelly, and head out to Hunt Valley for a bonfire party. There is a collection of people from all different schools: St. Xavier, Calvert, St Paul's, Grayson, Notre Dame Prep, Roland Park, all sorts of people. We wade into the crowd and within fifteen minutes are involved in drinking games.

I find some girls I know and Kevin is all over Lucy, trying to rekindle the spark he has had permanently lit for her. His problem is her spark seems to be dull or wet. She likes him sober, but doesn't find him quite so funny when he is drunk. And after about an hour, we are all drunk, just a continuation of the day after a minor intermission of a summer league lacrosse game.

By eleven o'clock, I've found Danielle and we make plans to go to her house. Her parents are at the beach and she is supposed to be home watching her little brother but has sneaked out for a little while to the party. The only problem I have is I have to drop my car off at my house so my parents can use it in the morning. I called them at ten and told them I would drop it off and get a ride to Timmy's to spend the night. I plan on staying at Danielle's but they don't need to know that. Since she drove to the party also, I ask her to follow me home.

As I drive down York Road past TSU and St. Joseph's Hospital, I see lights from a cop car turn on behind me. I look down at the speedometer and see that I am going 55 in a 35 mph zone. My heart drops, my head spins and I think for a second about making a run for it. No, that's not necessary, I can talk my way out of it.

When the cop comes to my window, he gives me the usual stern "License and registration please."

"Yes, sir," I say, "was I doing something wrong, sir?"

"License and registration," he says again, this time with annoyance.

I fumble around my back pocket for my wallet and hand him that, then I lean over in my seat and search through the glove box for the registration. After I look through every paper in there, I finally find it. The rest of the papers are now on the floor and I look up at the officer and notice he is looking down at me with a look of disgust. After he examines my license and registration, he doesn't go back to his car. Instead, he shines his flashlight onto the passenger seat and the floor of the passenger side, then into my face. As I look away from the light he says the words I have been dreading since I saw the lights.

"Have you been drinking?"

"No sir," I say.

"Where are you coming from?"

"I was at a friend's house."

"Is this person behind us with you?" he asks.

I feel a sense of dread. "Yes, she is following me to my house."

"Step out of the car," he says.

All I can think in my head is Shit, but I try to not show any emotion. I step out and stand straight up, looking him right in the face.

"Walk in a straight line, one foot in front of the other," he says, demonstrating for about four steps.

I put my arms out, step with my right, followed by my left and right until he says, "Turn around."

I start back and he says, "Okay, put your arms down when you do this."

I put my arm down and immediately feel my shoulder lean to the right. I hope he doesn't notice as I slow my left foot and carefully place my right foot in front. My balance is definitely off and I am hoping not to fall over. My breathing slows and my head pounds. My heart races and my nerves are shaky. Officer Bryant, as I see on his name tag, writes something down on his little pad and looks up at me and says, "Stand here. I want you to say the alphabet beginning at H and ending at S."

"Excuse me?"

"I want you to say the alphabet beginning at the letter H and ending at the letter S."

I start at H and go through the alphabet to S.

"Now I want you to do it backwards, starting at S," he says.

I start at S and go slow, not sure if I am doing it right or not.

Officer Bryant is giving no indication if I am doing well or not. I have no idea if I am right or not. It's a feeling of desperation and isolation.

"Step forward, I want you to blow into this," he says.

"I'm not blowing into that," I say.

"You are not required by law to take this breathalyzer, but if you have not been drinking, it will prove your innocence. If you do not blow into it, I will have no choice but to take you into the station and book you for DUI."

I know I am way past the legal limit and I also know I don't have to do it. So I look at Officer Bryant and I say, "I am not blowing into it, so you're going to have to do what you have to do." I have always heard that if you don't blow, they don't have a number to hold against you.

I know it is not going to get any better but I am surprised by the cop's demeanor change. "You are electing not to take this breathalyzer and to have me take you in."

I look him in the face and say, "I am not taking the breathalyzer."

As soon as those words come out of my mouth, his whole tone changes, his attitude shifts and he grabs me by the right bicep. My back is to his white Baltimore County police cruiser. He has hold of my bicep and spins me to face the car and kicks my right foot out wide. Suddenly I feel a hand push between my shoulder blades and my chest hits the hood of the cruiser. He has hold of my right arm the whole time and I feel his hand slide to my wrist. As I recognize his hand, I feel him kick my left foot out further. He cuffs my right wrist and grabs my left wrist, cuffing it. This is the first time I have been handcuffed and arrested and it doesn't feel anything like I thought it would. Really, it's anticlimactic. He starts with the "You are under arrest, anything you say can be held against you" that I have heard on tv so many times, but the feeling is numb, busted, caught. I am pushed into the back seat of his cruiser and he walks to the front seat. I look back over my shoulder and see Danielle in her car, looking at me with sad eyes. I want to wave to her, to let her know I am okay, but I can't lift my hands from behind my back, so I just nod. I don't know if she sees me or not, but she doesn't react.

The day started out so promising, so good, and now I end it in a cop car, about to face charges. When my right wrist gets handcuffed to the bar in the police station and I am told to wait until I am booked, I realize that I am screwed. My parents are going to kill me, my coach might find out. When I come out into the lobby at 3:45 a.m., Danielle is asleep in the chair in the corner. I look to the left and a male cop, a young guy who looks about twenty-five years old, looks at me and says, "I told her to go home, but she said she would wait. You have a nice friend there."

I lean over her and touch her arm. She looks up with exhausted eyes and squints in the bright lights.

"Hey, you didn't have to wait here," I say.

"I didn't know what was going to happen to you." She starts to stand up and look for her purse.

"Thanks for waiting," I say as she grabs her purse. I reach for her hand with my left hand and push the door with my right, hard enough for it to open for both of us.

We walk in silence to her car and drive to my house.

"I was really hoping to spend the night with you. Sorry about screwing it all up," I say as I get out of her little white BMW two-door.

"Don't worry about it, we'll do it some other time. Good luck with your parents."

"I'm going to need that," I say as I close the door. I lean into the open window. "Thanks again, you really are too good to me."

"'Bye, Mark," she says as she drives away and I wonder if that is the last time she says goodbye to me or if she will ever give me another chance. This is not the first time I've let alcohol get in the way of showing Danielle she is special to me. It just seems that no matter what I do with her, it ends with me blowing it.

|||||||||||||||||||||||||||||||||||||||||||||||||||||||||||||||

CHAPTER 03

|||||||||||||||||||||||||||||||||||||||||||||||||||||||||||||||||||

Kevin, Roy, Lucy, Stephanie, all of us make plans. There is a party tonight. The girls call their friends. We will meet at Karen McGarvey's house in Mt. Washington. This is a big old wooden house at the bottom of a long hill. By the time we come back from a beer run, there are fifty people outside in her cul-de-sac. We are heading downhill, a long straight run from the very top of Mt. Washington to the dead end of Aviator Way into this mass of people. Greg has volunteered to drive and inside his car are six cases of beer and two bottles of Jim Beam. We're loaded up and, regardless of whether anyone else brought any beer, I have plenty. I know we will be giving away a lot of beers but we'll put away at least three cases and one of the bottles. We can pass around the rest to get this party started.

While I am thinking this, I feel the car accelerate, shift gears and accelerate again. Greg is driving a five-speed manual Volkswagen Golf. He has just slammed it into another gear and I yell, "What the fuck are you doing?" as loud as I can. I look at Kevin, a guy that loves a good time, but when he sees things about to go bad, he just goes "fuck." He braces. The look on his face tells me "we are toast."

I look at Greg and reach for his shoulder. I look through the windshield and Greg flips the high beams. I can see faces, girls in winter jackets, talking to boys, guys in packs all suddenly turning and looking into the glaring headlights in sheer panic like their lives are about to end. At about 150 yards and Greg takes his hand off the stick shift and reaches down. He moves his foot from the accelerator to the brake pedal. I see Art in the front seat put his arms out to the side, one against the door and the other one towards Greg. At 100 yards, one-tenth of a second later, Greg slams the brake and pulls the emergency brake hard with his right hand. With his left he turns the wheel hard counter clockwise and we start to spin. Brakes scream, tires screech, I smell hot rubber and we all spiral inside a tin can, towards a crowd of frightened friends. We come to a rest, untouched thankfully, facing up the hill, crooked, having done more than a 180-degree turn. I look at Art and Kevin, and they both look like they are ready to explode. I look at Greg from the back passenger seat, and he looks crazed. I yell, "What the fuck are you doing?!" right into his right ear as loud as I can. "You fucking idiot!"

Greg looks straight ahead with a twisted smile and both hands back on the wheel, "Did you see their faces? They were scared shitless."

Art says in a monotone voice with great conviction, "You...are...a...fucking...idiot. That was so stupid. You are a fucking moron." He opens the door, looks left at Greg in his seat and says, "I will never ride with you ever again. That was so fucked up. You just played with their lives."

"I did not, dude, I was just fucking around," Greg says.

I am getting out of the back, I can't sit in this seat any longer. Kevin is already out, walking away to the side, not into the group of panicked people, post-panicked really, because they know what a close call it was. My friends aren't dumb and I imagine they are pissed.

Art puts one foot out of the car and looks back at Greg. "That is not 'just fucking around', that is fucking with people's lives. That's over the line, that's way over the line." He puts his other foot out, stands, takes the door frame at the corner of the window and slams the door shut as hard as he can. He rocks the car. By now, I have opened the hatchback, hearing everything, and with my back to the crowd, I grab two cases of beer and put them on the closest curb. As

I walk back to the hatchback, Art makes eye contact with me and says, "We need to find another ride home."

I roll my eyes and say, "No shit, that was way fucked up."

He grabs two cases and I take the brown bag with two square 750-ml bottles of Jim Beam and place them sideways on top of the beer. I reach back into the hatchback and get the other two cases. When I look forward, I see Greg, kind of frozen with his hands on the wheel. The car is still running and, his eyes, in the rearview mirror, are distant. He hasn't looked back or said anything else.

I rest the beer between my knee and the side of the car and close the hatch. I say to Art, "I'm going to take this over here. Go put that in Siz's car and we can use his trunk." I walk toward the curb and the crowd while Art walks the other way with his back to the crowd, blocking his stash. As I get there, Kevin has picked up the other beer and we all head to Karen's backyard. By the time we set them on the bottom step of her back porch, twenty-five people are coming into the backyard with more on the way. Kevin grabs a fresh beer and hands it to me, takes one for himself and without prompting, cheers mine as I am opening it. "Cheers, at least we weren't accessories to the murder of like twenty people. Dude, we could have killed all of them."

"I know, I don't know what that dude is doing, he's got problems," I say as I lift this cold beer to my cold lips. We are surrounded by people from all the schools, most talking in hushed whispers, trying to figure out if they are safe here, if anything else is going to come out of the woods. As I hand out beers to Lucy, Stephanie and her friends, we talk about Greg and his idiocy, parties, sports, music, school dances, and all the other things seniors in high school talk about. Art emerges through the crowd in the backyard with a beer in one hand and his hat in the other. "Donations for the next beer run," he says. Girls are putting money in the hat, I see guys digging into their pockets. It looks like a collection basket in church.

When I look back at Kevin and Lucy, Karen McGarvey surprises me by sneaking up to me. She says as soon as I look at her, "What was he doing with his car? He could have killed somebody."

"He could have killed more than just somebody," I answer. "I don't know what he was doing."

"I don't want him here, okay? I don't want him here. Tell him he can't stay."

"Alright, alright, I will tell him he can't stay," I say.

"Tell him he can't be here, okay?" she says, with emphasis.

"I will, Karen, I promise," I say as I lean down, pick up a beer and hand it to her. She takes it from me and opens the can. I cheers her beer and we both chug a little. "Thanks for having the party," I say.

"My parents are gone, but you can't let anybody inside. You and Artie have to help me keep everyone outside."

"We'll make sure everybody stays outside."

Lucy steps into our conversation. "Your friend Greg is a moron," she says as she puts her arm around my shoulder.

"You're right, Lucy," I say, "you're right. Now, listen, I need you to find me a nice girl who wants to take me home. There is no way I am going home with him."

"I hear your girl Denise is coming, with Stacey and Kristin," she says. Denise is the same tall beautiful girl that I always seem to mess up around. She is super kind, really patient and always happy.

"Good, you have to let me know when she gets here. Plus, you have to put in a good word for me, okay?"

"I will, you know I will, but I think she likes you already," she says. I hope so.

We party, I keep an eye out for Greg and drink with friends. Roy shows up, boys from Grayson show up. When I see Greg slinking around later, I tell him, "Dude, Karen does not want you here. You need to either leave or avoid her like the plague. If she sees you, she's going to kick you out."

Denise shows up fashionably late and we connect. She is one of the most easy going girls I have ever met. She looks great and I mention to her that I need a ride home.

"No problem," she says, "I can drop off Stacey and Kristin at Kristin's house and drive you home."

Sweet, I think in my own head. She is planning some time for us to be alone without my even suggesting it. Once I suggest it, I'm a pig, but when she does, it's a nice idea.

In the backyard of Karen's house is a big tree with a single swing coming off a branch that is at least fifteen feet in the air. People are taking turns sitting on it, with someone pushing them. As this night has gone on, the daredevil in everyone has increased and people take turns jumping off at higher and higher heights.

The tree is on a hill right next to the porch, as most of the party has drifted down the hill towards the back of the yard. Siz is pushing Stacey on the swing and she is not happy with the height that he is pushing her. Since she is screaming, Siz is laughing and pushing her higher and higher. I look up and see Siz. When the swing comes back to him, he starts to run and push the swing over his head as he runs underneath it for maximum height. Stacey yells, "Don't do that again and somebody please help me!" I see Siz circle back to push her again. This time as I watch, Siz pushes her as he runs under the swing. But this time, he can't stop. His momentum takes him to the end of the hill and down. His feet are moving too fast to slow down, his body hurling to the bottom of the hill. The thoughts of Greg's asshole move from earlier float back into my head. I see Art, standing at the bottom of the hill, facing sideways, towards me, talking to Kristin. I yell "Art!" right before impact, too late. I watch as Art looks to his right and up the hill as Siz runs him over. The collision of these two 200-pound football players sends beer in the air, bodies flying, cups and cans flying and crunching, bodies thumping and thudding, muffled girls' screams, guys' grunts and groans, people releasing short breaths as they try to recover. A party scene of forty to fifty people is in disarray as at least twelve are knocked over, ten are pushed back and at least another ten are soaked in beer and Jim Beam. I sprint the twenty feet to Art and Siz and look at both. Siz is getting to his feet as Art is on one knee. His hands are cupped under his face as blood streams into both hands. He hurls the blood to the side and continues catching the fresh blood.

I say, "Art, look up."

When he looks up, I see his upper lip, or what's left of it, dangling under his nose. Even in the dark, with just moonlight, I can see at least a two-inch slice of skin, basically from under his right nostril past the other side of his nose, down to his lip. It is a piece of skin, dangling on a 45-degree angle, gushing blood.

"Art, your lip is cut," I say.

He takes his right hand and grips the slab of skin. He starts to pull it off. My stomach drops.

"No, man, no, don't pull it, hold it on there," I yell, just to make sure he hears me.

By now, everyone is up and regaining their wits. No one is yelling or crying. I think that Art is the only casualty.

"Hold on," I say. I take off my jacket. I have a blue long sleeve Summer House tee shirt on, one of my favorites. I peel it off real quickly and wad it into a ball. I have a regular white tee shirt on underneath and the air hits me. It is cold. I press the shirt onto Art's face, under his nose and Art grabs it with his right hand. "Hold it there, try to stop the bleeding," I say as I zip my coat back on.

Siz is next to me and Kevin is on the other side. "Art, let's go, let's get you to the hospital," says Siz.

Siz grabs Art's left arm and I put my arm around his waist, while Art keeps his head down, nose in my bloody shirt. Kevin is walking with us and he opens the passenger door.

Art says, in a muffled voice through the bloody shirt, "I don't want to bleed all over your car."

"Don't worry about it, just get in the back," says Siz. Kevin opens the back door and Art ducks his head to get in. When I look at Siz, he nods his head towards the back and I start to get in the back with Art.

"Hold up," I say as Siz slides into the driver's seat with the keys in his hand. "Kevin, take these, we got him," I say as I hand the last three six packs of Schaefer beer to Kevin. "I'll call you later," I say as Kevin grabs the beer.

"Art, I'll tell Kristin that they are going to fix you up better than before," he says.

I can't tell if Art is smiling or not but he mutters a sarcastic, "Fuck you."

"Fuck you, too, Art, later," he says, equally sarcastic. "Get that mug fixed up."

Kevin closes the door for us and Siz already has it in drive. We take off for St. Joseph's Hospital, the closest one we can think of.

When we walk in and the nurse sees all the blood on the shirt and his hands, she ushers Art right past the desk and into the back. We both stand there bewildered, and I think she senses that. From over her shoulder, she says loudly, "Have a seat, boys, I will be with you in just a minute."

We sit down in the sterile, plastic Brady Bunch chair, looking around, seeing two random people on the other side of the Emergency Room lobby.

Siz looks at me and I say, "Damn, man, I think I had a chance with Denise tonight, she said she would give me a ride home. I think Art had a chance with Kristin, too, until this happened."

Siz says, "I know I had a chance with Stacey until I scared the shit out of her."

"Fucking Kevin, he ends up with the beer and Lucy. Damn," I say. Then I add, "I should have let him get in the back seat with Art." We both laugh.

When the nurse comes back, she asks us questions about Art, his name, his parents, his phone number. We take turns answering her questions and then we sit back down in the seats. This time we sit in silence, in our own thoughts, until we see Mrs. Arthur come through the darkness behind the automatic doors. She looks at us with a mix of concern and worry. She doesn't stop to talk to us, though, as she walks right to the nurse behind the desk. They talk in hushed tones and Mrs. Arthur follows her through the doors into the Emergency Room.

Siz and I look at each other and without saying a word, get up and head towards the same automatic door. As we get to the sensor and the doors slide apart, I say, "I think she looked worried."

Siz says, "I think she looked pissed."

Both of us walk straight to the car, seeing the condensation that comes from each breath, as the temperature has dropped since we have been in the hospital. Neither of us knows what will be the result of this most recent screw up, but without saying, we both know that our friend will not be seen for a while. Face surgery and a solid grounding from his parents will put him on the shelf, for how long we will find out at the lunch table at school next week. For once, I'm not the one in trouble.

III

CHAPTER 04

IIIIIIIIIIIIIIIIIIIIIIIIIIIIIIIIIIIIIIIIIIIIIIIIIIIIIIIIIIIIIIIIIIII

It's the weekend before Thanksgiving of my sophomore year when I hang up the phone with Roy and the plan is set. I will meet him at his house and Timmy Shaeffer will pick us up there. We have a cooler of beer on ice in the trunk of Timmy's old blue Lincoln Continental. We are going to the play *Annie* at the St. Catherine's School. St. Catherine's is an all girls school out in horse country in Baltimore County. I've met a few girls from there with Roy over the summer and they like to have a good time. St. Catherine's is a school with a lot of fairly wealthy girls who have a lot of freedom. Many of them have travelled around the country and Europe, so they don't have the usual hangups of most high school girls. Some of them are really pretty and I've met their older sisters with Jamie, Liam and those guys. I'm not sure where we are going after the play, but the girls are ready to party, so I know it's going to be a good time.

"Mom, can you give me a ride to Roy's by seven? We have plans," I say as I walk into the kitchen. I notice she is more dressed up than usual.

"No, honey, I can't. Your father and I are having some friends over and they'll be here in about an hour," she says.

"That's plenty of time for you to give me a ride," I say.

"No, it's not. I have to finish cleaning up and there's food to cook. You can ask your father, but I don't think he will have the time either."

I walk out of the kitchen and go out the back door to find Dad.

He's putting charcoal in the grill and looks like he's still dirty from yard work all day. Chances look pretty slim but I'm asking anyway.

"Dad, can you give me a ride to Roy's house? He wants me to get dropped off there."

"Mark, I can't. I have a few things to do before company comes over and I still have to take a shower," he says. "As a matter of fact, take that beer right there and put it in the cooler. There are two bags of ice in the freezer downstairs. Put the beer in there and go get the ice."

"Can't you give me a ride, please?" I say as I rip the cardboard off the case of Budweiser cans. As I stack them in the cooler, I plead my case. "I can spend the night at Roy's, it's okay with his parents, I just need a ride and I won't ask again, please."

"No, not tonight. You should have said something two hours ago," Dad says.

"Two hours ago, I had to cut the grass and then you made me clean the basement," I said, the irritation in my voice easily caught by Dad.

"There's no need to be a smartass, Mark. I can't give you a ride, your mother can't give you a ride. We didn't say you can't go, you just have to find your own ride."

I call Roy, but he can't get in touch with Timmy. Lauren isn't at home to give me a ride, she is at Martha Brune's house and it is not looking good at all.

Roy calls me back to tell me that he is going to meet Timmy at Windy Valley, a convenience store about a half-mile from his house. I don't have any way to get there. It is at least ten miles from my house and they are meeting in thirty minutes. I make one last desperate try.

"Come on, Mom, can't you just give me a ride, please?" I ask again.

"No, I can't and don't ask me again," she says. I mutter under my breath and head upstairs, determined not to be nice to any friend of theirs who shows up tonight.

Instead of partying with Roy, Timmy and some pretty, fun girls, I watch the Michigan Wolverines with Jim Harbaugh at QB beat Illinois in football. It's a boring game and it fits a boring night. Even though I'm hungry, I refuse to go downstairs and be nice to my parents' friends. I am sure it is the Brunes, the Talbots, people like that. People I have known my whole life, but I don't have any interest at all in talking to any of them. I don't want to be nice, I don't want to make small talk, I don't want to answer any of their questions. Instead, I mope in isolation, miserable in my own room.

When I wake up in the morning, I'm hungry and head downstairs to eat some breakfast. Dad is awake on the couch, reading the newspaper.

"Morning, Mark, how did you sleep?"

"Fine," I say, not interested in furthering any conversation, considering I had to stay home on a perfectly good Saturday night.

"Did you talk to Roy this morning?" he asks as he folds the paper and puts it down next to him.

"No, I just woke up," I say. "Are you going to want us to go to church?"

"Not this morning," he says, "but I think you need to give Roy a call."

"Why?"

"I just think you should give him a call," he says again.

"I'm going to get some breakfast," I say.

"No, I think you should give him a call right now," he says.

"Okay," I say curtly and quite honestly, disrespectfully.

"Morning, Mr. Wilkerson, is Roy home?" I ask when Roy's father picks up.

"Yes, Mark, but he's still sleeping. I'll have him call you when he wakes up."

When I hang up, my father asks if I've talked with him. "No, he is still asleep," I say, annoyed, and walk into the kitchen to get something for my growling stomach. "Are you done with the sports page?"

"Yes, right here," he says as he holds it up in the air. I walk back to the living room, grab it from his grip and walk back to the kitchen. I pour a bowl full of Fruit Loops, fill it with milk and bury my face in the sports section. The last thing I want to do is talk to my parents about anything.

An hour later the phone rings and I hear Mom call out, "Mark, phone is for you! It's Roy."

I pick up in the hallway upstairs and yell downstairs, "You can hang up, I got it!" As is customary, neither Roy nor I say anything until we hear the other phone click. Once I'm satisfied we can talk, I say, "Hey, Roy, my dad wouldn't stop telling me to call you this morning. Sorry about that. Did you guys have a good time last night?"

"Mark, it was crazy. Timmy crashed his car last night. He ran into a tree on Greenspring Valley road. Fred, Kathy and Marsha were with him. They were all hurt real bad. I was in Campanella's car and we were the first ones there. Fred and Kathy are in the hospital, I think Marsha is going to be okay, but I think Timmy might have died. He was messed up bad."

"What do you mean? How did it happen?" I ask.

"They left the play before us. We were in the parking lot drinking beers and a lady at the school told us to get off the school grounds. So those guys left first and we waited for Cassandra and Karen to come out. They had to take off their costumes and their makeup and stuff like that. So we waited for them and left about five minutes later. We were all going to my house since my parents were at your house. When we came down Greenspring Valley Road, we saw their car against the tree." Roy starts to whisper. "It was fucked up, they were all hurt bad. The front of the car was mangled in the tree. Me and Campanella pulled Marsha and Fred out of the car. Kathy was sitting up front, but we couldn't get her out of the car. She's in bad shape, her face was bloody as shit. I think she broke her cheek, her eye socket, her shoulder, she was messed up. Fred definitely broke his leg and his arm, he might have broken his hip. Marsha wasn't that bad, I think she's okay. She went to the hospital, too, but I think she is going to be okay."

"What happened to Timmy?" I ask.

"We couldn't get him out," he says, as his voice cracks and I can tell he is crying. "He was bleeding out of his mouth and his seat was smashed into the steering wheel and the dashboard and we couldn't move him. By the time the ambulance got there, he wasn't breathing." Roy sounds scared and exhausted just describing it. "The only reason I wasn't in the car is because I told Campanella I would wait with him for Cassandra and Karen. Otherwise, I would have been in there with them. I know, if you were with us, you would have been in there with them. Dude, we both could have died last night and for some reason, we didn't. But I think Timmy did. I don't know for sure, but I think he did. The paramedics made us all stand back. And wouldn't let us see him, but I don't think he was breathing. I'm not sure but I'm going to find out and I'll call you." He is crying and sniffling and, for some reason, I look at the clock. It is 10:15 a.m. and I realize that this day will change everyone's life. And there is still the rest of the day left.

"What did Roy have to say?" Dad asks.

"He told me there was an accident last night, that Fred, Kathy and Marsha got hurt pretty bad and that Timmy is in really bad shape," I say.

"I'm sorry to hear that. We got a call early today from Wilkie, and he wanted you to know that not going last night may have saved your life," Dad says.

"I don't know about all that," I say, although there is a sense of relief. I would have been in that car because the cooler was in that car. Maybe it would have been different if I was in the car, maybe it wouldn't have been different. I don't know, but I do know that I just dodged a bullet. But if Timmy is really dead, it changes everything.

Five days later, I'm sitting in St. Stephen's church in the city with several hundred other people–adults, students, friends, classmates. We are here for Timmy's funeral, and while some people joke and laugh, most of us, the high school students, are still shocked. We are here to bury our friend, our teammate, our classmate, our opponent, our peer. I sit with Roy, Charlie and Campanella about ten rows back from the altar, in this old, well-lit, stone church for a noon mass. Timmy went to St. John's with Roy, Charlie and Campanella. I've known him since eighth grade when he came over to my house with Roy. We played on the same summer league lacrosse team, drank at the same parties, liked the same girls, took the same risks. He was a good lacrosse player, a middie with good stickwork and a nose for the goal. I liked playing with him because he was tough. I can't say that about all St. John's players but Timmy was tough, not afraid to hit after the whistle or throw a hard slap check and was always willing to run through a check to get a shot off. He liked to take wings on faceoffs just to get a hit in on somebody. He always eyed up the wingman on the opposite wing and would try to run him over when he wasn't expecting it. He called it his free shot.

Timmy was not tall, kind of skinny and full of fight, that is what I liked about him. He always had nice clothes, but they were usually dirty and sometimes ruined after a night of partying. We would stay up late to throw eggs at cars or stop by a Loyola College party, just to see if we could get into it. Timmy lived in a big house in a nice part of the city called Roland Park. Roland Park sits in between the campuses of Loyola College and JHU, so we would use their lacrosse fields to practice and scout out the campuses for parties. We knew we looked young and would usually get kicked out, but it never stopped us from trying.

Now, all of that is gone and I am trying to understand how this could happen so fast. I understand Pop's dying. He was over eighty years old and had been sick. Timmy just turned sixteen, had his whole life in front of him and was in perfect health. We are not old enough to bury our friend, our peer. But, I guess we are, because this is what we are doing.

Just as I look down at the program, I hear a slow murmur and look up. Fred is being rolled into church in a wheelchair with a cast on his left leg, a cast and sling on his left arm and bandages on his face. He is rolled to the right side of the front row and a hush falls on the whole crowd. Timmy is dead and Fred looks like he barely escaped.

Within minutes, a fifty-year old priest flanked by a couple of altar boys walks down the main aisle of the church, singing a solemn hymn to organ music. His look is serious and he never looks right or left, just straight ahead. When he walks past my row, I look at the two altar boys. They could have been me four or five years ago. They look innocent and hopeful, all the while having no idea that the people in this crowd have now seen the reality of drunken behavior and careless adolescence end in death. A person, possibly an older brother, won't be at the kitchen table for dinner, or they won't be piled into a station wagon to watch his umpteenth game. I look at their innocence and surprisingly, envy it. Here I am in church and it is for all the wrong reasons.

As I zone out in my own thoughts, we all sit and stand together, listening to the familiar readings and passages, ancient words read to a dazed crowd, searching for meaning in today's circumstances.

When the priest stands at the lectern to speak, his voice is deliberate and controlled. He looks at the crowd and asks, "Who wants to be here today?"

In my mind, it is a question that has no right answer. Of course I don't want to be here. But, I would not miss the ceremony that says goodbye to my friend. I want to be here for his family, for his classmates. But I don't want to have to say goodbye. While I sit and ponder the question, the priest goes in an entirely different direction.

"While no one wants to be here, in church on a Friday morning, missing family matters, school or work related, everyday activities. We should want to be with friends and family. We all should cherish every moment that we have with the ones we love, the people that fill our hearts, the moments we have that are precious. I look out today at the youth in this audience, the vitality and futures that lie before us, on this day and each subsequent day. Our hearts grieve for the passing of Timothy, we express our sadness and invest in our healing. Timothy gave us an example of the preciousness of life. I have known Timothy since he was about nine years old, when I moved to this parish. And, I also know that he was never called Timothy, he liked to be known as Timmy, full of life and happiness and hope. He was mischievous, carefree, and a fun guy to be with," says the priest. "It is time now to speak about what can be done about Timmy's life and the need to use him as an example going forward. I have spoken with Timmy's parents and they have asked me to speak with you about his legacy. Timmy loved all people, young and old, rich and poor, sinners and saints, black and white, all people. Timmy laughed out loud with everyone but Timmy's death was brought on by alcohol use and drunk driving. He died because of it. Timmy's mother and father want this to be a lesson for you to learn from."

He keeps talking but I don't hear anymore. Timmy died because he drove into a tree after a few beers. He might have been distracted, he might have looked at the floor of the car for a cassette tape, he might have looked into the backseat, he might have taken his hands off the wheel to light a cigarette, I don't know. But I don't need this guy giving me a lecture about my friend. I want to walk out, but I can't. I sit, numb in my friend's death, sad and lost, trying to understand how we can put Timmy's loss, his parents' loss into a lesson for all of us in the crowd. Life isn't fair to anybody, no matter how rich, how smart, how nice. The good die young is what Billy Joel says, but it doesn't make it fair. Really, it makes life unfair. Timmy didn't hurt anyone, ever. He didn't treat people badly, he didn't steal from people, he didn't deserve to die.

By the time I wander out of the church, people want to make plans, but Roy and I walk downtown, towards the city. He has eight dollars and I have ten. We walk without talking, in sport coats and ties, to the harbor, where we sit by the water, silently, looking at people with eyes that have never been so jaded or desperate. I don't understand how life can be so cruel, so sudden and definite. How life can punch you in the gut and kick you in the balls at the same time? People who kill other people should die, not kids who drink a few beers and drive a car. I know it sounds arrogant or naive, I'm not sure which, but I never thought that kids from the suburbs died at sixteen. We were friends, teammates, drinking buddies, but now Roy and I will never see him again. I cry to myself, tears rolling down my cheeks, wiping snot with my coat sleeve. I look at Roy and he has his face in his hands, shoulders heaving, breathing deep through his nose. Two kids who have no idea what we have lost until it is gone and never coming back.

II

CHAPTER 05

IIIIIIIIIIIIIIIIIIIIIIIIIIIIIIIIIIIIIIIIIIIIIIIIIIIIIIIIIIIIIII

We are on the bus to UMBC for the championship game senior year of high school, having dispatched Grayson in the semifinals for the third time this year. Our opponent in the finals is Brice Academy, whom we'll face for the third time this season and for the third time in a row in the finals. We beat them this season at our place, first game of the year 7–1, and then at their place halfway through the season, 8–5. We know these guys, have played them a bunch of times through the years. The bus is loud, everyone's fired up but this is one of the times when I am not saying anything.

I look around, there is Kevin, ready to go. There's Garth, a year younger than I am and our resident lacrosse savant. He's a middie but he can do it all: faceoff, score, clear it, feed, everything. Shit, he is the best forward on the soccer team, can dunk a basketball as a point guard and runs the show in the midfield on this team. He and Kevin can both run like the wind. The difference is that Garth can shoot. He brings heat and he can sting corners. The two of them have been playing great over this last month of the season. There's Art, our hard-hitting, shit-talking defenseman, calling guys out. There is David Connors, my teammate since second grade and the quietest, most humble guy I know. He's our defenseman who guards every other team's best attackman. He and I work on each other in every practice. There is T Murphy, my co-attackman from the second grade. He, David and I have been doing this together for a long time.

There is Mark Talbot, my friend since I was born. Our parents were friends in their high school years. I never played with Mark until high school. He's one year younger than I am, too, and we were always on separate teams in rec league. But he is a perfect complement to T Burt and me, a lefty who likes to shoot. T and I are righties who play X and the right side. Mark is great on the fast break and he's a good cutter. Both T and I are good feeders, so it works out great for all of us. And there is Greg, miserable, not even looking up, messing with his stick. He got put on the second midfield a few weeks ago and hasn't gotten over it.

The banter on the bus is subdued, a low hum at this point. I sneak a look up front and see Coach is looking at the scorebook. I guess he is looking for their jersey numbers, but you can never know what is going to come out of his mouth. We like Coach, but we play for each other. He puts people in the game, but we make sure the best players play. Coach plays games with guys' heads.

After an embarrassing homecoming loss to Mount St. Joseph 6–5, we decided we were not going to let it happen again. I was hurt and didn't get to play in that game. I stood on the sidelines in street clothes watching their goalie make thirty-one saves. We could not throw it past him to save our lives and I had to stand helplessly and watch. If Art hadn't bent my knee backwards the day before at practice, I thought, I know I could have thrown at least two past him. Thankfully, after homecoming we were off a week from games over spring break and I played in the next one, a win at Severn. Both Mark Talbot and T got hurt in that game and I had to play with two sophomores, Willsy and JB.

We're perfect since homecoming, overall at 16 and 1, trying today for win number 17. Bresch, a defenseman, looks nervous and excited all at the same time. He has just started to hit his stride this year and he has been playing great. He's got a big assignment today, stopping their crease attackman and leading scorer, but Bresch has already played great against him twice this season. Brice Academy puts up a lot of goals against everybody but us. We have held them down on defense, and as an offense we don't let them get the ball back. T, Mark Talbot, Garth, Kevin, all of us hold the ball against them and force their goalie to make tough saves. Our team doesn't score a ton of goals, but other teams get jumpy against us, skittish. They shoot as soon as they get the ball because they don't know when they will get it back again.

Tommy G, our goalie, is five feet six inches tall, 140 pounds and cocky as shit. He is good and he knows he is good. We like to remind him in practice when we are lighting him up. He hates it, but it makes us all better. In looking around at my teammates, I check them off one by one. I see we are ready, I know we are ready. I tune my ears to the conversation, I listen. Garth is doing his usual routine, calling out the names of the other team's middies. I know I can get Garth going.

"Mark Daily! Trevor Boone! Brian Riley!" Garth yells with a pause between each name.

I interject with my common question to Garth, one I ask him before every game, "Garth, you want me to hold you back?" I ask, with a look of phony concern.

"Don't hold me back, Mark, don't hold me back," Garth yells.

"You bringing everything?" I ask.

"I'm bringing it all, Mark, I'm bringing it all," Garth almost chants, getting louder with each syllable.

"You bringing it, Kevin?" I ask the same way.

"Damn right," he says, a man of few words and many actions.

"Kevin is going to be running by guys in transition today, boys, better get open. He's going to be starting fast breaks!" I yell out loud to everyone. It is the start to our ritual.

"T Squirt is going to be riding his ass off today, boys!" Kevin yells.

T yells, "Tommy G's going to be stuffing guys all day, boys!"

Tommy G yells, "Bresch is shutting down that fat ass on the

crease!"

Bresch yells out, "Carl is going to murder Mark Daily!"

Garth interjects, "*I'm* going to murder Mark Daily!"

Carl yells out what someone else is going to do today in a confident manner, finds a fictitious play that they are going to make at some point in the game and when it comes true in the game, everybody goes nuts. We go around the horn, loud, high school, pumped.

I hear David Connors's soft voice. "Mark is going to stick bounce shots and over- celebrate." I look at David as he smiles, and everybody laughs. I know we are ready.

I yell, "Garth is going to sting some corners today, boys!"

Garth, who never ceases to amaze, yells, "And Whitey is going to ride home in the back seat!" as younger guys look around. Whitey is the manager, he rarely gets a mention. People hesitate until Garth finishes after a pause with, "with the trophy, boys!" and the bus goes nuts. This is it, this is what we do, this is how we get ready. Because when the doors of the bus open, we don't say much of anything after that. We don't yell or scream in pregame. We really don't raise our voices until the game starts. We talk to each other, but we don't hoot, we don't holler. We don't talk—we do, we act, we play. And, we plan to outplay you from the beginning to the end.

The pregame feeling out of the other team is the norm, but we don't pay them much attention. One thing I do know is that everyone is going to sneak a peek into the crowd. The story is that the place holds six thousand in the seats and with ten minutes on the clock before the game, the stands are full and the crowd circling the field is deep. There's a hill surrounding the field so you feel like you are playing in a pit with fans all around you. This the main event with players from every high school, college players home for the semester, lacrosse fans from everywhere. It is packed.

Kevin, T, David Connors and I are captains. We win the coin flip and defend the goal in front of our bench for the first quarter.

We will be shooting in front of our bench in the second and fourth quarters. We jump out to a 2–0 lead on a T Burt goal and a Garth worm burner. Mark Daily scores for BL to make it 2–1 before I cut and get a feed from Mark Talbot, of all people, to make it 3–1 at the end of the first quarter. Garth gets another at the start of the second. A Kevin fast break finds me feeding Mark Talbot on the doorstep and it is 5–1. The half ends with us up 6–2 and it feels like we are dominating them. By the time the fourth quarter starts we are up 7–2 and we are sucking the life right out of them. Our defense is suffocating them all over the defensive half of the field and we are dominating the ball on our offensive end. Garth gets a low-to-high highlight reel goal on extra man in the fourth and we finish them off 8–3. Coach subs out all the starters with two minutes left and we flood the field when the final whistle blows. We throw our sticks and gloves in the air, we dogpile. We have done this before at the JV level, but we act like we've never been here before. It is the one time that Coach lets us do what we want after the game. We high five the fans, we hug our parents, we yell with our fellow students.

Kevin stands in front of the fans, arms raised, while Garth sneaks behind him and pulls his shorts down to his ankles. Kevin stands frozen momentarily, in his spandex, before the funniest look of panic comes over his face and he reaches to his ankles and pulls his shorts up. I grab Garth in an embrace and we both fall over laughing. More than six thousand people just watched us dominate for the championship. The work, the runs, the hurt, it is all worth it.

By the time we get to the bus, sweaty and thrilled, eyeblack smeared on our faces, everyone clears a path in the aisle as Whitey walks to the back seat with the trophy. He is walking on his toes, in his tie and sport coat. And when he turns and faces us with a smile as wide as the city, he jumps up and plops down on the back seat. The bus explodes in noise so loud it shakes.

‖‖‖

CHAPTER 06

‖‖

Kevin, Art and I wake up around eleven o'clock and, after a bowl of cereal, head out to the 61st Street Beach in Ocean City, Maryland. The beach on 61st is wide and not very crowded. The wind is blowing 15 m.p.h. and it's only 70 degrees, so we just sit in a circle with some other friends until about two o'clock, when we decide to get lunch and a head start on drinking since Lucy, Stacey and Amy are having a party tonight.

I know it's going to be a good time because college friends will be in town and the other high schools like St. John's and Brice Academy will be down as well. It should be a great time. We play music as loud as we want, we live like adults and we do what we please. The carefree lifestyle of a high school senior heading into the summer before his freshman year of college, another level of freedom we have only imagined, is real and right before us. We only have one assignment: get a job by the end of senior week. Otherwise, we can party and celebrate our season, before we have to go back to Towson for senior prom and graduation. After that, it is back to the beach.

Art, Kevin, Bruce and I have gotten a place on 61st Street to work and party before college. We know it is a swan song of sorts, but we're not in a hurry to get away from our friends just yet. We knock down jobs, Art and Bruce in restaurants, Kevin at a beach stand renting chairs and umbrellas, and me in the Sunshine House, a surf shop. Once that is taken care of, the rest of these days are for fun, beginning to the end of each day. Freedom and fun.

Around four o'clock after the beer run, Kevin, Art, T, Bruce, Greg, Beau O'Neil and I are drinking and bullshitting when Trevor and Harry stop by with the *Baltimore Sun* newspaper. Trevor and Harry go to Brice Academy and they play lacrosse there. They brought the paper because today is the day that the All-Metro lacrosse team is announced. Trevor drops it on the table in the living room and says, "Read it and weep, boys, once again the teams we beat get all the recognition. Nothing new here. Harry and I have to meet my uncle for dinner tonight, but we'll meet you guys back here at midnight. Tell Lucy and them that we're sorry we're missing their party."

Both of them head out as quickly as they came in, but we want to look at the newspaper and check out this year's All-Metro section. All of us are riding a super high because we avenged our loss in last year's championship game to Brice Academy, beating them 8–3. We beat Brice Academy in the first game of our league schedule this year and then just beat them in the last game of the season, the championship game. We were definitely the two best teams in the league, possibly two of the best teams in the country, along with West Genesse in New York. It feels really good to finish off the season with the championship and avenging last year's loss.

When we open the paper to see who made All-Metro, it surprises us to see that only one offensive player from Loyola, Garth, is named to the first team. We outscored every team in the league in every game but one, but nobody else from our offense. The page is full of guys that we beat, whose hands we shook after they lost to us. And there they are in the paper, smiling with pride while the last time I saw any of them, they were looking sad and pathetic after we beat them. Two of our defenders, Joe and David, made it and so did our goalie, Tommy. Greg is pretty despondent, because he made first team last year but this year he didn't make anything. He didn't play very well this year, and a lot of other guys stepped up instead. I know he's bummed out, but it will not stop the party.

As a matter of a fact, I know what we can do. I grab a popcorn bowl from the cabinet, crumple the sports page in a ball, stick it in the popcorn bowl in the middle of the living room and light it. We all take a chug of beer as the paper burns, and when the flame goes out, we throw the ashes out the front door, a cleansing of bad news. Plus, we have the championship, who needs All-Metro.

During the course of the night at Lucy, Kristin and Stacey's party, we play quarters, chug beers, and do shots of liquor. We're on top of the world. Our team has achieved the greatest success and, because of that, we're feeling like life is not just good but great. Our parents are extra proud of us, their young boys made good. The culture of our community, the town of Baltimore is so lacrosse-centric, that to win the finals cements you as legit. We don't need anyone to stick up for us, make explanations about our skills, the result speaks for itself. We have taken an eclectic group of friends and turned ourselves into winners.

Throughout the journey of the high school season, the entire team has been inside our little cocoon. Our meals are made, our beds are warm, our houses and our parents are our safety blankets. Everything but school and lacrosse is our pleasure. We are carefree and we know it. In fact, we are so carefree, we can get careless. And, because of that, we look out for each other.

Around midnight, I ask if anyone wants to go back to 61st Street but they are all wrapped into a girl, a scene, a drinking game, something. So I head out solo on my new graduation present, a new blue cruiser bike. The party has been great but I tell Harry and Trevor that I'll meet them at 61st Street. Twenty streets and a curb hop later, I pull my bike up onto the porch and walk inside. Harry and Trevor are already inside with a friend. There are some people you just like to hang out with, and Harry and Trevor are two of those guys. We drink, we play cards, we laugh. By the time all the liquor hits me, I know I need to find my bed.

I make it to the bathroom just in time to throw up in the toilet, finishing off a spectacular night for a seventeen-year old.

Debauchery, drinking, games, friendship, girls, teammates, respect from older guys, the works. Instead of sleeping off the booze, I lie on my mattress on the floor, chin wet with slobber and breath stinking from vomit. I am unable and unwilling to do anything about either. I close my eyes, measure my breath and pray for sleep. Silence overtakes me.

My mind wakes but my body can't move. I feel pain, strong pain but I don't know why. I open my eyes and I see fire. It's on my bed, it's surrounding me. I hurt, I throb in pain and I know I need to get up. My bed is on fire and I must get out of it! I struggle to my feet but the flames follow me. It isn't the bed— it's my shirt, my clothes! They're on fire and I can't escape! I'm engulfed in fire and I scream in pain. It's unbearable but I can't make it stop. I try to run but fall to my knees. My body is consumed in flames but resistance is futile. I flail my arms, but each time I swing or pat to put them out, they just move up or down, not out. I feel skin blistering, I feel hair burning on my head–I am stuck in a suit of pain. I can see through the flames, but my vision is blurred, my movements in slow motion. I slump then try to stand again but I feel like I've been hit, run over really. I'm on the ground with my arms pinned to my side. The smell is repugnant. It wreaks of fowl air–the stench of scorched flesh, the mixed stink of burned hair, shirt and bedding. My nose burns, my ears ring and I start to go away. Then from somewhere behind me, I hear voices and I sense someone on me, hands on my back, slapping the flames.

The fire is suddenly gone and I am covered in a blanket. I am screaming and sick to my stomach. I think I've only been awake for a minute, but it feels like the longest sixty seconds of my life. Each second increased in pain, each second worse than the last, each second a struggle for survival. I vomit, I cringe, I feel lost and confused. My pain is a ten and my skin is gone. When I push the blanket off me and free my arms, my burnt shirt is stuck to my raw flesh and my exposed flesh is crippling me. The voices I hear are my friends Harry and Trevor, and they are telling me to be calm, to let them help me. It is living hell. This is the moment, the instant, that I feel like I am in a trauma, and, in fact, I am the trauma. This is the instant my old life ends and my new life begins. It hits me that I know I will never be the same again. The pain, the confusion, the panic are all over me. I am in more pain than I have ever felt or imagined and I am afraid it is only just starting. Put me out, please end this misery, please put me out.

Two drunken friends become my lifeline. You would think that survival instincts smash to the forefront. For me, it is a search for understanding. How did this happen? Who did it? For what reason? Those are the first thoughts in this instant. Those thoughts are fleeting as I change my mind to living, surviving, escaping this feeling of hell. Then the need to cease the immediate pain becomes the only goal. How long have I been on fire? They pat the remnants of the flames with a blanket and basically carry me to the shower. Thank God there is a girl there whose mother is a nurse. I hear her giving instruction on how to handle a burn victim. And that is what I have become, a burn victim. The water on my raw skin is excruciating. I stand, hand on the wall holding me up, barfing my drinks and eventually my bile. I can't lift my head, I scream out in pain. The smell of burned flesh is pungent and unforgettable. I become crippled in pain as I struggle for survival and understanding. I am on my hands and knees, on all fours, as the shower of cold water rushes over me. My pain is ferocious and the water both relieves and enhances it. I hold myself on all fours, muscles tense and shaking, my insides corrupt, my stomach vomiting with every breath. I hold my head to the drain, releasing alcohol, food, bile as I struggle for control, any control. Control of me, my body, my thoughts, my pain, my hope. I can hear voices assuring me of their concern, but I am alone in this new world.

Laura, a girl I have only met one hour ago, kneels down next to me. She helps me remove my wet, burned shirt in a way that causes me little additional pain. She is talking but her words are drowned in the water through my ears. As I turn to look at her, she is shouting instructions to the others. I return my face to the drain and my mind to nowhere, trying for numbness of feeling but not getting there. I scream through the shower floor and I hear the instructions get more urgent to the others.

Laura, through the water, touches my chin and moves my face towards hers. I see in her eyes and her mouth an assurance, but I can't hear her words. I can see she is helping but I don't know how. Her hand leaves my chin and I feel the water stop. My body cringes again and the dry air induces crippling body pain and vomit. Her hand touches the back of mine on the floor and I can hear her words.

"Try to get up, we need to take you to the hospital," she says.

I hear Trevor yell, "I got the car!"

Harry yells from a distance, "I got the ice water!"

Laura has unmistakably taken control. She gives instructions, she comforts me and demands attention.

"Open the door, cover him in the sheet but don't let it touch. Harry, every time he wants, pour the water on him." All of this is said as I am being led to the door. I exit the front door, the same front door I entered one hour ago on top of the world and bound for fun. I step onto the concrete front porch and into the dark night. The small two-door car is waiting, lights on, engine running. Trevor and Laura help me into the front seat, Harry stationed next to me, bag of ice filled with water and cubes at the ready. I sit and the sheet makes contact with my exposed skin. I yelp and Harry pours ice water on my neck and it runs down by torso. It does not relieve me as much as it changes the pain locations. I call out, "Do it again please, do it again," gasping. The rush of freezing cold water comes over again and fills my soaked shorts. By now, Trevor is behind me in the car, having scrambled through the driver's side door. Harry hands him the bag of ice and water and runs around to get in the back seat, behind Laura.

"I know where we can go, hurry up!" Laura barks as she almost closes the door on Harry's leg. "We have to get there *now!*" She drives 61st Street and makes a right, heading north. I try to suck it up, but there is no stopping it. They look panicked, so I stare at the floor, doubled over in pain and trying to find one comfortable place.

Trevor says loudly, "We are going to get help, Mark, just hold on."

I grunt, "I'm trying, man."

"We're almost there," he says.

"Did I see Greg?" I ask.

"Yeah, Mark, you did, I don't know what the—" he stops when I start to dry heave again.

It hits me as we drive and my mind races that I know the truth. I piece it together and I know without having to ask. Greg did this to me, Greg did this to me on purpose. I cannot imagine what my two drunken friends thought as they rounded the corner to see me on fire. My two friends, Harry and Trevor, have saved my life after my teammate tried to ruin it.

I am taken to the 75th Street Medical Center, which at 2 a.m. is closed. While we wait, first knocking on the door and searching for a pay phone, I see the looks of panic on their faces. I have two feelings: sympathy for them because they look scared, and sad because it makes me aware of how severely I'm hurt. I don't think any of us have seen anything this serious before now. Thankfully, a policeman sees us at the center and pulls over to help. An ambulance is called and I am to be taken to the hospital. While I wait, my friends alternate between covering me with ice and pouring water on me. This is the only relief from pain and the relief lasts only moments, not even full seconds. I don't know how long it takes for the ambulance to arrive, but by the time it does, I am in shock. I am shaking and writhing in so much pain that they strap my legs down to the gurney. Twenty percent of my body is ripped open and exposed and I must be strapped down and medicated.

Two hours ago, I was on top of the world with all my boys. An hour ago, I was on my way home to pass out and party another day. Now, fifteen minutes after waking, I am scorched, damaged, medicated, on the way to hospitalization and changed forever. How changed, how damaged, how scarred, I have know idea. It isn't anything but lights and bandages, stretchers and EMTs, medical language and urgency. I lie there strapped down and fill the ambulance with stench.

Thankfully, the medicine hits me and I fade to sleep knowing I am in bad shape. My body burns, burns so bad, my nerves are exposed. Even a breeze, moving air, or ointment sends me into agony. How could something hurt so bad? My head aches and throbs. Usually, you can feel yourself getting better, but not this, this only feels worse.

Hospitals to the injured are both havens and prisons. When you are stuck there as a patient, your needs are cared for in relation to your desperation. It hurts both physically and psychologically to be the worst person in the whole place. That is when you know things are bad. Emergency medical service is what is provided until experts or specialists can be found and alerted. These hours of personal isolation and assisted care leave you in a painful and desperate haze. Time stands still. Minutes are hours and hours are minutes.

The doctor in charge arrives and for one brief moment makes me realize things will be better. He tells me my situation and actually has a plan for my care. I can't hear much of it but do know that I am scorched on some parts of my arms, my shoulders, my chest and my back and I am still bubbling on my neck, ears and face. He doesn't show me what I look like and I don't ask to see. I'm trying to comprehend his words and stop myself from throwing up. Literally, my body has rejected everything I have in me. Puking from pain is something that I know, right now, I will never forget. Puking from pain is the epitome of going from bad to worse.

I am by myself, but the doctor tells me I only have to stay here until my parents arrive. The first hours after a trauma are the most desperate. My family has to find out. Their worry, their uncertainty, the thoughts that their child has been hurt. What does he look like? What's wrong with him? Questions only time and experience can answer. These hours for my parents must be hell. It has to hurt parents more than it hurts their kid. Will he ever be normal again? What kind of toll will it take on him? Does he even have the strength to overcome? All of these can be answered in time, but the future is distant and the need for care is urgent.

My mind drifts outside my body, and I am lost in thought. I go to a dark place in my mind, where I realize everyone of us has a friend or a friend's friend, who not just hurt themselves, but maybe even died in a car wreck, like Timmy. Almost every occurrence is alcohol-related. I am reminded of the finality of life often, and I won't say I ignored it as much as I dealt with it. It was a consequence of my actions. There is always a chance of horror if I am not careful. Talk about an odd contradiction, the safest and most wholesome actions pushed to the limits, which have resulted in deaths. It is a place many people have been and can only identify when they have been there themselves.

The time in what starts as these routine nights and what follows as major trauma always collapses into an instant. I'm not sure when mine changed to a trauma because of its bizarre nature. Was I followed home and stalked? Was it random? Was it planned? I know the result but I still desire the intent.

In order to think like someone else, you must put yourself in their shoes. Even so, I can't understand. I know Greg did this to me, but why? Was there a switch that was flipped in Greg's head when I burned the paper? Was a wound opened that needed to be dealt with? Did I forget that individual recognition is different from team success? The team is the one and only thing I've ever thought about. In my mind, team success was the only goal, individual acknowledgement hollow. The place to be is on top with your boys when the season is over. I think I took a shot at someone's individual accomplishment and belittled it in a hurtful manner. Everyone deals with hurt differently, some in ways you can't even imagine. I cry, this time not from pain, but from loneliness. I don't want anyone else on this journey, but I know I am on it alone, by myself. I drift away from reality again, this time hoping not to wake up like this again.

Unfortunately, when I do wake up, I'm in the same shape and apparently I need to go to a burn unit at a major hospital. Transportation is ready and my parents are on the way. The hospital I'm now in is three hours from my house in Baltimore. Those three hours must be a living nightmare for my parents. To understand what is in their heads is impossible. But I do know one thing: I know I have failed them again. They give their lives to my siblings and me and I treat that gift like shit. Was I drunk? Yes. Was I dumb? Yes. They love me again and again and I fuck up again and again. My heart hurts for them, and now I can't even stand up without puking.

I don't want them to see me. I don't want to see them cry. Complete strangers look at me with a pained look, every time. When my parents see me this desperate, I know my Mom will cry. I know my Dad cares, too. I know it's not their fault that I'm like this, but they'll think it is. Life makes changes and it is not always the fault of anyone or anything else, I tell myself. This happened because circumstances happened. Blame is for later, and it is definitely not for my parents. I hope they can realize this before they get here. All I can do is tell them I love them and that I am sorry, sorry for their pain.

I wake up to see them and the doctor. They're discussing me in low voices. I listen but don't hear. It's time to leave this hospital, but first I have to look Mom and Dad in the eye. I'm afraid of how they'll look back at me. Their love for each other and for us is what has always shone through all their actions. They've put us first in so many instances and ahead of their own ambitions so many times. Now, I don't know if they will be the same parents.

I speak but my throat is raw. I've breathed in fire and now my voice is a broken, raspy whisper. I say I'm sorry and my mom cries. They tell me I'll be okay and they love me. In the past, I have struggled to grasp their love. At this moment, I now understand. Love lasts forever and through anything. Mom holds the back of my head in her hands, Dad looks over her shoulder, both staring into my eyes. I look back at them from my bed, eyes filled with tears. I know I have been a typical teenage boy, resistant to their love and guidance, and now, at this moment, I realize that all they have ever wanted for me, is to know that I am loved by them. Their message has always been clear, they love me, they care for me. I just haven't always been interested in listening.

Moving at all sends enormous shooting pain in every part of my back and chest. From a bed to a wheelchair to a car is what has to happen and it takes everything I have not to pass out. Puking through the move only makes things worse. Thanks to the pills, I manage to sleep for the first hour of the trip with only one more hour to get to the burn hospital. The looks of desperation on their faces are enough to tell me my parents are sick with hurt. They never expected me to look and be like this forever. They sent me to the beach four days ago, a normal teenage kid and I have come back crippled and helpless.

In this next hour, each one of us cries and calls out to God, looking for answers. I tell them about my guilt, my love for them, my desperate sense of self. As lows go, I don't know how it gets worse. I have become the painful burden of the two people who not only loved me the most, but gave me the world as well as they could. The emotional weight of guilt wears heavy and hard. It feels like my world has imploded and I am now pulling the people who love me down with me.

My parents, however, refuse to be pulled down. An old family friend is a doctor specializing in burn patients and recovery. Turns out he is a renowned burn doctor from Germany whom I have met before as my fourth and fifth grade soccer coach. Dr. Andrew Munster meets us at Francis Scott Key Medical Center. He has already talked to my parents and told them what to do in transit and that he would be there when we arrive. He told them to prepare for the worst before they saw me, but I don't think they understood what he meant.

My dad is worried about how I am upstairs, in my head. He wants to know what I remember, what I did, who I was with last night. I can barely answer but he keeps asking. How I feel is a tough question to answer when it seems like this is death. My mom keeps asking God for answers as to why. God does not answer aloud that I know of.

When we get to FSK, I repeat the cycle of car to wheelchair to bed. Only this time it hurts worse. I have not had a pill in more than two hours and my skin feels like it's ripping apart again. I don't puke, though, and I don't know whether this is because I have built up a tolerance to the agony or not. Either way, it's an excruciating time until the next pill kicks in. Dr. Munster examines me on the bed after the next pills start to take effect and starts peeling off gauze over burns. Since there is no skin, the gauze is ripe with puss. Pulling it sends me into the fetal position, writhing. Dr. Munster is calm and composed throughout, voicing his treatment strategy to his nurse, who's writing away. He doesn't touch me but he moves around me. He bends down, looks me in the eyes and tells me, "You are going to be in pain for two months, but you are going to be okay."

I wish that felt good to hear but it doesn't. A hundred-degree cleansing bath is the first thing every burn victim gets and I am about to get mine. New pills are brought in and I take them without asking. I am scared, so scared I can't even see straight. Talking about moment to moment is one thing, but living moment to moment is entirely different. You swear to God and everyone else that you can handle everything that comes your way and then it comes, everything. Everything and more. I can't handle it and I know it. This is the kind of scared where you don't even know who you are. What I will become doesn't matter because I don't know who I am right now. I'm sinking and I don't know how to stop. I'm not sure I want to stop. Where will I go from here and who will I be?

The bath is sterile and ready and I must face the pain. From scorching to searing is what my body feels like as I don't know whether to go in slow or dunk my body to deaden the agony. In front of me is a big metal tub where I can either sit or stand. I choose to sit on a stool since my ass isn't burned. I guess some people don't even get that option. It is a ten-minute timed bath, so I must stay in, reminded of the torment in each tiny ripple of water. The nurses look at me but don't say anything. I cry. Surrounded by strangers in a sterile room, I cry because I can't stop the pain. "Pathetic" takes on a whole new meaning. No one but a burned, pained, naked me in a silver metal tub. I don't feel better because I am in a better place, I only feel worse. Where is rock bottom? I keep sinking and sinking and still can't see it. How can I be so pathetic?

I don't know how long I cry nor do I care. I blubber. My nose runs, my eyes water, I drool. It's the triple crown of balling. My world has changed and this new one is foreign. Its elements are pain, agony, uncertainty, remorse, guilt, sadness and fear, and they encompass me. I just want to sleep and there is no way it is going to happen now. When you live minute to minute, ten minutes can feel like forever. A sharp, throbbing pain that is excruciating hits the burned areas. Skin is fragmented on my body like a cheese grater. It flakes off and floats to the bottom, only to reveal raw flesh that shoots more pain. How can doctors and nurses say that I'm not that bad, that I'll be okay?

It is hard not to scream the whole time, but I do have to scream at times. I scream from my insides, which hurt almost as bad as my outsides. I close my eyes and go under the water, first my totally burned shoulder, next my burned neck and finally my head, with my burned ear and skin bubble on my face. I sink and I yell, muted finally, but in no less pain. My ears feel relief from the noise, but my head now throbs, pounding and hot. My eyes are open and my mouth is finally closed, the bubbles from the air are gone. As I sink in this metal tub, I think that this all happened last night, a normal night, with drinks and girls and on my own, partying. Now, I'm here. This is what last night has turned into, a pathetic pain that will go on forever. I'm not sure if it will ever get better, but I look up. I follow with a push and my head breaks the water. My mouth opens wide and I breathe, slowly to start, but shallowly so it doesn't hurt too bad. I look to my right and a nurse makes eye contact. I know my hair is flat against my head but I am not going to move my arms to fix it. She asks, "Do you feel any better?"

My eyes well up with tears, again, my lips quiver and I answer, "No, I don't."

"Before you get out of the tub, I want you to take this medicine," she says. She places a tray that stretches across the tub in front of me. The metal tray has three small paper cups on it, two cups each have two pills and one cup is filled with water. I look at her after she secures the tray and she looks back. "This should help with the pain. I want you to get out. In about three minutes and we are going to sit you down in the seat right there." I look over and there is an adjustable metal stool with four legs on rollers on a white floor. I lift my left arm, the one with fewer burns, out of the water and grab a cup. I usually eat and drink with my right hand so I try not to spill the pills. I pour them into my mouth and gently grab the water with my left hand. The paper cup falls into the water because I dropped it on the tray and it rolled in. The nurse picks the wet cup as I take a sip of water to wash down two pills. I do the same with the second pill cup but this time I place it back on the tray. I pick the water back up and finish it off. When I put the cup down empty, the nurse looks at me, smiles and says, "That should help you for a little while."

After she lifts the tray away, I can now see the water in front of me. It's brown and murky, and it has a smell of old medicine and wet bandages. I want to get out, but I know it will bring a new round of torture. It is tolerable right now and I don't want it to go back to the way it was. The nurse with short brown hair and a pretty face says, "Dr. Munster will be right in and he wants to take a look at you before I get you bandaged up, okay, so I'm going to need you to stand up."

"Do you have a towel I can use?" I ask.

"Of course I do, so when he comes in, I'll get you out of the tub," she says.

As the door opens, Dr. Munster walks in. "Mark, do you remember me?"

I nod my head. "Yes, sir." Dr. Munster, my grade school soccer coach at Cathedral, is from Germany and has an accent. I haven't seen him since eighth grade except maybe from a distance in church. I didn't even think he remembered who I was. And I would not have recognized him in these circumstances until he started talking to me.

"I want you to know, you are going to be okay, but you are going to be in pain for a while. I have a pretty good idea of your injuries and your treatment, but I want a better look, now that you are cleaned up. You are going to have to stand up, just to get out of the tub, and we can put you on this chair," he says.

He rolls the chair over to the bottom of the two steps outside of the tub. At this point in my treatment I'm able to sit even if I am in a lot of pain, but for some reason I can't stand up. Every time I have had to stand up, I get dizzy and start to barf. The whole time I'm standing, I bend over and heave, dry heave, all kinds of heaves. Only when I sit or lie down is it in any way tolerable.

When I look up from my seat in the tub, Dr. Munster is standing next to the steps, with a towel. I'm naked and I've been in front of the nurse since I got in, but now, getting out, I feel embarrassed.

The nurse stands on the top step and puts her wrist under my left armpit and her hand on my left shoulder. I'm able to take a big burp and I stand up. The water runs right over my burns and back into the tub and it buckles my knees. The rawest, deepest pain is all across my right side, my chest, my arm, my neck and my back. Now, my exposed nerves hit the cold hospital air and they are on fire. I have to sit on the side of the tub, naked, exposed, and I feel my gut ache.

Dr. Munster says, "Take your time, we have time."

I stand up again and lift my legs over the side of the tub, one at a time, step down two steps and sit my naked, burned, shivering body on the stool. I reach out my left hand as Dr. Munster gives me an unfolded towel and I at least can cover up. The nurse has all of the gauze pads and white cream sitting on the table as Dr. Munster puts his rubber gloves on his hands, and he now has his glasses on his nose. He starts talking. "Mark, I am going to clean off some of this skin that needs to be cleaned off and we are going to start getting you better. Please let me know if any of this gets to be too much, and I can stop. I will try to be as gentle as possible, but it is going to hurt. This is the starting point for your healing and I want to get you off on the best start that you can. We—Nurse Lennae and I, along with a group of others—are going to make you well again. Heck, Mark, we are going to make you better than well, we are going to make you great again." When he says this, we make eye contact and I shake my head side to side. "I know you, Mark, I remember those soccer games. We are going to get you back out there, running those fields, doing great things." The way he says it all, in his German accent, makes me smile and even laugh a little. For one second, it doesn't hurt.

Sitting on his own stool, Dr. Munster leans in to look at my body and starts talking a language to Nurse Lennae that I can not understand. I am hammered on pain pills, trying to sit up as he uses small utensils to pick off dead skin and a gauze pad to dab it dry. It doesn't hurt too much when he touches it with the tweezer, but it burns every time he dries it. He does this over my entire burned right side.

"Mark, Mark, are you listening?" says Dr. Munster.

"No." I try to concentrate. "What were you saying?"

"There are some things I want you to know, for when you are taking care of yourself."

I realize my whole upper body is dry, my burns are raw and exposed, and I think I must be numb, because it doesn't hurt as bad right now. The pain has finally dulled. My knees are weak, my body shakes, my breathing is slight and labored. My head is heavy and woozy, dizzy.

Dr. Munster continues. "I am going to put chromosomium cream on your burns and you have to keep them as clean as you can, at all times. If you think it is dirty or you spill something on it, or your gauze pads come off at all, you have to make sure we know. We will help you, we will fix it, we just have to know. We will be checking, but if anything happens, please tell me or the nurse. We will fix it, but you have to let us know.

"Now that I have looked at you, you should know that you have first-, second- and third-degree burns on your upper torso, your upper body. Your hand is one percent of your whole body. If you place your hands all over your body, you cover your whole body with a hundred handprints. Fingers together, thumb in, is one percent, did you know that?" he asks.

"No," I say as he holds out his hand to demonstrate.

"Well, you have about twenty percent of your body with burns, mostly second degree and some third degree. You have only two percent first-degree burns and they will heal fine with some cream." As soon as he says the word "cream" he touches my right hip with some cream that stings like a motherfucker. That must be his trick because I know he hears me tighten my gut and grunt "uuhhhh." He continues, "The second-degree burns, if we really take good care of them, will be okay, will recover nicely with little to no scarring as long," and he nods, "as we are diligent. Now, Mark, I think we only have three to four percent third degree and that still looks pretty good. Most of it is on the underside of your bicep and on your chest, but I don't think we will have to talk about skin grafts right now. I want to see how it progresses and we will keep a close eye on it."

He is continuing the application of the cream and still talking, but I have checked out of the conversation. Each touch stings, and the places he has already covered throb. I'm glad there is no mirror in here because I know I don't want to look at myself. Just as I think that, I look down at my chest. I have held my head up and my right arm out the whole time during the exam because this is the way to feel the least amount of pain, and I don't want to look. But I look down now at my chest and it is red, raw nerves, no skin on the right side. I have no nipple. I have one on the left side of my chest, but I don't have one on my right side. Part of my torso is charred, part of it is brown. Some areas are black, some red and raw, and all are blended on my skin like a puzzle. The smell of it is vulgar, sickly, raw. I can feel every one of my nerves, in full effect. My right arm is red, open nerves, no skin, and I think the worst is in my armpit. I do hear Dr. Munster say, "I think you were sleeping on your left side, and the liquid that was on you was on your clothing on the top, right side."

He holds my right elbow up with one finger and begins placing the cream under my forearm then my biceps. It doubles me over in pain. I hold my forehead in my left hand, left elbow on my knee, right elbow still up in the air held by Dr. Munster's finger.

"This area that I am touching is the third degree area. It is not in great shape right now, but I think we can treat it, keep it clean, and it will heal pretty well," he says.

Nurse Lennae now gets behind me and starts putting cream on my back. Either she is more gentle than Dr. Munster or my back isn't burned as badly because it doesn't hurt as much as the arm had. Nurse Lennae then puts her clean gloved hand on my left shoulder and presses my back straight up. From there, she smooths cream starting from the bottom and going to the top, what feels like my whole back. The more cream the more pain from the front, the side and the back. It takes my breath away. I feel like I have to throw up and, with my eyes closed, feel the touching stop. Ten seconds then twenty go by, each one hurting more than the last. I hold it in, I grimace, I gag, I whimper, "Get it over with." I know that there is more to do, more cream, more coverage and I want it to be over. Without ever opening my eyes, without moving my arm, like I have one hand up in court, the other on a bible. I remain as still as I can, shaking throughout my torso, and feel them continue, still gentle but with a bit more haste. I can't stand to look or smell, so I sit there, eyes closed, breathing through my mouth, slowly.

The only person I have ever seen burned is Johnny from *The Outsiders*, and he dies in the movie. I don't know how much better or worse I am than he was, but I can't believe he's worse.

"Dr. Munster, am I going to die? It feels like I am and I don't want to die," I say.

"Mark, you are going to live, okay, but you are going to be in pain for some time now. You are going to stay here with us and we are going to take care of you, let you rest and treat your burns until you are okay. I don't know exactly how long you will be here, but we are going to make sure you are healthy and healing."

He didn't say "healed," so now I have no idea how long I am going to be in pain. They finish all of the cream and gently place non-stick gauze pads on top of the cream all over my right side, my back and my arm. Within five minutes, they've wrapped me with rolled gauze. They swathe it across my thumb and up my arm, a long slow pain that finally gives my burns some cover. Nurse Lennae stops at the top of the arm and tapes it with the light white hospital tape. Next, she starts with a fresh roll of gauze and goes around my chest as I lift my arm. She goes around one time, and then another, and then another, until she covers my whole torso. She wraps up my neck and tapes that off, too. I am the Michelin Man in gauze pads.

Finally, I can get into a bed someone else has rolled into the room. I feel a little steadier on my feet and I climb in. As I step up on the bed, I catch a glimpse of my face on the window of the door, and I look like shit. *But...what is that?* "Dr. Munster, what is wrong with my ear? I can't feel it." My ear is the size of a lemon on the side of my head. I saw it in the reflection, but I don't feel like looking again. I just want to lie down.

"Your ear is a first-degree burn, similar to why your thumb is so swollen. You don't feel it because the second- and third-degree burns have all the attention of your nervous system. Your ear will be fine, I want to let it heal on its own. I don't want you to touch it with your hand," he says.

"Dr. Munster, I don't even want to move my hand at all, it hurts too much already," I say.

"Let's take you down the hall to your room and get you a little something to eat, some applesauce, and then you can get some sleep," he says.

We head down the hall and I realize I have no idea what time it is. How long have I been like this? I lie on my side and stare: the nurses' station goes by, an empty stall in the emergency area goes by, a tub—*was that my tub?*—I close my eyes. When the bed stops moving, I hear voices, it sounds like Mom and Dad. I hear Dr. Munster's accent but I can't open my eyes. I am aware of them but out of it. I drift and drift, in dull pain the whole time.

When I wake up, I have an IV in my left arm and pain screams along my whole right side. It's still not a dream. I was hoping that it was, but this is definitely real. "What day is it?" I ask the nurse when she comes into the room.

"Today is Friday, you just got here yesterday. I put your IV in last night so you could get something for your stomach and the pain. Are you feeling any better?" she asks. She's a new nurse, someone I've never seen before.

I'm lying in the fetal position on my left side, with my left arm out straight and the IV dripping liquid. "I don't feel any better, but I don't think I feel any worse and that is the first time I can say that. If it's Friday, what day did I get hurt?"

"You were hurt on Wednesday night and you got here yesterday around four o'clock in the afternoon. The doctor was with you for several hours. You must have been tired, because you slept through the night last night. I started last night at eleven and you were a great patient. I gave you your medicine at 3 a.m., and that is when we did your IV also," she says.

She touches my left wrist, looks me in the eye and says, "Let me know if you need anything, okay? Last night, you called out for something, but I couldn't understand what it was. Please let me know what you need and I'll try to help."

"Was it loud?" I whisper.

"Ah, um, yes, it was and that's okay, I just didn't know what you wanted or who you were asking for."

"Okay," I say, unsure if I was yelling out in pain or calling for someone for help. I don't know and I am not sure I even care. I do know I had some crazy, crazy dreams and I can only remember snippets of those.

"Your family just went downstairs to get something to eat. I'll let them know you're awake," she says.

"Okay," I say again, still staring straight ahead, lying on my left side.

When Mom and Dad, Lauren and Mary walk into the room, the look of sorrow is across all their faces. Mom keeps crying the whole time she looks at me, and Dad just shakes his head and says, "We talked to Dr. Munster and he told us you'll be okay. He said it's going to take a few months to get back to your full strength, but he's given us a pretty good idea about your injuries and your recovery. Mark, Dr. Munster is an expert in burn care, so I want to make sure we do everything he says in order for you to get better. You already look better. How are you feeling?"

As I get ready to respond I look at Lauren and Mary, and they both look pale and tense. Neither is changing her depressed expression but both their eyes narrow, as if trying to see inside my mind. Neither one is saying anything, and the way I look must scare the shit out of them. I do feel better, but it hurts really bad whenever I move at all. I am trying to lie still because it's the only way I can stand it. "Mom, Dad, I am really sorry about this," I start to cry, "I didn't mean for this to happen. I'm sorry you have to look at me like this. I really was trying to stay out of trouble."

"Mark, it's okay, you didn't do this on purpose. It's okay, we love you and you're going to heal," Mom says through her crying eyes and scratchy voice. I don't know how long they've been awake, but they both look tired, they look like their spirit is broken. I've failed them.

"I'm sorry, I promise, I'm sorry," I say.

Mom looks over and kisses my hair and touches the part of my face that isn't burned. Her touch makes me finally feel something good on my body, while the rest of my burn sears pain through my chest.

"I want you to keep resting. We're going to talk to the nurse right now, okay?" Mom says.

I nod my head and lie still, crying tears that roll across my nose and the side of my face. Lauren and Mary still don't say anything, they just drop their heads and look at the floor as they walk out of the room with Mom and Dad. Although the sun peeks through the closed blinds, the light is off and the color of the room is gray. The only noises I hear are background sounds in the hallway. The door opens and the new nurse walks in with four pills, two for pain and two vitamins. I take the pills while I am on my side and I spill water down my cheek and onto the bed, the same path that my tears took ten minutes ago. I close my eyes and ask God, "Why does this happen to me, why does this hurt so bad, what did I do to deserve this?" I cry and it hurts— my heart, my burns, my pride, my life.

|||||||||||||||||||||||||||||||||||||||||||||||||||||||||||

CHAPTER 07

|||||||||||||||||||||||||||||||||||||||||||||||||||||||||||||

"Mark, can you wake up? Can you talk to these policemen? They're here to see you," says Nurse Lennae. I try to pull my mind to attention. She's back and I feel better just seeing her.

"What did you say?" I ask.

"Can you talk to these gentlemen, they're from the Maryland State Police and want to talk to you. Are you okay to talk to them? Or... I can ask them to come back later."

"No, I can talk to them now, but what do they want?" I ask. I'm not comprehending.

"They want to talk to you about the fire and ask you questions, is that okay?"

"Yeah...okay, I can talk to them," I say. I look beyond her to two uniformed officers looking back at me. They're standing, holding their hats under their armpits.

"Good morning, Mark, is it okay if we ask you a few questions?" the taller of the two says.

"Good morning?" I say, perplexed. "What day is it?"

"It's Saturday morning. I am Officer Jones and this is Officer Smith. The nurse has told us that you have been sleeping a lot and that you probably will not be awake for too long, so we just want to ask you a few questions about Wednesday night in Ocean City," he says. "Do you remember anything about the day and what happened that night?"

"I think I do."

"Okay, just start with the afternoon. What did you do from noon until you had dinner?" he asks.

I tell him about going to the beach, sitting for a while in the cold and wind, going back to our place, playing quarters, getting pizza and making plans to go to a party.

"What time did you go to the party and who did you go with?" the same officer asks me.

"Around eight or eight-thirty. I rode my bike up with Artie, Kevin and Bruce," I tell them.

"How many people were at the party?" he asks.

"About forty to fifty people," I tell them.

"Tell me about when you left the party, how did you get back to your apartment?" he asks.

"Am I in trouble? I know I shouldn't have been drinking, but I didn't drive or anything."

"No, you are not in trouble, we just want to know what happened on Wednesday night," he says.

"I rode home on my bike about 11:30 p.m. I told Trevor I would meet him at my place and I just left by myself," I tell them. "Nobody wanted to leave when I wanted to leave, so I rode home by myself."

"Do you remember what happened when you returned to your apartment on 61st Street after eleven-thirty?" he asks.

"Yeah," I say, embarrassed. "Trevor and Harry were already there with a girl, and we started to play a drinking game."

"Did anyone else come in or join you four when you were there?"

"Greg came in about ten or fifteen minutes after I got there," I say.

"Did he participate in any of the games?"

"No, not really, he just said he wanted to watch and had a beer on the couch."

"So, when did you go to bed?" he asks.

"Well, I did a shot of vodka with Trevor and next thing I know, I ran to the bathroom to throw up. After I puked, I crawled into my bedroom across the hall from the bathroom. My mattress was on the floor, so I just got in bed. I knew I couldn't drink anymore, so I just wanted to go to sleep. It was probably around twelve-thirty."

"Do you know anything else that happened after you got in bed?" he asks.

"No, I don't. The next thing I remember is waking up and seeing the flames and—" I start to ache and sweat. My body starts to shake and I close my eyes tightly and moan. I try to be tough in front of these cops, but it happens no matter what, I can not stop it.

"Take your time, Mark, we're just here to help you and get some information," he says. They're both still standing in the same spots, and the shorter one, who has not said a word, has been writing on a pad ever since I started talking.

"I remember waking up and my clothes and my bed were on fire. That's about it," I say.

"Did anyone help you put out the fire?"

"Yeah, Trevor and Harry grabbed a blanket and wrapped it around me. That worked and then the girl who was there knew what to do. She helped me get in the shower, she helped me get my shirt off. I don't remember much else, I was pretty out of it by then. Harry and Trevor and that girl took me to the medical center. They helped me the whole time," I say.

"Do you remember Greg helping you?" he asks.

"No, he was just kind of standing there, I think. I'm not really sure."

"Mark, we have reason to believe that Greg Simonson started that fire. We believe he poured rubbing alcohol on you and on the bed and lit it. We are continuing to gather evidence, and your friends, Trevor, Harry and the young lady, Laura have been very helpful," he says.

"Are you saying Greg did this on purpose?" I ask.

"We're trying to determine the course of events from Wednesday evening and let the facts speak for themselves. We're not positive on anything yet, but it is beginning to look like that."

"Greg wouldn't do that. He wouldn't do that to me on purpose, would he?" I ask two men I have never met before.

"Mark, I'm not sure what would make someone do this, but we want to help you in any way we can," he says. "Is there anything else you can think of that you remember, that can help us in any way?"

I immediately think of the All-Metro page being lit on fire by me, and the fact that Greg made first team last year and didn't make anything this year. He was pissed about it, but who knows. "No, I can't think of anything right now," I tell them.

"Okay, I'm going to leave my card and my partner Officer Smith's card right here on this table. If you think of anything that may be helpful or just want to tell us something, please call us."

The shorter cop, who hasn't stopped writing, looks up from his pad, and with a voice way deeper than his appearance, says, "We are going to keep working on this to get you some justice."

I watch the backs of the cops as they walk out the door, and the hole that I'm in gets deeper and deeper. *Greg did this to me on purpose? He lit me on fire and he hurt me because why?* I'm limp and I don't know what else I can handle. I am crippled. I'm in pain and this was on purpose. It was not an accident. I don't understand. I pull the puke bucket up to the side of the bed and dry heave. Eventually, my stomach starts to empty into the bucket and I feel worse than ever, the physical pain now joined by the emotional pain of helplessness.

Nurse Lennae comes into the room because she hears me throwing up and says, "Let me get a towel and a new bucket." My head is sweating, my bandages are turning brown from the reaction to the cream and the blood that oozes from the burns.

She pats my head with a towel, reaches for the bucket and says, "Let me help you with that."

I don't know why I feel the anger–it certainly isn't planned–but I hold the rim of the bucket tight with my left hand and say, "I don't need your help, I don't want anybody's help."

She lets go and checks my IV. She takes my temperature, checks my bandages, changes my top sheet in silence and as she heads out the door says, "You'll be taking a bath in thirty minutes."

I lie still, same position as always. On my side. Broken.

||||||||||||||||||||||||||||||||||||||||||||||||||||||||||

CHAPTER 08

||||||||||||||||||||||||||||||||||||||||||||||||||||||||||||

By the time Mom comes in, I feel like I've been in this hospital for weeks but it's been just three days. People who are worse off than I am are being wheeled past my room. I am the last burn victim to be admitted, but we all follow the same routine: bath, cream, bandages, pain killers, misery. Some scream out like I did on my first night. I don't see any light at the end of this tunnel, and they haven't told me anything about when I'll get out. Unfortunately, I'm not sure I want to get out. What's out there? Who can I trust? What am I going to do? There are no answers to any of these questions.

Mom leans close to the bed and says, "Hey, how are you--What's wrong, Mark? What's bothering you?"

I start to tell her about the police visit, their questions, how they think Greg set me on fire, but I can't finish because I'm sobbing, my body shaking.

"Mark, we're not sure what happened. We just know that you have been hurt and that you were sleeping when it happened. I didn't know the police were coming by or I would have been here. Lauren took Mary to school, I went and picked up Thomas at college and your father had to go to work. I'm sorry, honey. There are a lot of things we need to figure out, but first we want you to get better. I just thank God that Trevor and Harry were there with you and were able to get you help. I talked to both of the boys and that nice girl Laura, who was there too. I promise I did not know the police were going to come by to talk to you. You're going to be okay."

"Everybody keeps saying that I am going to be okay and I'm the only one who thinks I am not going to be okay. Do you think Greg did this to me on purpose? Did he really light me on fire?"

"I don't know for sure, Mark, I sure hope not. Why was there rubbing alcohol in your room?"

"Kevin and I pierced our own ears and I didn't want to get an infection, so we bought it and some cotton balls," I say. "Sorry, but I knew you wouldn't like me having a pierced ear."

"Mark, a pierced ear is the least of my concerns right now. We're going to find out what happened, but my main concern is that you recover and begin to feel good again. I will not tell you that you are going to be okay, but I do think you can recover from this. It's going to be hard, but Dr. Munster has told me it *will* get better."

"Why would anybody do this to somebody else, and why would *he* do it to *me*?" I ask, knowing she can't answer.

Mom sits in the chair next to me, holding my left hand like I'm a small child. "I love you, I love you," she says, and as she repeats the words, my eyes get heavier and my heart gets colder and I fall asleep telling myself that no one will get a chance to hurt me again like this because I will never give them the chance.

When I wake up, my whole family is in the hospital room. Thomas and Lauren are home from college, Mary is done with school for the day and Dad has left work early to come here. I hear everyone talking to each other so I keep my eyes closed, listening. They're talking about school, summer jobs, my recovery. Mom is explaining to Thomas the last two days at the hospital and I can tell Thomas is getting agitated. What fills my head at this very moment is that my family, my parents, have been with me, giving me everything, throughout my life, and I repay them with heartache and disappointment. My father goes to work every day, my mother works the whole time we are in school, drives us all over town, and gives us all we need to succeed. And, for some reason, I keep hurting them. I don't open my eyes, and I can't face them right now, so I just drift into a painkiller-induced haze and fall back asleep.

"Mark, Mark, can you wake up? You've been asleep all day and we need you to wake up. Can you hear me?" I hear Nurse Lennae pull me up to consciousness.

I open my eyes and stare straight ahead, listening but not moving. I nod my head and say, "Yeah, I can hear you." I look around. Thomas, Lauren, Mary, Mom, Dad, and Dr. Munster are all in the room with me. Thomas, Lauren and Mary look at me with sad eyes and slumped shoulders and my parents' faces show a mix of concern and sadness.

Dr. Munster starts the conversation. "Hello, Mark, I'm glad you're getting sleep. I know that we've been giving you a lot of medicine and that makes you very sleepy. In the last thirty-six hours, your vitals have stabilized and you are responding to our care. Things are beginning to look better. Now I want to go over some things before I leave for the day. I have explained to your mother and father your continued care protocol, and I want to share it with you. I want to tell you what we are going to do to you and for you in order to get you back to your old self. Now, your burns have been diagnosed and they are being addressed. There is no quick fix or fast recovery when it comes to burned skin. It needs to remain clean, continually cared for, and I feel certain that it will heal itself over the next sixty to eighty days. We'll continually monitor the third degree burns and address them again after they are given forty-five to sixty days to heal. I am pretty confident that you know these things already.

"I also want you to go to physical therapy," he says. "A therapist will be up to see you tomorrow and will set you on a program for the next two months. Your skin, when it recovers, will need to be stretched. If you don't do any therapy, your movements and flexibility will be restricted. It may not feel great, but it is necessary. The physical therapist will put you on an outstanding program in order for you to have a full recovery. Also, there is going to be a psychologist who will stop by to see you. I would like you to talk to him about how you are feeling, if you have any questions, if you have any nightmares or concerns."

I lie there listening, not convinced I need to talk to anyone about any of this, especially someone I have never met.

Dr. Munster continues. "The nurses are going to continue to give you a bath every day and put you in clean bandages. This will be the routine for you while you are here and even afterwards, when you go home. I know that you have not been able to walk yet and have only been able to move with a wheelchair. This is only temporary. Your body is in shock and right now walking is too much for it. Eventually, you will be able to walk down the hall with the therapist. Then, you'll be able to walk all around the hospital and ultimately to run all over a lacrosse field. It will happen, it is just going to take time. Each step will take time. I know you don't want to hear anything about patience, but you will learn something about patience. Now, in the short term, you have some things happening in your life and we want to help you get there. I am sorry to say, but I do not think you will be going to your senior prom. It is a week from today and you will not be healed enough or have enough stamina to go. I know you would like to be there, but it is not going to be possible. However, you have a graduation ceremony in nine days and I am hoping you will be able to attend your graduation. This ceremony will be less taxing on your body. You can remain in the wheelchair and your environment will be controlled, so, barring any setbacks, I am hoping to see you leave here in a graduation gown and get your diploma. It beats a hospital gown, that is for sure, right?

"Now, you will come back here after graduation and spend three or four more days while we monitor your burns. At that point, I think you will be ready to go home. In less than two weeks, you should be back at your own house, sleeping in your own bed. Also, your appetite should be coming back because your body needs nourishment. The cafeteria staff is going to address your needs and give you a healthy diet that will feed your body's needs. So, they will be by to talk to you and get you started. Now, I know I have given you a lot to think about but I wanted to set your expectations for your time here and your time at home. Mark, these injuries are going to take sixty to eighty days to heal but even longer to heal fully. You and I have to be diligent and, here is the word again, *patient*, and you can have your full recovery. I am going to go and leave you with your family but I feel really good about the road we are on right now."

He may feel good about this road but I think it sucks.

Thomas looks at me after the doctor leaves. "Can you do what he wants you to do?" he asks.

"I don't know, Thomas, I can't even sit up in this bed. I'm sorry, Dad. I'm sorry, Mom, I'm sorry, guys," I say.

"First, sit up in the bed," Thomas says, "then you can work on the next step. Don't keep saying you're sorry, just start by sitting up in bed. Then you can do what's next. He gave you an idea about what to do, so just try to do it, one step at a time."

Easy for you to say, you're not immobile in a hospital bed, puking every time you move.

When I wake up the next day, I begin the routine. Clean bath in hundred-degree water in a sterile metal tub. My flesh still looks like ground beef on my body and blood pools here and there on the surface of the water. I look down at my chest—still no nipple on my right side. My right arm has all the gauze stuck to it, so I keep it on as I slide into the water. Eventually it loosens and floats to the top of the water. Nurse Lenae pulls it out with the rubber gloves and puts it in the trash with the rest of the dirty bandages.

By the time I am set back up with new bandages and clean sheets, I'm ready to go back to sleep. The process has been exhausting and painful and the painkillers take their toll. When I wake up from the sleep, another nurse tells me that there are people that are here to see me. I ask her who they are.

"They look like priests," she answers as she leaves the room.

Two gentlemen walk into the room and I recognize them both,

Father McDonough and Father Joseph. Father McDonough is the headmaster of St. Xavier High School and Father Joseph is the assistant. I'm not sure what to say to them so I start with, "Hello, Fathers, sorry you had to come all the way down here to see me. You really didn't have to come by."

"It's okay, Mark. We wanted to check in on you and see how you're doing. How do you feel?" asks Father McDonough.

"Better than yesterday," I answer.

"Good to hear," says Father McDonough. He pauses for a moment before continuing. "Mark, we want to talk to you about your accident. Apparently the police have already stopped by to see you. I understand that Greg Simonson played a part in what happened." Another pause. "We're wondering how you are going to handle it with the police. Both Father Joseph and I"–he nods in Father Joseph's direction– "have discussed your situation and we want to make a suggestion to you. I would imagine that the police will present you with charges against Greg."

"What do you mean about 'present me with charges'? I didn't do anything wrong."

"No, I mean that the police will give you an option to press charges on Greg for assault, manslaughter, things like that. What Father and I have been speaking about is how that would reflect on the school and the effect it may have on future enrollment. I know this is a lot to deal with right now, but we're hoping you'll forgive Greg, set the example of turning the other cheek. We're very proud of you as one of our students, and we want to believe that you'll do what is right for your school, your classmate and your family. If Greg has charges pressed against him, there's a chance he'll go to jail. It would be difficult on you, knowing that your decision led to your classmate's spending a long time in jail. We just want you to think it over, show compassion for your fellow man. With graduation next week, Father and I are hoping this won't be a distraction and you'll show Greg the forgiveness we both know you are capable of."

"Yes, sir, Father, I'll think about it. I didn't realize that the police were here to charge Greg with anything. I just thought they were here to ask about what happened."

"Mark, I'm fairly certain that they are building a case against Greg and we know that that kind of publicity will be very bad for your high school. While what has happened to you is sad, we want to make sure your decision on Greg doesn't make it worse. We are here for you, Mark, and we want to help you get better. I know that both your father and your brother are proud of their St. Xavier education and we hope you are, too. In order for you to do the right thing for yourself, your family, your classmate, your school, we're encouraging you to forgive Greg."

"So you want me to make sure the police don't arrest him?" I ask.

"We just want you to let the police know that you don't want your classmate to go to jail for his mistakes. You don't want his family to suffer. So yes, you do not want him to be arrested," he says.

Father Joseph is standing behind and to the right of Father McDonough the whole time and nodding his head whenever Father McDonough speaks. "Mark, we spoke to your doctor and he told us that you should be well enough to attend the graduation ceremony. We look forward to seeing you there with your family and will help you in any way we can. Please, Mark, know that St. Xavier is your friend and we want what is best for you. Father Joseph and I must be going but we look forward to seeing you at graduation. Take care of yourself, Mark."

"Forgiveness is not something I'm really thinking about right now, but thanks for coming to visit, Father, and you, too, Father Joseph." I say the words out loud, but inside it feels like they're not interested in how I was feeling at all, just how they look.

||||||||||||||||||||||||||||||||||||||||||||||||||||||||

CHAPTER 09

||||||||||||||||||||||||||||||||||||||||||||||||||||||||||||

"Hey, honey, how are you doing?" Mom asks as I lie on my side. Father McDonough and Father Joseph left only a few minutes ago and I'm deep in thought about what they just said. Mom has startled me and I respond with one word: "Fine."

"You're feeling fine? Well, that's good to hear," she says. "I saw Father Joseph and Father McDonough as they were leaving. It's really nice of them to come down here and check on you. Did they have anything to say? Do they know you should be able to make it to the graduation?"

"Yeah, they talked to Dr. Munster and he must've told them that I can go. Is Thomas coming down later?" I suddenly ask.

"Yes, he's coming down with your father after work. They both should be here around six," she says. "Are you alright? Something I can do?"

"No, I just want to ask Thomas about something," I say. I know I can tell Thomas and he will listen. Mom will just jump in and take over, calling people and making it a big deal. Thomas will just tell me what to do.

"Okay, well he'll be here pretty soon. I want to tell you that your aunts and uncles have called and want to give you their best wishes. I saw Brian and Mary Joe and they were asking about you," she says. As she continues to list all the relatives who've called or stopped by the house, I try to listen and follow along, but I cannot stop thinking about Father McDonough and Father Joseph, jail time, the cops, manslaughter–what the fuck is really going on right now? I am lying still in a bed right now because every time I move it feels like I am being stabbed with a thousand knives all over my chest and arms and I'm somehow supposed to make sure "my classmate" is forgiven. I feel myself drifting into a whole feeling of worthlessness. Do what I am told, don't do what I'm told. I don't know what the fuck to do, I only know that I just want my old life.

By the time Thomas gets to the hospital, Lauren, Mary, Mom and Dad are all in the room. I can't talk to him alone so I tell him that I'll call him tonight at the house. Mary and Lauren have some cards for me from some of my friends, and I have gotten some flowers from my parents' friends. The room is starting to fill up with balloons, flowers, and cards. I know these are nice gestures but they don't make me feel any better and it's not making me heal any faster. I have been here for three days and I have to be here for ten more.

While everyone is talking, I deflect any questions about me. I tell Lauren and Thomas about the person across the hall who is much worse than I am. He was painting his house and cleaned his body off with turpentine to get the paint off his arms, legs and face. Before he got in the shower to rinse it off, he lit a cigarette and his whole body got burned, everything but the palms of his hands and the bottoms of his feet. I haven't seen him without his bandages. He's wrapped from head to toe. He looks like a mummy.

A small child came in last night. The nurse said a pot of hot water fell from the stove on him and he has burns like mine. But he's only three years old so he's been crying a lot and loud. I tell Thomas about the guy that has been here for two months. He crashed his motorcycle going about seventy miles per hour and burned the skin off his chest, back side and legs. He's getting skin graphs on sixty percent of his body. They're taking skin from a dead person and putting it on him. It sounds gross and it looks gross. I saw the guy go by in a wheelchair and his exposed skin was disgusting. I hope I don't look like him when I'm done. His whole face has been covered in bandages the whole time, so I have no idea what he even looks like.

Mary looks at me sadly, still not saying much. Thomas keeps asking what happened. Lauren just chats. She talks about her freshman year of college, about her lacrosse season. Her team just won the Division Three national championship, so she's leaving tomorrow to go back to school. Dad is driving her up there for an end of the season banquet.

In the past three weeks, my parents have watched me win the MSA lacrosse championships, my brother lose the Division Three national championship for the second year in a row, Lauren win the Division Three national championship, and have sent me off to the beach for a fun senior week before graduation only to return home wrapped in bandages, barely recognizable, crippled and damaged.

Sometimes having people around me at the hospital makes me feel good and sometimes it makes me feel more alone than when I'm here by myself.

‖‖‖

CHAPTER 10

‖‖

Later that night I call home. My mother picks up and I negotiate my way through a few more questions before she passes me to Thomas.

"What's up, is something going on?" he asks.

"Are you upstairs by yourself?"

"Yeah, what's wrong?"

"Father McDonough and Father Joseph came by to visit me this morning and want to make sure that I don't get Greg arrested. They want me to turn the other cheek and make sure he doesn't go to jail. They said it would be better if I just forgive him and then he won't get charged with manslaughter. What the fuck is manslaughter? I don't know, I don't know what to do. I don't think he meant to hurt me like this, I don't know. They kept saying that they don't want this to hurt more people and be a bigger issue, and I don't want that either."

Thomas says, "Forget those guys, do what you think is best. What did the cops tell you?"

"They just asked me a bunch of questions about the beach and the party, stuff like that."

"Well, the phone here has been ringing off the hook and I do know that a couple of reporters have called. Mom and Dad just keep telling them 'no comment,' but I don't know how long that will last."

"Thomas, I don't know what to do. I just want to get out of here and get these bandages off and forget this ever happened. I want to go back to the way things were."

"Listen, Mark, don't worry about Father McDonough, don't worry about the cops, just do what you want to do," he says.

"I don't want to do anything," I say.

"Then tell them you don't want to do anything."

"You mean tell them I don't want to press charges?"

"Tell them the truth, that you don't want to tell the cops anything. Mark, remember, you didn't do anything wrong," he says.

"All right, I will, it's just Father McDonough scared the shit out of me. He just kept telling me to forgive, to not let it get worse."

"Fuck him, he isn't hurt, he just doesn't want the bad publicity. Don't worry about him."

"Easy for you to say, you don't have to see him next week to get your diploma," I tell Thomas.

"True, but don't let him bother you, just do what you think is best."

"All right, I will. Thanks, man, I'll see you sometime," I say.

"See you," says Thomas as we continue our lifetime commitment never to say goodbye to each other and instead use expressions like "see you" or "later" or "catch you on the rebound."

‖‖

CHAPTER 11

‖‖‖

Two days later, I am visited by the same two cops. This time I can actually sit up, although I don't lean back because the burns on my back hurt when there is any pressure. Also, my IV is gone and I can eat a little food now. The painkiller pills are still coming every four hours, so I do get some relief.

"Mark, I am Officer Smith and this is Officer Jones. We spoke with you the other day and want a chance to talk to you again. Are you okay to talk now?"

"Yeah, I'm okay to talk," I say.

"Good. Well, we got some additional information from some other people who were with you on June 3 in Ocean City. After speaking with you and the witnesses, we are able to determine the course of events for the evening. As a result of our investigation, we feel the following charges will be applicable to this case: assault, manslaughter, attempted…"

And before he can get any more words out that I don't understand, I just blurt out, "I do not want to press charges."

Officer Smith looks up from his notepad. "Excuse me. You do not want to press charges, are you sure about that?"

"Yes, I'm sure. I don't want to press charges and I don't want this to go on any longer," I say.

"Are you sure you do not want to reconsider this?" asks Officer Smith. "You've been through a lot and I don't want to rush you. Please, take your time and think it over."

"I don't need to think it over any more. I am not going to press charges, I am not going to court and testify. I'm not going to relive it, I don't want my parents to have to hear it all over. I have thought it over and I don't want to do anything. I just want all of this to go away."

"Are you okay if Greg gets away with hurting you?" Officer Smith presses.

"I don't care about him, I care about me. I don't understand how pressing charges on him makes it better for me. It doesn't, it only makes it worse. What I want is to get better, get out of here and never come back. So, I don't want to do anything but get better."

"Alright, Mark, but if you change your mind or if there are other things you want to talk about, please call us. We're always available, and if we find out anything more–anything you don't know about– we will be in touch with you. Good luck in your recovery."

"Thanks, I'm sorry you have to deal with any of this. I just want it to be over."

II

CHAPTER 12

IIIIIIIIIIIIIIIIIIIIIIIIIIIIIIIIIIIIIIIIIIIIIIIIIIIIIIIIIIIII

Graduation day finally comes, and I have a chance to leave the hospital. I have to spend it in a wheelchair because I still can't stand up for more than a couple minutes. But it's a chance to see and feel the sun, be outside and change the scenery. The only problem is that there will be hundreds of people looking at me in a wheelchair, whispering about me as I roll by or as they see me across the lawn. I have not talked to anybody since it happened and I don't know what they've been doing. What I do know, since it's Towson, is that everybody is going to be gossiping about the fire. I almost don't want to go but I don't want to give anyone any ideas about me. They can look at me, they can talk about me, they can have their opinions, but I can't let it matter. Nobody but me knows what I know, knows how I feel, thinks what I think. They all can just judge from the outside.

When we roll up to the parking lot, we go through the whole routine: Get the wheelchair out of the trunk, climb in it and start towards the lawn where the graduation ceremony takes place. I did manage to get myself dressed pretty well. Up until now, I haven't worn anything besides shorts since last week. Mom has gotten me an XL white button-down shirt that fits over my bandages without pressing on them and I tie a really loose knot on my necktie. It's too hot for a sportcoat, so I go with khaki pants, white shirt and tie for the ceremony. Thomas is pushing me in the chair when I get to a crowd of my classmates. Everybody stops talking and stares at me as I literally roll up. "What's up, guys," I say to no one in particular and several of them look startled to hear me talk. "Nothing much," someone says and there's awkward silence as no one else knows what to add. Out of the crowd comes Kevin. "Hey, man, how are you feeling?"

"I feel like shit," I say, "look at me, stuck in a wheelchair because I can't stand up without puking." More silence. I can tell people are listening to our conversation.

"That sucks," Kevin says. "Are you going to be all right for today?"

"I hope so, man, who knows."

"Thomas, I'll take him from here if you want to get a seat in the crowd," says Kevin.

"Alright, sounds good," Thomas says, and he leans down closer to my ear. "If you need something, just wave me over, I'll be looking for it."

Kevin starts pushing my chair and we head over to the gym to meet all the other seniors. While we walk, Kevin and I catch up on the last week.

"What the fuck happened, Mark? I stayed at the party with Lucy, and Trevor came back at like one o'clock and they told us you got lit on fire. What the fuck was Greg doing?"

"I don't know, man, I just woke up and it was in my face–oh my God, man, it was fucked up."

"It must've been, dude. My parents were freaking out, calling all over to get hold of me. All the parents were freaking out and we didn't know where you were. Trevor said you went in an ambulance, but nobody knew where you went. Were you by yourself?" Kevin asks.

"Yeah, dude and I was out of it. I didn't know where I was either. Apparently, I went to the hospital in Salisbury first."

Just as I say this and right outside the gymnasium, Father McDonough walks over to us. "Hello, Mark, I'm really glad you made it. We've been talking and think it best if Greg Simonson takes you up to get your diploma. It would show great compassion to your classmate and help him with his grief. He's told me how badly he feels and we want to give him a chance to feel better, is that okay with you?"

"I guess it's okay, it just seems weird, that's all," I say.

"Well, Mark, I think it will be great for both you and Greg that you two can show everyone that, despite the circumstance, you are both Men for Others," he says.

"Okay, Father, I will. I just want to graduate. I want to get it over with."

"That's great, Mark, this will be a great thing for St. Xavier High School." He walks away, black robes and ceremonial hoods trailing after him.

Kevin looks at me and says, "Dude, that was fucked up."

"Yeah, you should've been there when they came by the hospital. He and Father Joseph spent the whole time telling me not to get Greg arrested. It will look bad on the school and stuff. I was laying there, it hurt to move, and they're like, turn the other cheek, try to find forgiveness. It was fucked up."

"Yeah, dude, that's crazy. Let's go inside and catch up to Art and Bruce and those boys."

By the time we all head outside to the lawn, the gym is getting pretty loud. Everyone is excited about graduating, and they also realize that they can't get in trouble anymore. Any threats from the teachers do not carry any weight, so guys are saying stupid shit and punching each other in the arm. Guys wear sunglasses inside. All the little things that we haven't been able to do are now "no big deal." I sit and watch guys who never smile let out big laughs, shy kids are wearing sunglasses and grinning, nerds are yelling song lyrics, stoners are wearing their Walkman earphones. I feel like a fly on the wall as I scan the gym. When people see me, they mostly stop talking and stare. I keep my head up and say, "Hey, Billy," "What's up, George," "Looking good, Jeff" to people I know. In the back of the gym are all my boys, sitting in the bleachers cracking jokes, making fun of each other and talking about girls. The usual. When Kevin and I get there, everyone's smile turns to a straight face and they either look down or straight at me with sadness in their eyes.

I look at Art and say, "What the fuck, it's not like I died or something."

Art replies, "Mark, for a while we were not fucking sure. Nobody knew. Damn, though, you look better than I thought you would."

"I feel fucking worse than I look, that's for sure."

"Well, it's good to see you," says Art.

"It's good to be seen, that hospital will make you crazy," I reply and it seems to lighten the mood. People go back to talking to each other, giving each other a hard time.

Father Joseph stands in the middle of the gym. "Gentlemen, the graduation ceremony is to begin in ten minutes. I'm going to need you to get in line according to your last name, and be ready to walk to the lawn in five minutes. Take off your sunglasses, remove your earphones and be ready to go. A's beginning this row, H's in this row, M's in this row and R's in this row. Please do it quietly in an orderly manner."

Kevin and I stay put. Father Joseph approaches and says to Kevin, "You need to get in line in order to be ready. Mark, I'll push you to an area under the trees so you will be in the shade for the ceremony. Then, when it is your time to receive your diploma, Greg will come for you."

"Father, if it's okay, Kevin can take me to the shade and then find his seat. I would like to be in with the students for the procession if that's all right."

While I can tell he doesn't want to say yes, he nods his head. "Okay, Mark, get in line in front of the H's. And, Mark and Kevin, no funny business."

"Father, it's not like I'm going to jump up and start dancing or anything," I say.

Father Joseph just shakes his head and says to Kevin, "You'll see a spot under the tree behind the stage we have set up for Mark and his family. Take him there and then find your seat."

We head out of the gym and out of the corner of my eye, I see Greg coming into it, tying his tie and putting on his jacket. He's rushing to catch up to his spot in line. Father Joseph grabs him by the arm and points to where he is supposed to be. We're in front of Matt Hall, Tom Harriman, the Harris twins. When he walks near me, we don't make eye contact. He spends the whole time looking away from me. Everyone else around us either is silent or whispers to the person closest to him. The mood in the whole crowd has gone from laughing, joking and relief to quiet and somber, just like that.

Kevin rolls me under the tree where my parents are sitting and heads to his seat. After fifteen minutes, even in the shade things started to get uncomfortable. I listen to the speech from our valedictorian, Tim Evans, and by the time Father McDonough speaks I am hurting pretty bad. I down a pain pill my mother has brought. I look down at my white shirt and see the discoloration from the bandages coming through the fabric, the combination of sweat, healing cream, and the heat as my shirt has turned a yellowish brown.

Finally, they start the procession of graduates, and students start to make their way towards the stage. After the B names are finished, I see Greg get up from his chair and walk over to me. He doesn't even look me in the eye but goes behind me and starts to roll me to my place in line. We just skid a couple of feet on the grass and I say, "You have to unlock the wheels, just push on that," pointing to the brake on the wheelchair.

Greg unlocks the wheels and we start towards the line. I say, "Get behind Lou Demedio and in front of Jeff Deaver" as we head to the graduates. As I focus on some of the people in the audience, I hear some rumbling and look up long enough to see fingers pointed in my direction. Greg doesn't say anything to me and I don't say anything to him as we both wait for the chance to roll in front of the stage. When Lou Demedio walks up the stairs, I tell Greg, "Just push me across the front."

Father McDonough comes down the steps, the same ones that everyone uses to exit the stage. He meets me at the bottom. Greg stops the chair and I reach out my hand. Father McDonough shakes it, places the diploma in my lap, leans down and whispers to me, "I am really proud of you for this," then smiles as he stands up.

I look down at the diploma in my lap and see my shirt stained yellow and brown on the right side and soaked with sweat on the left. Greg hesitates on what to do next, so I say, "Please take me back to the shade." Between the heat, my nervousness, and the unwanted attention, I feel dizzy and sick to my stomach.

As I'm headed back to the tree, I look up and make eye contact with Mom. She's smiling, a fake smile, and looking only at me. She will not look at Greg. When she sees my face, her smile disappears and a look of concern clouds it. Greg rolls me to the same spot as before and heads to his seat. As he lets go of me, the chair starts to roll slowly. Thomas grabs it and puts the brake on. Mom leans in. "Are you okay?"

"No, I'm not. I don't feel good and I can't really be here anymore. Can we just go?" I say.

"Sure, honey, we can go, let me get our things," Mom reaches for her purse and the water and the supplies from the hospital. She leans towards Dad and my brother and sisters and says, "Mark needs to go, do you want to come with us?"

I hear them say, "Yeah, let's go," and Thomas grabs the handles of the chair and releases the brake. As soon as the chair starts to move, I feel a wave of emotions wash over me. I heave tears and hide my face. I can't stand to look up and I don't want anyone to see me pathetic and crying.

By the time I get back to the hospital, I feel weaker than at any other time in my healing. What started out as a chance to get out and be normal has turned into a painful and pathetic episode. I realize

I have no strength–no physical strength, no mental strength, no personal strength. I'm worse than I thought. I lie sweating in my bed, covered in disgusting gauze. I close my eyes and pray for help. Please, God, make this better, make this go away, make me normal. And I realize I will never be normal again.

When I wake up, Mom and Dad are still at the hospital, but it's dark outside.

"You slept for four hours, you must have been really tired," Mom says.

"Can I have some water?" I ask.

"Of course, let me get you some," my mother says.

As soon as she leaves the room, I look at my father. I want to talk with him alone. "Dad, I'm sorry for all this, I'm sorry to embarrass you, I'm sorry that this happened."

"Mark, you don't embarrass us. We have always been proud of you and we love you. You don't have to apologize to us, okay? We're your parents who love you. You don't owe us anything, let's just work on getting you better," he says, and before he can say anything more, Dr. Munster walks in the door.

"Mark, how do you feel?"

"I feel better now," I answer. Of course, I'm lying.

"Good, I understand you were pretty tired from being outside today. Now that is normal, your body is spending all its energy on your healing and you are going to be tired pretty quickly." He talks about the importance of taking it easy as my body heals, about my compromised immune system. "Now, Mark," he continues and locks eyes, "I am glad you went out today and congratulations on your graduation, but let's keep you in a controlled environment and keep you rested. Your time will come but for now, let us take good care of you and get you back to full strength."

I just nod and say, "Okay, Doctor," followed by a long drink of cold water from a straw. The cold water going down my throats is the first thing that feels good in my body all day.

In my mind I accept defeat, I accept my pain and think, *Don't fight it, just give in and let the healing begin.* I don't know if God hears me ask for help, I don't know if he cares, I just know that I'm weak and fragile and I'm not leaving the hospital weak and fragile the next time.

For the next ten days I sleep, bathe, watch TV, do physical therapy, nap, eat, read, sleep and do it all over again. I finally see some of the wounds start to heal. The skin on my ear and thumb looks like skin from a grape, discolored and wavy. I can lift my arm up to ninety degrees. I can stand up and walk down the hall. I stop throwing up, I sit up without being dizzy, I can even bend over and pick up an orange off the floor. Each step is a step in the right direction.

||||||||||||||||||||||||||||||||||||||||||||||||||||||||||||

CHAPTER 13

||||||||||||||||||||||||||||||||||||||||||||||||||||||||||||||

I've been home from the hospital for about two months and follow the same routine each day: bath, gauze, movie, nap, movie and sleep. My appetite is back and I eat three meals a day as I sit in my air-conditioned house.

But today is different. Today I will finally get a taste of freedom since I can go out to lunch with a girl I've been talking to on the phone during my recovery. She's been really nice and has visited me in the hospital and at the house. We first met during last year's lacrosse season at a Hampton High School party. She's a year younger than I am, and I really don't know her very well. I talked to her just a few times before the fire.

Her name is Rachel. She's short and thin with blond hair and a nice tan. Her light blue eyes have a hint of shyness. Today she wants to pick me up and take me to lunch. I'm eager to get out of the house, eager to do something, anything, and Rachel is the kind of new girl I want to do it with. She's borrowing her mom's black Chevy Blazer. I'm looking out the window when I spot it and I walk back into the living room so it doesn't look like I'm waiting for her to show up.

When she rings the doorbell, I feel the uneasiness well up inside me. I still have my right arm and hand wrapped in gauze pads and tape. My chest under my shirt is wrapped the same way and I wonder if she thinks I look like a freak. I've already warned her that I am not totally healed, but she hasn't seen me yet so I walk to the door slowly, afraid of her reaction. As I open it, she smiles through the glass of the storm door.

"Mom, my ride is here! I'm leaving!" I yell in the direction of the kitchen.

Mom yells back, "Mark, hold on!" She comes through the dining room, her face serious and her voice measured. "Be careful, okay, just go to lunch and come home."

"Okay, I will," I answer and head for the door as fast as I can.

Rachel looks awesome in her little blue sundress as she walks in front of me down the front steps. Her legs are tan and her shoulders look sexy and when she turns to look back, I am caught off guard and kind of stumble on the bottom step. *Did she see me gawking? I hope not.*

"Are you okay?"

"Yeah, yeah, I'm good, just ready to get out of here."

"Well, let's go then!"

I climb into the passenger seat and Rachel walks around to the driver's side. When she gets in the car, I look over at her and say, "You look really nice today."

She looks back and says, "Thanks, but I don't like my haircut."

"I think it looks good," I say and then realize I don't remember her hair ever looking any different.

"Where do you want to go for lunch?" I ask between music and small talk as we head towards the middle of Towson.

"Not sure yet, but we have to make a stop real quick before we go," she says.

We drive past The Crease and Charles Village Pub and head east towards Kenilworth. I don't ask where we're going, just happy to be out, listening to the radio and driving around with Rachel. I can't help but look at her legs while she drives. She has beautiful tan legs, nice thighs, muscular and smooth. She runs cross country and has thin, strong legs and they have my attention. She looks so good, I have been isolated for so long, and I am nervous. She's the one who came onto me when we first met and kept calling me when I was hurt, but now that I am finally with her, I am unsure.

We pull up in front of a ground level entrance to a townhouse and she parks the car. "Come on in, I have to get something real quick," she says.

She opens the door and I ask, "Whose place is this?"

"It's my mom's place. She's in Bethany with her boyfriend."

"Oh, okay, what do you have to get?"

"A kiss from you," she says and stands on her tiptoes and French kisses me right inside the front door. We kiss for a little while, then she says, "Come on in, do you want something to drink?"

"No, I'm good," I answer as I sit on the couch.

Rachel goes into the kitchen, comes out with two cokes and puts them on the table next to me. I look up at her.

"I don't want to hurt you," she says as she leans over to kiss me.

Between kisses I say, "I'll let you know if you're hurting me." When she puts her knee on the couch, I grab the other one and hold it next to my waist. She's sitting on my lap with my arms around her. One of her hands is around my head and the other on my back. She smells like fresh-cut flowers and her skin is smooth.

We keep kissing and she stands up and pulls her dress over her head. She isn't wearing a bra, and her small boobs are all white compared to the rest of her tan body. While I'm looking at her, she slides her underwear off. I fumble with my shorts button as she grabs them by the side. I lift my butt off the couch and she pulls them to the floor, right next to her dress.

She sits on top of me, puts me inside her, leans her head back and rides me on the couch. I don't know how long it lasts, but it's not long, not long at all. All I know is that I cannot get this girl pregnant, so I lift her off of me and cum on the couch and the floor.

"Sorry about that, let me clean it up," I say.

"Don't worry about it, my mom's gone for the weekend," she says.

"Okay, that's cool."

Rachel walks naked into the kitchen and I just sit and stare at her from the back, stunned that I just lost my virginity, that this girl is so hot and so comfortable walking around naked, so mature but younger than I am, with a place for the weekend without her parents.

"Are you staying here all weekend?" I ask her while she is in the kitchen.

"No, I have to stay at my dad's house. It's lame, I know," she says as she walks back into the room, naked, carrying paper towels in her hand. I stare at her body and she gives me a sly smile when my eyes finally meet her eyes. I know what I look like–no shorts, shirt still on, gauze down my right arm and hand.

Once we wipe up the mess, Rachel grabs my left hand and says, "Let's go upstairs." I hold her hand as she walks one step ahead of me upstairs to her bedroom. She is naked and beautiful and, at that point, Rachel becomes the love of my life.

I can't help but look at her white butt and her tan lines from her bikini, it's beautiful. All the trying, all the talking to girls, all the effort and this is how it happens. This is how it goes down. In the middle of the afternoon, in a place I have never been, and with a girl I barely know. I didn't bring a rubber, but I certainly didn't think I was going to need one when I left the house.

By now, we're at the top of the steps and she turns, her hand in mine, and walks toward a doorway with a half-open door. Inside, her room is spotless and sunny. She looks over her shoulder, as she pulls me gently into the room. This girl is tender, way more beautiful than any of the other girls I have known before. She kisses me on the lips and starts to unbutton my shirt, as I hear the door close behind me. She must have pushed it closed with her foot. I open one eye to see if she is looking, and her eyes are closed. I close my eyes and touch her with my left hand as I hold my right hand to the side and let this dream become a reality.

Round two goes much more smoothly than round one, since we

are on the bed and I feel more comfortable. When we're finished, neither of us is in a hurry to move, and we lie together. I think we both fall asleep for some time.

When we wake up, we just leave the house and go back to the car. We stop at Towson Deli for a sandwich before she drops me off at my house. She kisses me softly when I get out of the car and I tell her, "I'll call you tomorrow and let's try to get together before I leave."

"Call me," she says. It's not like we're boyfriend or girlfriend at all, so this just feels weird. We have only been out a few times together a while ago, but she chooses to sleep with me now. I wonder and stare at her car as she drives away. I shake my head and head up the front steps to the house.

"How was lunch with your friend Rachel?" Mom asks.

"It was good, we went to Towson Deli, then went out to Loch Raven," I say.

"You didn't sit out in the sun, did you?" she asks.

"No, we sat under a tree and hung out, it was fine," I say. "I'm going upstairs to lie down."

When I call Rachel the next day, she tells me she's headed to Bethany Beach to meet up with her mother and won't be back until school starts. By the time she gets here, I will have left for college. It's weird. I'm not her boyfriend, but I feel like I just got dumped. I shared with her the moment I had wondered about, the feeling I had searched for, the conquest we, as boys, desired. Now, I don't know when I will see her again. I'm confused. I know that she isn't the only girl in the world, but she has my attention and now she is disappearing for the rest of the summer. This must be how it is in college, girls sleep with guys, no strings attached.

|||||||||||||||||||||||||||||||||||||||||||||||||||||||||||||

CHAPTER 14

|||||||||||||||||||||||||||||||||||||||||||||||||||||||||||||||||||

In seven days, it's time to leave for college and I can finally smell the chance to be normal, to get away, to leave "Smalltimore," (a nickname for Baltimore because everybody knows your business there) and just be another person, a freshman in college. I don't have to wear any gauze except for my upper arm. My nipple has grown back and except for always wearing a shirt and hat outside, I look normal.

Kevin is home from summer school and I have a chance to get out of the house. Kevin got into Duke to play lacrosse, but he had to go to summer school with some other athletes to make sure he's ready for the academic part of school. Lucy is having a party–her parents are out of town. I know Kevin is looking forward to seeing Lucy, and I am hoping to see her friend Danielle.

"Make sure you're home by eleven tonight, Mark, and please be careful," says Mom.

"I will, it's just a chance to see some guys before we leave," I answer.

Kevin knocks on the door and Mom gives him the talk about looking out for each other and not doing anything stupid.

By the time we get to Lucy's, I've had two beers and they taste good. I've missed the flavor and the feeling. It's great to see everyone and know the more things change, the more they stay the same. The leaders of the party take control, work the drinking games into the mix. Girls look at what other girls show up to the party, look to see what they are wearing. They welcome old friends and new ones into the crowd. The girls' attitudes seem to be relaxed, knowing that the microscope of high school is over and the freedom of college is around the corner. The guys haven't seemed to change at all. We all talk about sports, the beach, summer jobs. I can't wait to get to college and make this lifestyle the norm.

Lucy's parents are from the Dominican Republic, so her house is different from everybody else's house. Most of us live in two-storey colonials or Cape Cod houses with living rooms and kitchens on the first floor and bedrooms upstairs. Lucy's house is like a Caribbean home: one level, tile floors everywhere, a sprawling living room/kitchen combination and bedrooms down each hallway. She has a cool patio and pool off the back of her house, and this is where all the action is tonight.

I wade into that action with an eye out for Denise. I haven't seen her all summer except for the time she visited me in the hospital. She has lived at the beach and is back home before she starts at the local college, TSU. I am there for about an hour when Denise comes into the party and she seems intent on finding me. Denise was going to be my prom date but we didn't get a chance to go. We've talked on the phone during the summer. I know I'm excited to see her, and I think she is excited to see me. We've always gotten along well. She's a kind, generous person who has always made time for everybody. I think that's what I like about her the most. She is kind to everyone—her friends, my friends, parents, everybody. I even took her to lunch with Cleta one time, and she spent the whole time talking to Cleta about her family and its past. It was really cool to see someone my age be so nice to my grandmother.

By the time she rolls in, I have had about six beers and I feel great. Denise doesn't have much interest in the party and I'm fine with stepping away, so we duck out. I tell Kevin, she tells Lucy and we leave, and I don't think anybody else even notices. Her car is a Ford Explorer and we head out to a spot we've gone to in the past,

Loch Raven Reservoir.

It's a warm night, no humidity, so it feels like a warm blanket on my skin—not hot, just a warmth in the air. We have four beers with us and Denise has a blanket in the car. By the time we pull the car over and find a place to sit, I can tell Denise seems different from the way she usually is. Her interest in our conversation is genuine but super-excited. She has swerved twice in the car on the way here not from drinking but from looking at me while driving.

The place we sit is isolated and quiet. We've come here many times during the day to go swimming, but this is the first time at night. The moon is in the shape of a crescent and the stars are many in the sky. There's no other light in the area, so when the headlights of the car finally go off, a stillness and peacefulness surrounds us, very much different from the party. We both crack open a cold beer and she asks me how I feel. I know I can tell her the truth.

"Denise, I am so sick of that question, it is not even funny. I'm okay, at best. Sometimes I'm fine, sometimes I'm okay, sometimes I'm angry, sometimes I feel worthless, sometimes I'm pissed off. I feel like I don't know how I am, and really, I have no idea how I am supposed to be."

"What about now, how are you with me?" she asks.

"This, right now, is about the best I have felt the whole time and I know that I'm not in any hurry to go anywhere else," I say.

"Good," she says as she puts her beer down in the grass and leans in to me. I put my beer down on the other side of the blanket and we kiss. I roll her to her back and lie on top of her. Denise is soft and pretty, with blond hair and long legs, which she wraps around my waist. I am as gentle as I can be, as much for myself as for her. In five minutes we're naked except for some bandages on my arm, and five minutes later we're finished making love. We both lie on the blanket, looking at each other and Denise says, "Do you want to do something tomorrow, go to lunch maybe?"

I say, "Yeah, l would love to. I have to go see a shrink at eleven in the morning. My parents are making me go a few times before I leave for school, so I have to go tomorrow and the next day." We make arrangements to meet around noon the following day.

She leans up, resting on her elbow, and her naked torso is right in front of me. There is sweat on her chest from the warm air, and I try to act cool, but it's one of the most beautiful sights I have ever seen. She looks down on me as I lie on my back, and her body is gorgeous, naked and inviting. "Let's not think about tomorrow just yet," I say as I sit up. I kiss her on her shoulder, neck and lips. She lies back down and kisses me back.

By the time we put our clothes back on and drink the last two not-so-cold beers, our conversation slows and we're both in our own thoughts. I don't know what she's thinking, but I can't help but wonder why girls are coming on to me. For years, I've tried to pick up girls, tried to get them to like me, tried to make time with them, with mixed results. And suddenly, the last two times I go out, two girls make it a point to find me and be with me. It's weird.

I must have a funny look on my face because Denise leans her face into mine and asks, "What are you thinking?"

"Nothing, it's just such a nice night that I don't want to leave. This has been the best night I've had in a long time," I say.

"Good, because I wanted you to have a good night," she says and kisses me. "Let's see what happens next time we see each other," she says.

In my mind, I think *Sweet, there's going to be a next time.* I am not sure what love feels like but this is the closest I have ever gotten to that feeling.

CHAPTER 15

I'm sitting in a psychiatrist's office looking back at an older, bearded, hippie-looking guy who asks, "How are you feeling?"

I am not totally an open book. I respond, "Doing great, how about you?"

"I am doing well, thanks. So tell me a little about yourself, what do you enjoy?"

"My hobbies are fast cars and fast women, that's why the guys in the car club call me the cruiser," I say, straightfaced. I have taken the line right from the movie *Stripes*. No reaction. He goes on with his line of questions:

"Have you had a chance to reflect on your accident?" "Do you remember your dreams?" "Have you had a nightmare about your accident?" "Where do you see yourself in five years?" "What is the most important thing in your life right now?"

I answer in any way I feel like answering, with any answer I want to give him. Most of the time it's not even true. I have to sit through one hour and then I can get out of here. I told my parents that I don't need therapy or a psychiatrist, but Dr. Munster thinks it's a good idea, so here I am.

If I am getting on this guy's nerves, he doesn't show it and my hour ends. Denise picks me up from his office and we go to lunch. She tells me that she has a meeting with her advisor at TSU and we can't spend the whole afternoon together. Time with her is so much better than the time with the shrink. We laugh about last night. We talk about next time, but she has to go to dinner with her family tonight and I leave in a few days. I can't wait to go away, but it would be nice if she could come along, too.

More appointments with the shrink. By the time my third visit is over, I am diagnosed with Post Traumatic Stress Disorder, whatever the fuck that is, and I am given a book, *When Bad Things Happen to Good People*. What do I know? I know I don't have to go back to him until Thanksgiving break and I can put this book on the shelf in my room and never open it.

Unfortunately, I don't get a next time with Denise, and we promise to find each other at Thanksgiving. Her parents have her getting supplies for college and picking out stuff for her room. My parents throw a monkey wrench into our plans and make me go to dinner and see family in Frederick. What I've anticipated all summer is suddenly right here, right now: out of high school, out of my parents' house, and onto the college scene. It's September 3, 1986 and I'm ready for anything.

But I can't shake the recent past entirely. My first day at RMC is unlike that of any other student in my class, that's for sure. Since the fire I've developed ulcers in my stomach, and occasionally I get sick and throw up for no reason. I find out right before I leave home that I have to change my diet. No fried foods, no spicy or greasy foods, no caffeine, nicotine or alcohol. I can do all of that, except for alcohol.

As we pull away from the only home I have ever known, the old wood-paneled Ford station wagon is filled with my clothes, books, cleaning supplies, food and all the other necessities of a college freshman. Both Mom and Dad are taking me to school and I settle into the back seat as we head off to Route 95 south. For some reason–maybe stress or anxiety–my parents have to keep pulling over to let me throw up on the ride to campus. It is a three-hour drive and we pull over three times. By the time we get to school, I am ready to say goodbye to my parents and move on.

Two pleasant surprises are part of my new life at RMC. One is that the school sent out too many acceptance letters and enrolled too many freshmen. As a result, my roommate and I are given a room at the Holiday Inn as our dorm room for the semester. Unlike a dorm room, it includes cable TV, maid service, sheets, towels, a conference room as our study hall and a shuttle bus to campus. It's a nice setup.

The second bonus is that my roommate is my teammate from high school, Art, and I know several other people from Baltimore who are also freshmen. Kevin's girlfriend Lucy is one. A girl named Stephanie, whom I have known since I was five years old, is Lucy's roommate. It's going to be a good time and I can't wait for the freedom college offers me.

As soon as Mom and Dad pull out of the Holiday Inn parking lot, Art and I head out on bikes to explore the campus, find old friends, make new friends and have some fun. Within two hours, we have met most of the people on Lucy's and Stephanie's hall, invited them to the Holiday Inn and are currently hosting a pool party. Most of the guys (it's all guys at the Holiday Inn) are pretty cool and are happy to help with the party, bringing beer and liquor that they have in their rooms. It seems that as long as all drinks are in a cup and no alcohol is in view, nobody at the Holiday Inn cares what you drink. Lucy and Stephanie are introducing the girls from their dorm to the guys at the inn, and our freshman class promises to be a good one. Most of us are private school kids, many from the state of Virginia.

Art is playing football for RMC, so he's been here for two weeks already with summer practice. He's invited a couple of football players over, and after about a half hour they start acting like meatheads who can't handle their liquor. One guy jumps on a chair and breaks it, then another falls onto a table and breaks that, too. My friends and I like to drink and laugh, make fun of each other, talk to girls. Destruction of property is not really my thing, but I can't stop these guys from tearing stuff up, and at this point, I don't want to. Pretty soon, the front desk people are sniffing around the pool and tell us to break up the party. "Only invited guests may swim in the pool." We explain that everyone is invited and it gets us nowhere. Around six o'clock we decide to head back to our room with Lucy, Stephanie and some other friends to drink before we head to dinner.

There's one girl who stands out from the rest of the others. She's shy, she won't take her clothes off and swim in her bathing suit in front of us. She doesn't drink much, but she's very cute. She likes music, so she's taking care of the tunes. She's a little too big on country music, but there is classic rock that we agree on. She has caught me looking at her a couple of times, but I can't get her to relax very much. She's like the private school girls from Baltimore but better looking. She doesn't need makeup and is sexy without trying to be. Her smile takes my breath and her southern accent makes her seem really vulnerable. It doesn't take long to realize that she's from a small town, but she likes to travel, plays guitar and is close to her family. I'm getting her out of her shell and she brightens as we laugh together. Her name is Stacey and she lives right across the hall from Lucy and Stephanie. Stacey has a boyfriend from home, but that doesn't matter to me much. Since she's playing hard to get, I let all the other guys try and just sit back. Lucy, Stephanie and the other girls are having fun and, once the football players leave, we head back to the pool. Who needs dinner, we can always order pizza.

By the time it gets dark, we take our traveling party on the road and head to a frat party. Stacey is in and out of my sights but I can't help noticing all the guys that come up to her. It makes me feel both jealous and desperate. She is coy and beautiful, and when I try to be cool, it comes off as arrogant. She dismisses me as drunk and I can't disagree. Since I know a few older guys on campus from home and lacrosse, they take me upstairs to meet other players on the team. After that, I don't remember anything.

I wake up in my bed in my room, 10A at the Holiday Inn, with all my clothes on and a ringing headache. It was my first night at college and it was my first blackout. The shrink had asked me if I ever blacked out and I didn't know what he was talking about at the time, but now I do. It's a weird feeling, but by the time Art wakes up and we head out to breakfast, I dismiss it. I mustn't have done anything too stupid.

It's a month into the school year, and I have blacked out at least three more times. I don't go to every class and no one seems to care except for my lacrosse coach. I've not had a haircut since I got there. I feel like I'm a typical freshman, drunk half the time and hungover the other half.

In November, Big Dave, who lives in Richmond, comes by to pick me up to go to Baltimore. Big Dave's dad and my uncle, Francis, is the athletic director at Georgia. Georgia is playing a football game against Navy at Memorial Stadium in Baltimore, a place I've been to many times, and I want to see the family. Big Dave has told me that he has an extra ticket for me, and I ask Stacey if she wants to go. She said yes and we are headed up I-95 to the game.

I introduce Stacey to Brian, Hugh and Billy. All the crew is here and we have a great time. Georgia wins, so we have a big post game party in the parking lot. We throw the football, but beer replaces tackling and we act like college kids. I watch myself because Mom and Dad are here and I don't want them to say anything about the drinking. Plus, if I bring Stacey all this way, I want to show her I can be a gentleman. God knows I haven't shown much of that at college. When the party ends, we pile into Big Dave's car and head back to RMC. Big Dave's wife, Jean Marie, has packed a cooler full of food and she feeds us, two hungry college students, the best we've had in months. We sit like kids in the back seat, holding hands, as Stacey leans into my ear and says, "I've had a great time today, you are so much more fun when you don't drink that much." I'm not sure what she means by that, but I've had a great time too.

Within two weeks I've blacked out again. Stacey has gotten

sick of my sloppiness and instead enjoys the attention of the older guys. She doesn't seem to be with anybody in particular, but they all notice her. I am immature and shallow, so I resort to teenage bravado and act as if I don't care. I move on to other girls, with my eye on Stacey when we're both sober. We both take on different personalities when we drink and compatibility-wise, it won't work. The thought of not drinking is not even a flicker in my mind. Why then do I want a relationship with her to work? Why do I say I don't care, when I do? Because I feel something for her that I haven't felt with anyone else. Because my heart is stronger than my head, it always has been. Unfortunately, the pull of the bottle is stronger than all feelings and logic.

||||||||||||||||||||||||||||||||||||||||||||||||||||||||||

CHAPTER 16

||||||||||||||||||||||||||||||||||||||||||||||||||||||||||||||

By the time spring of my freshman year rolls around, my top-down priorities are partying, lacrosse, and school. I have team-mandated study hall and I make sure to go–who wants to run extra sprints? Otherwise, I go to class only when I have to. Partying has not affected my play too much as I am the second leading scorer on my team, playing out of position at midfield. The leading scorer is one of those guys that loads up on cupcakes and doesn't show up against anybody good. He even scored eight goals against Bridgewater, a first-year team, shooting and scoring long after all the rest of the starters had stopped. But, against W&L or Roanoke, he doesn't score a single goal.

Against W&L, I'll get a chance to play against Roy and Charlie, and I am really excited. Like a dumbass, I go out the night before the game and get drunk. During the night, an old girlfriend from Baltimore, Maria Ellison, shows up on campus and it turns into a very late one. Maria is one of those extremely wealthy girls who have no cares in the world, so she stays up late, sleeps late and still gets everything done. She's really smart, kind of artsy, and likes to get drunk. She's also really pretty, with one of those elegant faces that make her look good when she's happy and when she's sad. Every time I'm around her, guys always do a double take. Several of my friends doubt that she even likes me, but, for some reason, she calls me or I call her every few months and get together. She goes to the University of Richmond and just shows up on this Friday night half-drunk and looking to get fully drunk.

I make the suggestion that Maria get in the shower with me, but she rejects it and instead waits in my room while I get cleaned up. We both have fake IDs so we head out on my bike with her on the handlebars to a bar right off campus called the Train Stop. There is a guitar player, plenty of friends and a bar filled with beer and liquor. Wouldn't you know it, Stacey is there. I try not to notice her, but she makes it really difficult. Stacey is dancing for the guitar player, pulling other guys on the dance floor and generally drawing attention from every guy she can. Maria even says, "What's the deal with the blond girl, did she not get enough attention in high school?"

I just laugh. "Yeah, who knows, let's do a shot."

By the time the bar closes at 2 a.m., Maria and I are too drunk to ride the bike back to the Holiday Inn. Instead, we walk, stumble, fall, occasionally sit and finally hitchhike the mile back to my room. We fall on the bed, fully clothed, with the intention of getting naked, but because I drank too much and getting an erection is out of the picture, we give up and both pass out.

I wake up. The clock reads 10:15 and I realize I have to be in the locker room by 10:30 for a noon game. I leave Maria passed out in my bed and head out. I look for my bike to get there quicker and remember that it's sitting, unlocked, outside the Train Stop. Who knows if it will be there by the time I get back to it, but now is not the time to check. I start jogging to the locker room and pick up my speed as I get closer. I pass the cafeteria and turn the corner towards the gym and run directly into Roy and about six of his teammates.

"Hey, man, what are you doing?" I say to Roy.

"We've been looking for you. We got here at nine-thirty and I've been trying to find you. I saw your team, those guys didn't know where you were," Roy says. "Hey, this is Brian, this is John...." He introduces them all to me but I stop listening. I have met these kind of arrogant, asshole players from W&L before and I am not really interested in being too nice right before we're about to play them. And now that I have stopped running, my head is starting to pound.

"Damn, dude, you smell like a brewery," Roy says.

"Do I?" I ask as I breathe into my hand and smell it. "I ran out of my room and didn't even brush my teeth. Any of you guys have some gum?"

One of Roy's snobby buddies has some, so I ask for a couple more pieces.

"Where are you coming from?" Roy asks.

"Dude, Maria Ellison showed up last night half-drunk, and we ended up drinking until three. It was a shit show, both of us wiped out on the walk home."

"Where is she, is she coming to the game?" Roy asks.

"I don't know, I left her in my room, still asleep."

Roy looks at me with a smile and starts nodding his head, "You and Maria stayed up all night last night, didn't you? She's hot," he says, looking at his friends, "and she has always had a thing for Mark. She's way out of his league."

"Fuck you, dude, let me tell you, we didn't stay up too late. We ended up at the town bar until closing, headed home, drank more, and" —as I say this, I look at Roy's friends. A couple of them are looking at me like I'm crazy, but the others are starting to laugh— "we passed out cold and I just woke up about ten minutes ago. I have to get to the locker room or I'm in big trouble. Safe to say, Maria is not showing up today after last night's pitiful performance. I'll make it up to her sometime, though, you can bet on that. But in the meantime, I have to get ready to beat the shit out of this W&L lacrosse team."

Roy just nods and smiles as I grab him by the shoulder and give him a hug. When we separate, I make eye contact with a couple of their guys and lift my eyebrows and my head at the same time and say, "Nice to meet you guys, enjoy the tour of campus." None of them say anything, and I know I just got in their heads for the game.

We lose, which is to be expected, but I end up with three goals and three assists in a 14–10 loss. Roy's buddies might have looked down on me earlier for my middle class background, my use of foul language, my abuse of alcohol the night before a game, my lack of judgement when it comes to women. But I also know that they cannot look down on me because of my lacrosse ability. On a level playing field where everyone begins as an equal, your ability to perform is all the matters. People's connections, their parents' bank accounts, their country club status–all major W&L bragging points–hold no weight in a game. It is either you can or you can't. And today, I know that I can because they sent a bunch of different guys to cover me. Charlie tried for a while and did a good job, but I got him one time and they put someone else on me. Going through the handshake line after the game, I hug Roy again and say, "I'll see you in the summer, man."

Roy responds, "My friends don't know what to think about you, you stay up all night and light us up. Damn, man, good game."

"Thanks," I say.

"Now go brush your teeth, your breath could kill a small dog, you nut."

I smile and know this guy is my friend first, no matter what.

|||||||||||||||||||||||||||||||||||||||||||||||||||||||||||

CHAPTER 17

|||||||||||||||||||||||||||||||||||||||||||||||||||||||||||||||

The very next week, I start drinking at happy hour and continue into the fraternity party at Phi Delt. I have plans to meet Maria tomorrow for brunch. She wants me to come to Richmond and meet her at the Shockley Slip Cafe. I know that Art is tied up with his girl and I have very few prospects at this party, so I call an audible. I duck out of the party and head back to my room in search of Art's keys to his turd-brown Volkswagen rabbit. I plan on taking it tomorrow, but no time like the present and, being ten drinks into my day, the idea of surprising Maria overcomes me.

I find the keys, grab a collared shirt and a pair of khakis, find the car, and head out, starting the twelve miles straight down Route 1 south. I've done this ride before, and it's an easy ride, with the University of Richmond right off the highway.

A few miles in, I look in the rear view mirror and see police lights behind me. I pull into the right lane to let the cop go by and he pulls over right behind me. *Oh shit*, I think, *what does he want?* I lean over and slide the beer I brought with me under the passenger seat. As I come up, I hear the shock of the sirens behind me and it sends panic into my arms and hands. It jolts me in my upper body as I use my blinker and pull to the right side of the road.

The policeman comes up to the driver's side window, and as I roll it down, he leans in and asks, "Do you know why I pulled you over?"

"No, I don't," I say, trying to minimize my words, hoping not to breathe on him.

"Do you know the speed limit on this road?"

"Umm, is it 50?" I ask.

"Yes, it is 50, can you tell me why you were going 67 miles an hour?"

"What?? I wasn't going 67," I respond quickly, sure that I wasn't speeding.

"Excuse me, son, are you telling me I'm lying?" he snaps back. I can tell he's pissed off. Right then, I see a flashlight come into the front seat from the passenger side. I lean my head down and look that way, only to see another cop shining the beam into the car.

"Looks like he has some beer in the front seat, Joe," I hear him say to the officer on the driver's side.

"How old are you, son?" Officer Joe asks me.

"I am eighteen, sir," I respond, hoping that some "sir" and "please" will help me. "That beer was there when I got in the car. I'm just driving to Richmond, sir."

"Where are you coming from?"

"I am coming from RMC, sir."

"You know it's against the law for anyone under twenty-one to have alcohol in your possession at any time, son. Have you been drinking?" he asks, inevitably. The one question I have been trying to avoid and the one question I am afraid of.

"No, sir," I say with all the assurance I can muster.

"Why don't you step out of the car," Officer Joe says.

"Yes, sir," I say, unsure of how this is going to work out, but confident in my abilities to both hold my liquor and hide my intoxication. I stand up straight and look at Officer Joe, who's taller and thicker than he appeared while he was leaning into the window.

"Since you haven't been drinking, you shouldn't have any problem blowing into our breathalyzer, would you, son?" he asks in a way that isn't really a question.

I respond the only way I know that may save me. "No, sir, I don't think I need to do that."

"If you don't blow into this breathalyzer, I'm going to have no other option but to arrest you for transporting alcohol by a minor, son," Officer Joe says, looking at me like he knows I'm guilty.

"I don't think you have to arrest, me sir," I say.

"Don't tell me my job, son. Look, Billy, this guy doesn't want to take a breathalyzer, wants to transport beer and then tell me that he shouldn't get arrested. Listen, I am going to give you one more chance, you can take this breathalyzer or you can go to jail, what's it going to be son?"

"I am not taking it," I say, and before I can say anything else, I feel a hand hit me in the middle of my chest and I stumble backwards onto the side of the Volkswagen.

"Billy, this boy doesn't think he needs to take our test," he says across the car to his fellow cop.

Before he can say anything else, it's my turn. I have tried to be respectful and tried to be nice, but since it's not looking good and I know I am about to get cuffed, I fire back, "Don't call me boy, don't call me son, you're not my dad."

"Look at this, Billy, we got ourselves a smart ass college boy," he says as he smiles at me.

"It's a shame he ain't going back to college tonight," Billy says from the other side of the car.

"Turn around," he says to me, "and put your hands on the hood of the car."

As I turn away, I feel a forearm shoved between my shoulder blades and I stop my face from hitting the hood with my hands. Just then Officer Joe grabs my left wrist, and I feel the same hit between my shoulder blades, this time slamming my chest and the side of my face against the hood. He presses his hand and leans with his body weight against my back, smashing me against the hood. He grabs my right wrist and cuffs my hands behind my back. He shifts his hand to the back of my head and shoves it into the hood of the

Volkswagen.

"Son," he accentuates, "you are under arrest for driving under the influence, you have the right to remain silent, anything you say can and will be used against you in a court of law." As he continues, I try to turn my head to get it free from his grip, only to have the other side of my face smashed against the hood. He finishes his rehearsed lines as he continues to push my head into the car.

I wait with no resistance. When he finally lets me up and turns me to the patrol car, we make eye contact and I say loud enough for him to hear, "Fuck you."

Just as quickly, I feel a knee to my gut, doubling me over. In an instant, while bent over, I barf. Some of it lands on his shoe. I see his feet try to get out of the way of the next round of puke and hear him say, "Shit." I smile as I am looking at the ground, happy knowing at least I got him a little. The remnants of barf on my jeans is a small price to pay for at least a little satisfaction of fucking with Officer Joe.

The rest of the night is a blur of booking, fingerprinting, holding cell and sleep. When the sun rises and I wake from a rough night on a cot in a cell by myself, I hope that I get out soon.

I sit alone in a Hanover County jail cell, thinking of where my night began and where it ended. My idea the night before was to surprise my friend and sleep in Richmond, my reality is a night in lockup and a DUI offense. I don't know where to turn. I decline my chance to make a phone call from jail, only asking for a chance to call a cab when I get out. Art's car is on the side of the road on Route 1 somewhere and I have to pick it up and get it back to school. Hopefully it is still there and hasn't been stolen or broken into. I know they took my keys last night, so hopefully I get them back, too. All these thoughts are swirling around in my head when an older, overweight white cop comes in front of the cell and jolts me out of my thoughts.

"Wake up and get out of bed, you're free to go," he says flatly. The rattling of keys and the noise of the lock ring through the hollow room as I scramble out of the cot and put my feet on the floor. Without stopping, I keep moving forward and continue to walk through the door.

He looks at me and says in typical small town expression, "Slow down, son, what's your hurry?"

"I don't want to be here any longer than I have to."

"Then don't come back," he says matter of factly and opens the door to the lobby of the police department. On the counter is a tray with my keys, my wallet and the contents of my pockets from last night, some gum, change and a condom. "Here's a card for the local cab company, you can use the pay phone outside. Your car is on Route 1 about eight miles south of here. You're free to go."

I walk outside and use the payphone to call Jimmy's Cab Company. They tell me they will be here in twenty minutes. While I wait, I lift the phone book that hangs from the metal wire, look up Big Dave's phone number and put my quarter in the slot. Big Dave is a lawyer in Richmond, and I am about to call for some legal advice. The only place to turn is to family. The lecture from my parents and the disappointment in my actions can wait until later. For now, I just want to find out what my punishment will be, and Big Dave will know.

||||||||||||||||||||||||||||||||||||||||||||||||||||||

CHAPTER 18

||||||||||||||||||||||||||||||||||||||||||||||||||||||||||||

It's a cold, rainy November Saturday night–Thanksgiving break sophomore year– and I am home in Baltimore in a downtown bar, Alley Oops, with all my friends and our fake IDs. The bar is aptly named because it sits at the dead end of an alley off Cross Street in the heart of Federal Hill. The alley is actually named The Alley, and it has to be the most stolen street sign in all of Baltimore city. The bar itself is like a lot of downtown bars in residential neighborhoods: exposed brick, a narrow feel, loud music and the smell of stale beer throughout. It's a college bar, friendly to any kid with a fake ID and cash in his pocket.

By the time Trip, Art and I have drunk our fill it's 1:30 a.m. We walk out of the short alley onto Cross Street, see the activity from the other bars and people in the streets, and follow the smell of fresh grilled beef. We put our money together and order three pit beef sandwiches from a man who looks like he's maybe sixty-five, maybe older, as he serves them in his winter coat, oven mitt and dirty apron. I cover mine in barbeque sauce and barely taste it as it fills a void in my stomach that I didn't know I had.

"That was the best sandwich I've ever had," I say to both Trip and Art, who have finished theirs as well. "Let's get another one." I dig into my empty pockets and pull them inside out. "Who's got some money I can borrow to get another? All I need is four dollars."

Art pulls his pockets out. "I don't have anything."

Trip says, "I spent the last of what I had on the sandwiches."

"All right," I say as I stumble away, heading towards Trip's car for the ride home. As I walk down Cross Street, I get an idea. *How about if we get one of the pieces of beef off the grill? What if we bring it home, I'm sure we have bread at home. Wouldn't be hard to get. It's just a sixty-five-year old man standing there, he won't be able to do anything about it. It'll probably be pretty easy. We'll need to get some barbeque sauce.*

"Wait, guys, I got a good idea, we can make a bunch of sandwiches at my house," I say.

Art asks, "How are we going to do that?"

"I'm going to grab one of those pieces of beef off the grill. It'll be easy. But I need you guys to go around the corner and have the car ready. What I'm going to do is grab the beef and run, make the turn and hop in the car. Just be ready to go, all right?"

"Yeah, okay," says Art. Art and I have pulled off some capers like this before, so he's always ready.

"Trip, just have the car running, I'll be there in like, ten minutes," I say.

"You're not going to do that," says Trip.

"Dude, just have the fucking car ready, okay?"

Art and Trip continue walking down Cross Street as I turn back and head towards Alley Oops. Cross Street is a narrow, one-way street that has a lot of traffic, so it is not unusual for people to be walking in the middle of it. I take a look at the old man standing by his grill, waiting for more customers. He stands alone with foot traffic and car traffic all around him including the bar right in front of him, Hightops. I've pulled a few heists in my day, and this one looks to be an easy one. The guy looks like a sitting duck, and a getaway car sits one block away. This looks like a pretty good setup.

I keep walking past Alley Oops to the end of the street. I don't see any cops. Since I know the beef is going to be hot coming off the grill, I need something else. I reach into a trash can right outside the closed Cross Street Market and find a brown lunch bag, clear the contents, and place it over my hand. I start a slow jog towards the stand. When I get a few feet away, I spot the piece I'll grab on the top part of the grill, reach out with my covered hand, grab it, tuck it like a football under my armpit and haul ass. I feel the initial heat on my jacket and hear the man yell, "Hey, get back here!! Boys!! Boys, he—"but I now hear only my breathing and my feet hitting the pavement. It's about 150 yards to the corner. Trip and Art should be there, ready, with the car running.

But now comes more yelling and more than one voice. "Hey! Stop!" I look over my right shoulder as I hit top speed afraid of seeing cops, but instead it's five or six guys, older guys, city guys, chasing me. I kick it up another notch. By the time I make the turn, these older guys are gaining on me. I look for the exhaust of the running getaway car but instead I see both my friends outside it, Trip on the driver's side, Art on the passenger's. I swear I hear Trip say, "I don't even think he's going to do it," as I run past them and yell, "Start the fucking car!" By now, the city guys are right behind me and I start to swerve and zig zag down Lancaster Avenue, like a kickoff returner trying not to get caught from behind.

I can feel the pack right on my back. A second later one of them kicks my foot and I lose my balance, sliding on my shoulder and my side, beef fumbling from my grip as I eat pavement. Before I can regain my senses or get to my feet, I feel kicks to my back and my ass and my side. I crouch into the fetal position and cover my face with my forearms as blows land all over my body. I lie there, trying to roll away as a hand grabs my wrist and knuckles graze my now unprotected head.

I pull my forearms back and cover again as I hear Art yelling, "Break it up, break it up, what's going on here!" The thuds keep coming one after the other as I hear talking–yelling, really–in the background. They slow after about a minute, but I don't dare stop blocking my face or my eyes or even attempt to get up. When I haven't been hit for at least thirty seconds, I sneak a peek through my forearms and see Art's pants and shoes next to my head between me and the crowd. While I lie there, I hear the unmistakable signal that cops are on their way: radio noise, stern voices, loud shoes on the street.

"Gentleman, stand back, stand back," one yells from a short distance. I hear one of the officers talk into a radio, mumbling indeterminate words or instructions. I get the sense that I am okay to get up from the pavement. My jacket is ripped, and my pants are torn. I push myself up with my right hand, brown bag still on it, and get on one knee. When I lift my torso to breathe I immediately feel pain, real pain, in my side. I don't know if this is what a broken rib feels like but this hurts, bad. By the time the cops are next to me, their whole crowd is talking, telling the cops what happened, why it happened, how we ended up here. Finally, I hear a cop say, "Please, be quiet. We will get to the bottom of this. Sir, let me ask you a few questions," he says to me..

One of the guys steps forward and starts talking to one of the cops. The other cop spends his time holding back other guys from kicking my ass some more. I hear the conversation between guy and cop. Turns out he's the old man's son. He, his brother and their buddies hang out and work as bouncers at Hightops in case anybody messes with the old man. Sounds like a pretty good plan, much better than my plan.

When they finish talking, the cop comes over to me, asking questions that he already knows the answer to. At this point, there's no use lying or trying to push the blame. I tell him that he has the story straight, yes I did that, etc. There's no point arguing, all I know is that I don't want to go down to the police station. I've been there before and I don't want to go again. If I give this guy some "Yes, sir" answers and act contrite, maybe he'll give me a break. Officer Bentley pulls out his ticket book and explains what my charges will be.

"Son, I don't need to take you to the station, but you will be charged with a crime. You are being cited for theft of a personal property of less than two hundred and fifty dollars. You are being released right now under your own recognizance and will be given a court date in less than fourteen days. It is your responsibility to contact the magistrate in Baltimore City in order to arrange your hearing. Do you understand your responsibilities?"

I nod my head. "Yes, sir."

"You sign right here. If you do not respond to this summons within fourteen days, there will be a warrant for your arrest issued. Do you understand?" he asks again.

"Yes, I understand." I hold my right side with my right hand, convinced I have at least one broken rib. The crowd around us has grown as the people leaving the bar slow down while they walk by, like rubbernecking at the scene of an accident.

When the officer rips the ticket from his book and hands it to me, I fold it and put it in my jacket pocket. I hear the group of men give me shit as I walk away but I am determined not to make eye contact. "You're lucky the cops saved your ass," one of them says loudly.

I hear the cop say, "Gentleman, everyone go home, it's time for everyone to go home."

"Don't come back down here, or we're gonna to kick your ass again," the same voice says.

By now we're halfway down the street. I take a look over my shoulder to see if anyone is following us. As soon as I do, I hear the same voice. "Damn right, you should be looking over your shoulder. You keep looking over your shoulder, because we're coming for you!" I don't say anything. I just quicken my pace to the car and slide into the back seat, lie down on my good left side and resume the fetal position. Guilt washes over me, the guilt of stealing, the remorse of getting caught, the impending doom of the consequences. My pattern of not thinking through actions only to be left with scorched bridges, leaves me despondent and depressed. *How can my parents spend so much time teaching right from wrong and I still always choose wrong?* My sober self knows, while my drinker self rolls the dice every time, willing to live with the results. The result of this drinking binge is an ass kicking in the street, which I asked for and deserved.

By the time we pull up at my house, tomorrow's plan is set: We'll wake up early and leave right away. I'll tell my parents we have school work to do and we want to get back to campus. We creep up the stairs. I empty my pockets of change, the bar tab and my ticket. Art sticks his wallet on my dresser. When Trip empties his pockets, out comes change, his keys and a twenty-dollar bill.

"You had money the whole time?" I ask as I punch him in the arm as hard as a man with a broken rib can punch. It hurts me more than it hurts him as I fall into bed on my left side. Just making contact with the mattress sends a jolt and I say, "You dick, you could have bought three more sandwiches."

"I need to get gas tomorrow, it was my last twenty," Trip says.

"I would have gotten you twenty tomorrow. I can't believe you let me go down like that," I say.

"That was your dumbass idea," he says laughing, "but I would have eaten that beef, that was good."

"Fuck you," I say as I search for a comfortable position and crash.

When I wake up at 8 a.m., I roust the boys from bed. We put on our clothes, pack our bags and head straight for the front door.

"Mom, we're heading back early to get some schoolwork done," I say as I poke my head into my parents' bedroom. "I'll call you when I get to school."

"Okay, drive safe, guys," she says but we barely hear her. We're already heading down the front steps towards the car.

‖‖

CHAPTER 19

‖‖

Two weeks later, the hall phone rings in the dorm. "Mark, phone for you!" I hear. I walk down the hall and pick up the receiver. "Hello?"

As soon as I hear my mom's voice, I know what's coming. "Mark, some policeman came by the house tonight to give us a ticket and a court date for you. Do you want to tell us about what happened at Cross Street with a side of beef?"

"Mom, I didn't know how to tell you–" I start.

She cuts me off. "How about you start with the truth? You got arrested for stealing, you were in a fight, you got a ticket and you didn't think you had to pay it." I hold the phone out away from my ear and wince.

"Mark, are you listening? Do you know what this means?"

"I'm sorry, Mom. I'm sorry," I say.

"It means you have a warrant for your arrest. The police came here tonight to arrest you, do you know that? You didn't do anything they told you to do and because of that, they came here to arrest you. 'Sorry' is not going to cut it!" She's getting louder as she talks. I hold the phone out again and search for words. There is silence.

"I didn't know how to tell you, Mom. I'm sorry." *Again.*

"Your father is going to call Tom Bodie tomorrow and see what can be done, but I promise you this, you will pay every dime of the fine and the lawyer and you will pay us back for anything else that comes with it. We're disappointed in you and expect much more from you. Your father and I are extremely disappointed, extremely disappointed," she says. "You can't keep doing these things. You've been given an opportunity to go to school, to fulfill your dreams, and you seem to me like you're blowing it. You haven't been honest with us in God knows how long. You come home for a break from school and get arrested, are you kidding me?"

"Mom, I—"

"Don't 'Mom' me," she interrupts and I swallow any further comments. "It's like your father and I don't know who you are anymore. The child we raised, sent to the right school, taught right from wrong, gets arrested, and has a warrant for his arrest. Mark," she continues as my heart breaks and tears, disappointment washing over me, "your grades are not good and I don't see them getting better with this kind of behavior."

Everything she is saying is true, I can't dispute it. Her clarity and truth sting. "Your father and I are making great sacrifices to send you to school and give you the life you have and it is apparent that, not only do you not appreciate it, you are determined to ruin it. This is not going to go away, you will fix this, you will make this better, you will do whatever the judge tells you to do, you will be accountable for your actions." She pauses, anger in her tone and exasperation in her breath.

"I'm sorry, Mom, I'll pay for it all." There is silence as I wait for her to pick up where she left off. As the silence continues, I take the opportunity to say, "I'm going to go, okay? I'll talk to you soon."

"Yeah, you go now," she says in a tone of utter contempt.

"Who was that?" Art asks when I get to my room.

"The cops came by my house tonight. They know about Cross Street."

"Oh, man, you are fucked." I can't disagree. My record gets longer and my future grows dimmer.

Almost instinctively and without hesitation, I reach into the mini fridge next to my disorganized desk and grab a Milwaukee's Best. I see there are about eight or nine and make up my mind to drink all of them over the next couple of hours. At this point, it doesn't matter if anyone wants to drink with me, as the social side of drinking is not too big of a concern to me anyway. This night leads into others just like it and I am not sure I have a sober day for the rest of the semester.

|||||||||||||||||||||||||||||||||||||||||||||||||||||||||||

CHAPTER 20

|||||||||||||||||||||||||||||||||||||||||||||||||||||||||||||

Needless to say, getting blackout drunk, skipping classes and being irresponsible don't lead to good grades and a diploma. After the first semester of my sophomore year, my dad informs me that I will not be returning to RMC. My GPA has dropped to a 1.75 and my drinking has only gotten worse. When I get home and my grades arrive a week later, my chance at RMC is over before I can make it worse.

I discover this dismal fact one morning right before Christmas when my Dad shows up at the doorway of my room. "Mark, I want you to call your coach and let him know you will not be going back to school. If he's counting on you, he needs to make other plans because I have other plans for you."

"What plans?" I ask.

"Don't you worry about that, just call Coach Richards and let him know that you won't be there next semester. When you're done that, come downstairs and help your mother clean the house for Christmas," he says.

"Yes, sir," I say, grab the phone from the hallway and pull it into my room.

I call Coach Richards at his office and speak with the secretary. She tells me that he's not in but will call me when he returns later today. I say thanks and hang up. By the time I get downstairs, the look on Mom's face makes me want to cry. Not because of my circumstance, but because of the pain and disappointment in her eyes. She conveys to me without ever saying a word that this is the most disappointing thing I have ever done. It is heartbreaking for her and for me. I don't say anything either, I just start picking up jackets and hanging them up, I take the full trash can outside and empty it, I sweep the kitchen, one thing after the other. About an hour into the day, Dad asks if I've heard back from the coach.

"No, he hasn't called," I say.

"Your mother and I have to go to the store, we'll be back in about an hour. Keep cleaning and when your brother and sisters wake up, have them clean their rooms," he says and turns away abruptly.

Once the door closes, I sit in a chair in the dining room, surrounded by Christmas decorations and our nice dishes–serving dishes, serving bowls, glasses for special occasions. I start to cry. Is it desperation or is it faith? I don't know. But I get on my knees, put my head in the seat of the chair and start talking to God.

"Please God, let me stop hurting my parents, help me stop making them miserable, help me bring some light into this darkness. I know I have fucked up, I know that this is my fault but please don't hurt them because I am an idiot." My cheeks are covered in tears and my breath is getting deeper. "Help me find a way, help me make things better. I beg of you, help me be better. I am so tired of feeling like a disappointment, so tired of making them unhappy, please help me make it right." Nothing comes into my head as an answer, so I just keep talking. "Please God, help me find somebody who likes me, who likes me for who I am, who likes me for me. Please help me find someone that I can love, that I can feel good about. Please let her be someone I have never met before and doesn't know me, doesn't know that I am fucked up already, someone that will give me a chance. Please help me make things better. Please help me get out of this life and into a new life. I am sorry for being an idiot, I am sorry for the pain I have caused my parents, my family, I am sorry for being such a fuck up. I don't want to be a fuck up anymore, I want to be part of the solution. I don't want to be the problem anymore.

Please God, please help me, please give me a chance, please, for my parents sake, please help me make a difference." I don't have any idea how long I've been kneeling but when I lift my head up, I hear someone moving around the first floor. When I turn my head to see who it is, Thomas is in the kitchen.

He looks at me and says, "What did you do this time?"

"Dad won't let me go back to school. He got my grades and told me to call Coach and let him know. He said he has plans for me."

"You shouldn't go back there anyway, you need to take a break from that place," Thomas says. I look up to Thomas, he's my older brother, plays sports, has good friends. I want to be like him, so when he says stuff to me–whether it's nice or not–I take it extra sensitively. He is the only guy in the world who can make me feel good and feel like shit all at the same time. But when he takes any time to give me advice, I listen. And then, like any good younger brother, I act all sarcastic so he thinks I don't care.

"What kinds of plans is he talking about, do you know?" I ask Thomas.

"No, not really, maybe he wants you to get a job. Either way, you need a change of scenery, you were screwing up down there," Thomas says, then changes the subject. "Hey, I want to take you to meet somebody later today, make sure you're around."

"Who?" I ask.

"A buddy of mine from college, John O'Donohue. He wants to meet you, thinks he can help you out," Thomas says.

"With what? I don't need any help," I say.

"Based on what you were just telling that chair, sounds like you need a lot of help," Thomas says.

"Shut up, you dick. Dad says to clean up your room before they get home."

"If I know Dad, he's not worried about me cleaning my room, so you better get back to whatever they had you doing," Thomas says.

"Shut up," I say, but I know he's right. Dad is only going to be mad at me right now, and the shitty thing is, I deserve it.

An hour later, Thomas finds me again. "Let's go. Grab your wallet," he says and heads out the front door. I look at Mom, who says, "Go with your brother, I'll finish this." I drop the rag that I'm using to polish silver and stop at the sink to wash my hands. While I'm there, Dad walks in.

"When you meet John, I want you to keep your ears open and listen to what he says. You think you have all the answers and I want you to listen. Maybe, just maybe, you can learn something from Thomas's friend. He's taking time out of his day, so listen to what he has to say."

"Okay, Dad, I will, but what does he have to tell me?" I ask as I dry my hands.

"He has a lot to tell you about himself, and it would do you well to listen to it," he says.

When we get to lunch at the Mt. Washington Tavern, John is there already. I've never met him. He went to college with Thomas, though, and is great friends with my cousin, Brother Bry. We sit down, but before we order anything, Thomas suddenly gets up and says, "I have to pick up Julie in Towson, I'll be back in a little bit." Something's up, of course. Thomas leaves almost as soon as we arrive, and as if that's not strange enough, now I'm forced to have lunch with some guy I've never met.

"Mark, Thomas tells me you are at RMC, how do you like it?" John asks.

"Well, John–" I begin but he interrupts me.

"Call me OD," he says. OD is a tall handsome guy with brown hair. The cadence in his voice is measured, not rushed.

"Okay, well, OD, I like it but I won't be going back next semester," I say.

"How come?"

"My grades are terrible," I tell him.

"I know how that is. At Washington College, I had a 1.85 going into my junior year and a 1.90 going into my senior year. I was barely skating by, but I got a 3.5 my senior year and brought my GPA up to a 2.2 and graduated," OD tells me.

"How'd you do that?" I ask.

"I took a semester off and I came back to school with less distractions and a better attitude," he says.

"What did you do, move off campus or get your own apartment?" I ask.

"No, I lived in the same place with Brother Bry. But I just cut one thing out of my life, and my grades got way better."

"What did you cut out?" I ask.

"Alcohol, I stopped drinking it and I had so much more time to do my work. And I feel better because of it, too," he says.

My stomach drops and I'm sure my face is white, like I just saw a ghost. Now I get it, the lunch plans, why Thomas left so quickly, I got set up. But I told Dad that I would keep my ears open and listen, so instead of going into a shell or being a smart ass, I just keep talking. I remember Mom talking about the sacrifices and I know my Dad has made plenty, the least I can do is listen.

"How did you quit drinking–did you go to AA?" I ask.

"I went to rehab for a month and then, when I got out, I made sure to go to a meeting at least every other day. It opened up my head. The rehab taught me about addiction and the AA has helped me find other people like myself who are going through the same things," OD tells me.

"I'm not really going through anything," I say, knowing I'm lying but not sure where to start or what to tell him. I stick with the old standby of "nothing wrong."

"I'm not saying you are. I am just telling you how it has worked out for me so far," OD says, "You should do whatever is best for you. Listen, I'm not here to tell you what to do, preach to you, tell you what you need to change. I'm just here to lend a hand if you need a hand up. Let you know that there is another way to live." He seems gentlemanly in his mannerisms and authentic in his intentions.

He stops talking and there is silence. I'm not sure what to say or if I should say anything. I realize I haven't looked at the menu and I'm starved.

"Where did you go to rehab?" I ask

"Hidden Brook, up in Monkton, it was good for me, definitely learned a lot," he says.

By the time we order and our food arrives, we're talking about football and lacrosse, Grayson–where OD went–and St. Xavier's. He throws in comments about life being better without alcohol and he sounds like he really means it. I can't picture it at all. Why would I want to go out and not have a drink? I got drunk too much and screwed up in school, end of story. I am not an alcoholic, I am not addicted to it.

Thomas and Julie make it back to the tavern by the time we get the check. OD will not take my money and pays for lunch. He couldn't be any nicer. When he shakes my hand and says, "If you need anything, do not hesitate to call," he seems to genuinely mean it. Of course, I know already that I'll never need anything from him although I say "I will" just to make him feel better.

I get in the car with Thomas and Julie and we head for home. Thomas says, "How was lunch?"

"Next time you're going to set me up, at least warn me first," I answer.

Thomas simply replies, "OD is a good man, isn't he?"

"Yeah, he seems like a good dude," I say.

"He is, and if you ever want to talk to him again, call him, he means it," Thomas says.

"I doubt it," I say, holding onto my stubbornness with all my might.

||||||||||||||||||||||||||||||||||||||||||||||||||||||||||||

CHAPTER 21

||||||||||||||||||||||||||||||||||||||||||||||||||||||||||||||

The next day, I wake up late and walk downstairs. Dad looks up from his chair. "Get dressed, we're going to get a tree," he says.

I nod, in my usual foul morning mood, and head back upstairs to put some warm clothes on. Finding a Christmas tree can take a while. Mom likes to find the perfect tree even though there is no such thing. A group consensus is never reached, so I usually stay out of it and just carry it to the car.

When I come downstairs, Mom and Dad are at the front door, coats on, and Dad has his hand on the door knob. "Kids, wrap your presents and clean up the kitchen," he says loudly. The house is small and a raised voice can reach all the rooms, closed door or not. "We're going to get a tree."

"Okay" I hear Lauren say from the TV room.

Mary comes running down the stairs. "Can I come?" she asks.

Mom's tone changes entirely to a pacifying, soft voice."Not right now, honey, we'll be back soon and you can help me bake cookies."

Mary has an obvious look of disappointment. "Okay," she says, nodding her head to the side, then turns and heads back up the stairs to her room, still in her pajamas.

Dad holds the door open and looks at me. I can tell that this moment of alone time with my parents is not some bonding time. No one else is coming with us to get a Christmas tree because no one else is invited. Mom and Dad get inside the front seat of our yellow, old, battered station wagon and I slide into the back seat, head down, waiting for the inevitable lecture that I know is coming.

As I sit there, my mind wanders. Mom has not said anything and that is unusual. She always has something to say on all subjects. Mom is a complicated person, a person of big ideas and small favors. She sits on the Board of Directors at Vill Julie College and has taught preschool. She has been a lacrosse coach to me and to a lot of other guys, some of whom have gone on to be all-Americans. She coaches boys, works for Catholic Charities and socializes with everybody. Wherever we go to a game, a school, a party, she knows everybody and, if she doesn't know them, introduces herself and her family, much to my chagrin. She talks to athletic directors and coaches, priests and nuns, parents and kids. There's nobody she won't talk to and share her opinion with. All of my friends who are girls find her to be funny and nice. I find her to be overbearing and embarrassing, probably like all other boys feel about their mothers. She is a product of her environment, the youngest of six kids, totally comfortable in any setting in any area of Baltimore. She is never at a loss for words, so this time of quiet is offsetting.

Dad is driving, one hand on the wheel and the other cleaning the fog off the windshield. Dad is a great counter to Mom's somewhat opinionated, outgoing nature. He's more reserved, open-minded with a gentle nature towards all kids, teenagers, and adults. His calm demeanor always puts my friends at ease. Dad rarely raises his voice, but when he does, it gets my attention. Instead, he usually teaches his lessons through parables and examples. He always gives everyone the benefit of the doubt, believes in the goodness of others and welcomes everyone into his world. He is easygoing, nonjudgmental and understanding. He prays at church and before bed every night.

I am caught in a web of my own doing by two very different people. My mother is the outgoing, direct and opinionated one, while my father loves being in the company of others and listening to their stories. While I don't feel I am closer to one or the other, at this point, in the backseat, I am further away from both than I have ever been in my life. I have ventured into my own world, intentionally eschewing any of their teachings because I don't care about outcomes, I don't care about their messages, I don't believe they love me, I don't see the benefit to living right, I don't believe in good.

As I sit in the back seat, head turned to the window to my right, watching trees and buildings, people in cars, I wonder why I can't get past this constant shit from my parents, from my coaches, from my teachers, from anyone who is above me. I'm now falling behind the people that are equal to me and the people who used to be behind me are passing me every day. I feel stuck in quicksand with a weight around my neck. I spiral into negativity so easily that the thought of redemption is not even possible. My self-induced pity party is interrupted by a simple question from Dad. "Do you want something to eat?"

"Um, yeah, I am kind of hungry," I say.

"Good, because we're stopping here anyway," he says, as he pulls the car into a crowded parking lot close to JHU. I recognize the place, a greasy spoon frequented by locals and students. We walk in and I head toward a table.

"Mark, we aren't eating here, order at the counter. Margare, get me a sausage, egg and cheese on white toast, okay. I'll be right back," he says.

I turn around and stand next to Mom in line, uncomfortable in our silence as she fidgets. I know she wants to say something but she doesn't open her mouth. We get our food and walk outside. Dad is standing next to the car. I open the back door. "Don't get in," he says, "we're going this way."

We walk down the city sidewalk, hats on, coats zipped up. I don't have any interest in starting conversation, but the tension makes me feel like one is coming and it won't be good. My mother is a strong woman. She stands five feet tall but has an outsized personality. Her heart is on her sleeve. If you want to know what's on her mind, just ask, because she'll tell you. The silence eventually becomes too much and she blurts out, "Are you trying to screw up everything?"

I play dumb. "What do you mean? I'm not trying to screw this up," I say as I put my arms out and my palms up. "I'm trying to go get a Christmas tree."

"That's what I am talking about," she says, frustration bubbling.

"You said everything, didn't you?" I say, being difficult on purpose.

"You know what I'm talking about. You're in a terrible mood around the house, your grades are poor, you're constantly fighting with your brother and sisters," she continues.

"Go ahead, what else am I screwing up? You said everything," I fire back, searching for a reaction.

"Don't do this, Mark," Dad says, "Don't do this."

"Don't do what, Dad? Defend myself? Stick up for myself?"

"Don't make this an argument. Treat your mother with respect, that's what I mean," he says.

Mom interjects, "We want you to be okay, we want you to be happy, and you seem a long way from happy." Random people turn their heads as they walk by us, hearing snippets of our angry words.

"You giving me shit about screwing up everything sure as hell isn't going to make me happy," I say, balling my fists, shaking my head and staring down at the city sidewalk.

"Sit down," says Dad. I look to my right, and on a side street is an entrance to an apartment building. In front of the building are two benches, one on each side. They're green and weathered, with chipping paint and exposed rust. "Come on, have a seat."

Mom and I sit down on opposite sides of the bench, basically as far away as we can be and still be on the same bench. Dad sits down on the gray concrete stoop of the big brick apartment building, facing us. He says, "Mark, we want you to trust us, we want you to believe that we want what is best for you and we know what is best for you."

Mom interrupts again, as she often does, and continues passionately, "We want to know how you're doing. It seems to us that you've changed. You don't let us in, you don't want us to know anything anymore, and, as your parents, that is a scary place to be. You shut us out, you don't let us in anymore. You used to talk to us, we used to laugh together and now, you just don't. I don't know why," she says, and I start to turn off. I don't need to hear more stuff about what I don't do, who I'm not anymore, how I let them down. Every time I'm with them, I get another bullshit lecture about what a disappointment I've become. I am numb and silent and just want to give them lip service.

Mom seems to be coming to a close so I open my ears again. "We love you, it's just that your father and I want to help," she says as she finishes. The thought of their helping is both noble and futile. *If I want your help, I will ask for it and that is not going to happen. I am not here for therapy.*

"I'm good," I say without a hint of a smile, "if I need help, I'll ask for it. I know I can do better." I look at the dirt and dead plants around us on the ground.

"Mark," Dad says, "I want you to look me in the eye and tell me you're okay."

I look him in the eye with a cold stare and say as robotically as possible, "I'm okay."

"I'm not sure I believe you," he says.

Mom starts in, "You just need to talk—" and Dad cuts her off.

"Margaret, let me finish." He continues, this time to me. "You can try it your way if you want, but it doesn't seem to be working out too well. Or, you can start taking some suggestions, start taking better care of yourself, and start acting more responsibly and a lot of your problems will start fixing themselves." Dad is an old school kind of guy. He'll give me a hug and tell me he loves me, but he expects me to do right. He doesn't yell or scream at his family, at a sporting event or at another person. He's reserved until he has to speak up. He's always willing to lend a hand but also knows what it's like to pick yourself by your own bootstraps. I've known since I was a kid that he graduated from the University of Baltimore and got a master's from George Washington University. What I found out later from my grandfather Henry was that he paid for it himself. I guess his father wouldn't pay for it, so Dad did it on his own. He never talks about that stuff, and now he wants me to open up and talk about what's bothering me. I'm not doing that because there's nothing wrong with me.

Dad gets up from the stoop and stands in front of me, reaching out his hand. I take it and he yanks me to my feet. "A journey of a thousand miles begins with a single step. You are going to come home and you are going to get some help." He puts his arm around my shoulder and squeezes with his right arm. With his tight grip, he makes me walk forward, saying, "The Lord helps those who help themselves. Mark, as hard headed as you are, I want you to learn how to get some help." He lets that sentence sit there, out there. *What kind of help?* "Let's go get this Christmas tree," he says as he loosens his grip on my shoulder and steps back on the sidewalk. When I turn, Dad is helping Mom up the same way he helped me, and we walk together. I feel Mom wanting to say something, but for the first time in a long time, she bites her tongue. We walk together among the crowd, ears open, mouths closed.

We walk another block to a small alley between two restaurants. What is normally gated and closed, filled with empty kegs and trash cans, is transformed. The alley gate is open and on both sides are cut trees, lights hanging from above and a Salvation Army bucket at the front. We look around at the trees, find one we agree on, pay the older man wearing a money apron who seems in charge. He cuts a length of twine off a roll and hands it to me. Dad and I each grab one end of the tree—he's got the base and I've got the top—and carry it the three blocks back to the car, rope in my left hand, tree in my right.

||||||||||||||||||||||||||||||||||||||||||||||||||||||||

CHAPTER 22

||||||||||||||||||||||||||||||||||||||||||||||||||||||||||||||

Christmas comes and goes, not nearly as exciting as when we were little. I get a chance to see Billy and Hugh on Christmas night. Billy's having a great time at Roanoke, while Hugh and I are in the same boat with academics. He's struggling at Wesley College and I've done just about everything wrong at RMC. The days after Christmas have something of a black cloud over them, with me walking on eggshells and my parents looking pissed at the very sight of me.

After New Year's Day, Dad says to me, "RMC goes back to school on the sixth. I want you to go down there on the fourth and get your things. Your mother or I will drive you down and help you pack."

"I can do it, Dad, I'll call Art to see when he's going back and he can help me. I don't want you to have to do it, I'll do it myself," I say.

"Well, if you have help and it's okay with your mother, I'll think about it," he says. "You need to get your transcripts from there so you can take classes up here. But for now, I just want you to get your things from RMC."

I call Art and talk him into going a day early, Saturday, January 4. We leave midday and get to school at about four o'clock. By the time we get there, we know there's a party at the Kappa Alpha fraternity and just like that, we're right back into the routine. But this night is different for me. I tell a couple of guys that I'm not coming back, and I feel like I'm letting the lacrosse team down right before the season.

During the night, Art's girlfriend, Tiffany, introduces me to one of her friends. Her name is Allison and she is a freshman. She is beautiful, with long, dirty-blond hair, a pretty smile and a gentle demeanor. We sit on a windowsill, watching the crowd, drinking beer and talking for the whole night. She's easy to talk to. She tells me about her hometown, Rehoboth Beach, Delaware, and about her family–divorced parents, one brother, stepbrothers, a stepsister–and her friends. She tells me about herself and her dreams. She wants to help kids from underprivileged homes in a school setting, so they can have better lives. It seems like something both admirable and hopeful. Her willingness to help others makes me think she has a really kind heart. She's one of the first girls I've ever met who actually asks me about *my* dreams.

I explain to her that I'm leaving school, that I'm a screw-up with bad grades. I tell her that I drink too much and I'm pretty sure my parents are going to send me to rehab. None of this seems to scare her away, and at the end of the night, I don't want her to leave. But, she has told me repeatedly, she will not stay overnight. I ask her if she'll at least sit on the couch with me so we can talk some more. It's late and the party has broken up and most people have gone back to their rooms or upstairs. We sit and talk and next thing we know, we fall asleep on the couch.

At 3:30 a.m., I feel her shaking my arm and hear her tell me she's going home. In my stupor, I say, "Let me take you," and we head to her dorm. When we get to her room, she turns. "Thanks for walking me home," she says, gives me a kiss and says, "Good night."

I stumble back to the same couch and fall asleep. As soon as I wake up, I find Art and Tiffany and ask about Allison. There's a concert today in Charlottesville, only an hour away, and I want to invite her. I call my parents and inform them that I'll be home on Monday morning and set about trying to find this new girl.

Within the hour I discover Allison in her friend's room helping her move in. I tell her my idea and give her the details. But, I explain, we have to leave for Charlottesville pretty quickly. "That sounds like fun," she says, "but I told my friend I'd help her. If you want, though, come find me when you get back and maybe we can hang out."

"I'll find you when I get back," I assure her.

When we get to Charlottesville, Art, Tiffany and I find our UVA friends from home, Bruce and T Burt, and I tell them that I'm leaving school and that for some reason, I feel that there's a sense of inevitability about it. When I get back home, I think my parents are going to take me to rehab. It's just a feeling, but it's a pretty strong feeling.

We all head to the concert to see Indecision, New Potato Caboose and this guy Dave Matthews. It lasts all day and we head back to RMC around eight o'clock. When I get there, I ride my bike to find Allison, who's in her room with her roommate, and she agrees to go out with me. We go to another party at another fraternity and have a great time. By the time the party breaks up, it's late. Allison tells me again that she won't sleep over, so we walk back to her dorm again. Since I have no idea when I'll see her again, I ask her for her phone number. She gives me the number to the phone on her hall and says, "Call me when you get back to Baltimore." I promise to call her and ride the bike back to Kappa Alpha to sleep on the couch again. But when I get back there I'm not tired, and I start throwing all my stuff in my parents' car, a blue Chevy Cutlass. By the time I'm finished, Art and Tiffany show back up and we sit down for a late night of pizza, liquor and beer. I have no idea when we go to sleep, but I cannot get Allison off my mind.

The next morning as everyone is waking up and heading to their first classes of the new semester, I climb in my parents' car and drive away, lamenting my lost opportunity at RMC and my uncertain future, with a glimmer of hope of a nice new girl who fits the profile of an answered prayer.

||||||||||||||||||||||||||||||||||||||||||||||||||||||||||

CHAPTER 23

||||||||||||||||||||||||||||||||||||||||||||||||||||||||||||||||

I'm on my way home from Shaffer's pub. I've failed out of school by my Dad's standards and I'm drunk. My friends are back at college and I am stuck in Baltimore, drinking with TSU and Loyola College students. Some of them are people from high school, but all my close friends are off at college. The nights in Towson aren't the same with all the out-of-town college students acting cool and tough. My attitude is, go back to your hometown but leave your girlfriend. I'm not making any friends and I'm not looking for any. The bottle, the weed, the older crowd that is already out of college are my only companions. Tonight, it is only the bottle and the weed that accompany me as I head home, driving the speed limit with two hands on the wheel, eyes straight ahead. I don't care about the radio, I don't care about the traffic, all I care about is the cops.

As I head down York Road about to make a left into my neighborhood, I notice the familiar whirl of red and blue lights far behind me on York Road. *They can't be coming for me, I've been driving straight, staying in my lane, under the speed limit.* I look in the rear view mirror as I turn on my blinker. I make a left and head straight down Anneslie Road, a narrow street with parked cars on both sides. I hear the siren as I look in my rear view mirror, hoping they don't turn and chase me. The siren gets louder and the reflections of the lights get brighter and brighter. Through the rear view I track the police car as it closes the distance to me, then heads straight down York Road, past the end of Anneslie Road, past me. I look again in the mirror and feel relief as the siren fades. I'm moving slowly, still glancing backwards when I feel the impact, hear the crunch and smell metal. I have just run into a parked car.

It takes me only a few seconds to recover and figure a way out. *I don't think anybody saw me, I don't think anybody knows.* I shift the car into reverse and back up, pulling metal from my Volkswagen Beetle away from the metal of this businessman's sedan. It's dark on the road, with street lights only on corners. The street is quiet. I shift the manual transmission into first gear and head straight down the road. I have to hold the wheel real tightly in my hand as the car is pulling hard to the left, but I only need to keep it straight for three blocks and then I'm home free.

I see a parking place in front of my house, pull in and get out of my car. But just as I close the door to run up the steps, a car pulls up next to me. "Green Volkswagen, you just hit my car," a male voice says.

I look at him in his open window and lie. "I just wanted to park the car and then I was going to go back up there." There was never a chance I was voluntarily going back, but now that he saw me, I try to cover my tracks.

"Is this where you live?" he asks.

"Yeah, this is where I live."

"Are your parents home?"

"Um," I say, "I think so. But I don't want to wake them up."

He puts his head just a little further out the window and says to me matter of factly, "You are going to need to wake them up."

I just bow my head and walk up the steps. When I walk in the front door, I look around the dark living room, flick the lights on, knock on Mom and Dad's door and whisper, "Mom, are you awake?" I hear Dad mumble, "Mark, what do you need?"

"I need you to come outside," I say.

"Right now?" he asks.

"Yeah, right now," I say, with both embarrassment and dejection in my voice.

I walk into the living room and wait for Dad. I sit on the sofa to wait and when I look up, both Mom and Dad are wearing wrinkled clothes and worried looks.

"I hit a car on my way home and the guy is out front of the house," I say right out.

"Where?" Mom asks.

"Up on Anneslie, right off of York Road. The guy is out front."

"He is out there right now?" Mom asks.

"Yeah, he is out there right now," I say. Dad looks at me with disgust, grits his teeth and says, "Get your ass outside right now." I crash his car, wake him up and ask for help, all while drunk. He is a patient man not to punch me in the face.

I stand up from the couch. He looks at Mom with raised eyebrows and almost in lockstep they walk towards the front door. They slow themselves so that I go out first into the cold night and look at the neighbor standing at the open door of his running car, lights on inside and out.

After they introduce themselves and talk briefly, I get in the back seat with Mom while Dad gets into the front. As I lean down to get in, I catch Mom's eye and she looks like she'll kill me when we're alone. There is no way out now.

By the time we get to the damaged car three blocks away, Dad and the owner have worked out how it will be handled. I'm not interested in insurance or blame, but I breathe a sigh of relief when the man says out loud, "As long as we can take care of this, I won't call the police."

Dad says, "You'll be doing us a big favor if you don't call the police. I assure you we will take care of it."

The rest is a blur as I sit on the curb with my head in my hands and remain silent while the three of them survey the damage to this man's car and the bumper of the Volkswagen that lies on the pavement in front of it.

When I wake up the next day, I have panic in my heart. *That must have been a dream. That didn't happen, I just dreamed it. I know it was a bad dream, it has to be a bad dream.* I get to the bottom of the stairs, I make my way across the living room to the big window at the front of the house. *Please let it be a dream, please let it be just a bad dream.*

I look out the front window, and in an instant, any shred of hope or optimism I had comes crashing down, replaced by regret, disappointment and dread as I see the car bumper lying mangled on the front porch.

My life, my situation, my circumstances get worse, again. Just when I think for a moment that last night was a dream, just when I think I have a chance, I screw up again. I think maybe this has been my last chance–maybe not, I hope–and I just flushed everything down the toilet, again. And, again.

||||||||||||||||||||||||||||||||||||||||||||||||||||||||

CHAPTER 24

||||||||||||||||||||||||||||||||||||||||||||||||||||||||||||

I'm lying in bed, three days after crashing the car. My subconscious mind takes over my thoughts. The power of letting go overcomes me as I resign to my sins, I ask to be taken, I accept my plight. This will never get better unless I take a step in the right direction. There is no eureka moment, no come to Jesus meeting, just resignation that the way I am doing things is not getting any better, the way I am living is only getting worse. I am the walking, breathing, living definition of being sick and tired. And hurt and broken. All of it.

As part of my DUI conviction and sentencing, the judge made me go to AA meetings twice a week, get a slip signed and show it to my parole officer once a month for a year and a half. I sat in those meetings back row and all I wanted was not to be called on to participate. I heard what those people said, I became familiar with their refrains, listened to their stories. Being sober did not interest me at all. I got my note signed and got out of there. When it came to AA groups, I did two things: I didn't show up drunk to the meeting and I didn't raise my hand. Otherwise, I drank every chance I got, every time I wanted to. Those people in those meetings were different from me. Those people had a problem with alcohol, they couldn't control it. Their stories were interesting and funny and sad, but they weren't me. I didn't have a problem, it didn't affect me. Or so I thought.

Within a week of the parked car disaster, I am about to be checked in, assigned to, committed to, voluntarily enrolled–

whatever you want to call it– at Hidden Brook Hospital/Addiction Treatment Center. This is a long, long way from keg parties and fake IDs. Mom and Dad are pulling up in front of what looks like an old age country home with a small pond in the front and a lake in the back. I look around, and I am not sure where the boundaries are, so if I make a run for it sometime, I think it looks like a long run. As I turn my head to the front, I see a middle-aged blond, stocky guy walking towards us through the open front door.

"Mister Di'Antonio," he says, mispronouncing our last name just like everybody else we meet for the first time.

"Daniel D'Antoni, nice to meet you," Dad says.

"Mr. D'Antoni, it's nice to meet you," he says. They exchange words but I can't hear what they say. By now, Mom is standing by my side, looking around in uncomfortable silence.

The welcome guy turns to Mom and says, "You must be Mrs. D'Antoni, it's nice to meet you. My name is Brendan. We prefer to use only first names here, so do you mind if I call you Daniel and Margaret?"

"Yes, that's fine," says Dad. Mom says, "Of course."

He turns to me. "And you must be Mark."

"Yes, I am." I try to make eye contact when I shake his hand, but I can't. I look at the ground, and he gives me a good hard squeeze and holds on until I meet his eyes.

"I'm glad you came," he says. "I think you're going to like it here. Let's go inside so we can talk."

We all walk in together. Brendan's office is painted yellow with a big window on the wall that overlooks the lake. Photos of Brendan and what looks like patients sit on his desk and table tops. There aren't any pictures of anyone who looks like his wife or kids or any other family member. I scan sayings on his wall, his desk, and the corner table: "One day at a time." "Let go and let God." While I'm looking around, Mom, Dad and Brendan take seats, Brendan behind his desk, Mom and Dad to the right. One seat remains. I realize I might be holding them up, so I grab it and say, "Sorry."

"What are you sorry for?" Brendan asks.

"I wasn't paying attention and didn't want to hold you up," I say.

"So, are you truly sorry about that, or is it just a reaction to say sorry?" he asks.

"Yeah, I don't want to mess you up," I say.

"Okay, okay, well we take words like 'sorry' seriously around here. We do not want you just saying 'sorry' when you don't mean it. We want to make sure that what you say is what you mean, that your communication here and going forward is honest and open. So, those are some reasons why I ask you if you are truly sorry," Brendan says in a compassionate but firm tone.

Silence sits in the air because I'm not sure what to say next. My parents are quiet, having turned the conversation over to Brendan.

"Now, Mark," Brendan continues, "I will make sure my communication with you is open and honest. I understand you're here because your drinking is causing your life to become unmanageable. I understand you also are having trouble with your schoolwork and that is mostly due to alcohol. Instead of going any further than this at this point, are those two items correct?"

"Yes, they are," I answer, knowing that my DUI and abrupt exit from college are true and there's no reason right now to debate whether my life is manageable or unmanageable.

"Well, before I go on, I have to tell you that only thirty percent of our patients remain sober after leaving our facility. That means seventy percent of the people who leave here pick up a drink or use drugs again. The percentages are not in your favor. You need to know the facts, so that you can accept them for what they are and form your own thoughts. Our system, the program that we follow, works for those who accept it, those who turn their lives over to it. The program will not work right away and it will not be easy, but if you commit yourself to following the steps and living one day at a time, you can achieve all that you want in life. Now, while that is all well and good, the first step is admitting you are powerless over your addiction; in your case, I understand it is alcohol. But, whether it is alcohol or drugs, you must admit that you are powerless over it and your life has become unmanageable because of it. Can you admit to me and to your parents, that you cannot control your alcohol and instead, the alcohol controls you?" Brendan asks.

"Yeah, you could say that," I say.

"The thing is, Mark, *you* are the one who has to say that you are powerless over alcohol," Brendan says.

After going to meetings for a year and a half, I recognize the question and feel a sense of panic. I know what he means and I know he is right, but I have never been asked this question directly.

"Yes, I am powerless over alcohol," I say.

"Has your life become unmanageable because of it?" he asks as my parents sit silently. I see compassion and confusion on their faces when I glance at them.

"My problem with alcohol is what got me here," I say.

"But, will you admit that your life has become unmanageable because of it?" he asks again.

"Yeah, it has, with school, my family, it got me in trouble with the law, it has gotten me in bad spots, so, yeah, it has made it pretty unmanageable," I say.

"Well, good Mark, that's the first step, so now we can work on helping you to identify your addiction, start your recovery and give you the tools necessary to remain sober. Mark, no one can do this for you. No matter how badly your parents want this for you, no matter how your siblings want to help, you are going to have to do the work. You are going to have to confront your demons, you are going to have to accept who you are as a person and work to improve who you are. The sky is the limit and you can be whoever you want to be, but you are the person who determines that. We keep a very strict schedule here and we do not accept excuses or unnecessary interferences. You are supposed to be at every appointment, group meeting and meal on time. Your attitude will be determined by you, but we have a program that will work for you if you let it. We want you to be well when you leave here and, speaking from experience as a person who has been through this program, you can be well if you give it a chance. Give it more than a chance, give it your best effort and see where you are when you leave here. Now, we'll get you checked in, introduce you to your points of contact and get you to your room."

Mom and Dad look my way. I am embarrassed, ashamed, exposed again. The hits just keep on coming. I guess I didn't think it was going to get this far, but it has. It's real. I look at Mom and Dad and just say, through tears, "I'm sorry, I'm sorry for all this."

Dad puts his hand on my shoulder, looks me in the eye and says, "Mark, this is where you are going to be all right. Do what they tell you to do, listen to what they say, tell them what you think, talk to them about yourself. Everybody here is here to help you. Let them help you. Then, you can help yourself. We love you, we are here for you, but you need to help yourself now. Do the right thing."

"We'll be back to see you on Sunday," he continues, while Mom stands there crying, with both hands pressed against her chest. "Until then, know that we love you."

We hug and I turn to Mom, and for one of the only times in my entire life, she doesn't say anything. She bites her bottom lip, takes a deep, deep breath and I see her eyes fill with tears. She closes her eyes, lowers her head and gives me a hug. When we separate, she looks away and I don't get to see her face, but I can feel the break in her heart.

Dad turns to Brendan and says, "Do what you have to do with him, he needs all the help you can give him because he won't listen to us, he won't listen to his brother and sisters, he won't even trust his own better judgement. Deep down, there is a really, really good son and brother, but right now, he won't let it out." I realize he wants me to hear everything he is saying but he never breaks contact with Brendan's hand. "Anything you can do to help will be greatly appreciated." It is belittling and humiliating to be spoken about like a failure. And, unfortunately, it is all true. We all know the truth hurts sometimes. And this time, it hurts a lot.

Dad takes his hand away from Brendan's, turns, and walks out the same door Mom did thirty seconds ago. I look at Brendan. "Follow me, it's time to get you to your room," he says. It's eight-thirty right now and we have a group meeting at nine o'clock."

It's eight-thirty in the morning, but it feels like a full day already. "I want you to put your bags in room 210 and go to the nurses' station," Brendan says.

He's headed out the door, so I grab my two bags and go. The nurse takes blood, gives me a ten-minute physical, weighs me and hands me a bag of clothes. Attached to it is a tag with "Mark" written on it. She says, "Wear this name tag for the first twenty-four hours and keep it on, the punishment is worse than actually wearing it." I don't ask what the punishment is because right now I don't want to know.

People are all over the halls, everybody dressed the same in hospital clothes, and the rehab workers seem to blend in. Some of them wear hospital clothes, too, and some wear regular street clothes.

"You can change your clothes in that bathroom," says the nurse. Since Brendan told her to have me at the group meeting by nine, she's moving me along pretty quickly. I would rather miss the meeting, but it doesn't look like that will be the case.

"Put your clothes in this bag and we'll get them back to you later in your room," she says.

When I come out of the bathroom, I hand her my bag of clothes. Now I look like everybody else, except I have a name tag.

"Here are some vitamins," the nurse says, "take these and get downstairs to the meeting. It's in the big room at the bottom of those steps right there. It is now 8:55, so you have five minutes to get some coffee and find a seat." I walk down the steps and a man in hospital clothes says, "Hi, Mark, I'm Dave," and keeps walking past me. When I get to the bottom of the stairs, I see a big room with windows surrounding it and chairs all around, all facing towards a rolling chalkboard. People are standing around drinking coffee, and whenever someone sees my badge, they greet me: "Hi Mark, I'm Steve, Hi Mark, I'm Jane." There must be twenty of them calling me by name.

As I make my way to the coffee maker, head down, the door opens and all kinds of people stream in from the outside. This must be the smokers because with them comes the smell of cigarettes. The smell is what I notice first, but gradually I recognize the disparity, the definite contrast between these people and the kind of people I'm usually around every day. They look different–older, rougher, like life has taken a toll.

But they also look hopeful. They have smiles, they're in conversations with each other. Everyone who walks by me introduces himself. "Hi Mark, I'm Claire. Hi Mark, I'm Fred." I just nod and say "Hi" to each one. I don't know what to do. I stand with a coffee in my hand and look around at the people milling about, taking seats, making coffee, running to the bathroom.

A man–not Brendan– seems to be in charge and speaks to the group. "Good morning, everyone. I hope your breakfast was good. We have a big day ready, so I'd like everyone to find a seat because we'll begin in two minutes."

I sit in a folding chair with no one around me and watch as the other people start to get settled. While I am looking to my left, I hear a chair move right next to me and I turn. A tall, brown-haired white guy sticks his hand out and says, "Hey, Mark, I'm Jeff."

I say, "Hey, Jeff" as I look down at my name tag and back at him. Jeff looks a little older than I am but not weathered like a lot of the others.

"Don't worry about that, I just took my name tag off two days ago. I've only been here three days, but it feels like a week. I know

it's weird with everybody knowing your name when you don't
know anybody else's, but you'll get to know all of us. Unfortunately,
there's a lot of stuff that'll be tough to get used to. Wearing name
tags is the easy part, listening to everybody's crazy shit is what
really gets weird."

"What happens if I take this tag off?" I ask.

"Ah, don't do that. They make you carry the bucket from the
spot-a-pot to the dumpster," he says as he points at the green port-
a-toilet off in the distance by the woods. "I am telling you, that is
worse than wearing a name tag, that's for sure. So, what's your deal,
why are you here?"

"My parents think I have a problem with alcohol. I got a DUI
and they took me out of school, so now I'm here," I say. "What about
you?"

"My company drug tested all the employees and I came up
positive. My choice was to get fired or come here and get cleaned
up. I just had a kid, a baby girl, and I can't lose my job so here I am,
ready for group therapy," he says, somewhat sarcastically.

"Everyone listen up," says the leader, "we want to get started."
The crowd of people– must be twenty to thirty–are now seated and
stop talking, so Jeff and I do the same.

"I'd like to start off by welcoming our newest arrival. Mark,
would you please stand up?" he says. I stand and look around,
embarrassment washing over me. "Please introduce yourself to
Mark if you haven't already done so. Mark," he says as he looks
at me, "welcome, my name is William and we're glad to have you.
Whenever someone new arrives, it's important that everyone
introduces themselves and is welcoming. You'll introduce yourself
to a new person soon yourself." I nod my head and he says, "Go
ahead and have a seat, we'll get started. This morning, I want you all
to take out your Big Book and open it to Chapter Three, page forty-
nine."

"We are going to read about forgiveness, both forgiveness of others and forgiveness for ourselves. This is important to making amends to those we have wronged through our addictions, those we have taken for granted and used because of our addictions, and this is also important to having the ability to forgive ourselves. We have to be able to forgive ourselves for our shortcomings and to forgive those who we feel have wronged us. Those we feel have done things to us, both real or imagined, need to be forgiven in order for us to move forward, to grow as people, to focus on our new selves."

He continues for another ten or fifteen minutes, reading and speaking. I've been to plenty of AA meetings in the last few months, so this is pretty much the same routine. William's talk is definitely more in-depth than ones I've heard at AA meetings before, but it's the same principle. Forgive yourself, don't blame yourself, you are afflicted with the addiction gene, blah, blah, blah.

I can't help but feel weird looking around at all these random people. The staff moves freely around the room while we patients have to stay seated and listen to the message. I see old guys. I see women who look thirty, forty, fifty years of age; white guys, black guys, most of them in their forties or fifties too. I am twenty years old. Jeff is the only person who looks close to my age and he just told me he has a kid. I wonder if the others are looking at me at all. Probably not, they've seen my kind before. Young punk who hit rock bottom. They probably think I'm some spoiled kid, cocky to a fault. They're probably right, got me pegged. The thing is, though, I haven't talked to any of these people in this room, ever. I can be anyone I want to be. I don't have to be the arrogant prick that these people think I am. I can be anyone I want to these people. I can be the person they don't think I am.

I notice that William is asking for people to share about their forgiveness experiences. It jolts me out of my daydreaming as the familiar panic hits me, the worry that I may be called on to speak.

But someone else steps forward. He's white, balding and has a beard. He looks to be at least sixty years old, probably older. He starts talking about his boyhood, being ten, eleven, twelve years old and watching his dad get drunk. Now that he's been in rehab for twenty-eight nights, he feels the need to tell his whole story. He wants everybody to know that, in order to give himself the peace of mind he needs to leave with, he needs to share.

"No one is making me do this," he says, "I just know that I have to do it and I want to do it. My dad, when he started drinking for the day, would usually start in the basement. We lived in a rowhouse in downtown Lancaster. He worked in a steel mill and did shift work–twelve hours on, twelve hours off, four days a week. The other three days were crazy. I have a younger brother, and he and I would make ourselves scarce for the whole day, but by the time we came home for dinner, it would get violent. It didn't matter what you did, he found a reason to get pissed off about it. He was violent with my Mom, he got violent with us, and I probably got it the worst since I was the older son. I've never talked to anybody else about it and I realized that I was keeping it all in. I turned to alcohol and drugs to get away from it and it took me in the wrong direction. It didn't numb my pain, it made it worse. Sharing this, I hope, will help me recover.

"One night, just another night of getting hammered, he starts in on Mom's cooking and won't stop. He keeps telling her how bad it is. He gets up from the table when she is doing the dishes. 'You can't do anything right,' he says.

"He was blackout drunk. He hears me try to defend my mother. 'I thought it was pretty good,' I say.

"Well, that set him off. 'Oh, look who wants to be a wise ass,' he says.

"I get up from my chair, and we go back and forth until he starts swinging. I'm fourteen, eighth grade, so I am big but not grown-man big. He's really pissed and he swings hard. I get out of the way with my face but his fist hits me in the side of my neck. I realize he's unsteady on his feet, but his punch still hurts like hell. When we lock eyes again, I say, 'That didn't hurt,' and he punches me straight in the face. He broke my nose and my cheek. I fell straight back into the refrigerator. But when he hit me, he slipped. I don't know why or how because I was laying on the ground, bleeding from my mouth and eye.

"I'm there curled up on the floor and nothing happens. I don't get hit, I don't get lifted up for more. I wait for about thirty seconds and nothing happens. When I lift my head from between my hands, expecting to get hit again, I see Mom and my brother looking at Dad and then at me, back and forth. It's like they can't believe their eyes. Finally, my Mom comes to me and helps me off the floor. Dad fell when he hit me and hit his chin on the corner of the kitchen table, at least that's what they told me.

"Well, when he was there on the floor drunk, knocked out, unconscious, and then my brother kicked him. And then I kicked him, and then Mom kicked him. And then it started. We kicked him in the ribs, we kicked him in the ass, we kicked him in the legs, we kicked him as hard as we could. I hated him, and I kicked him as hard as I hated him. It was like the pain was real and it came out.

"Well, everything changed after that. I went to the hospital. My father never came to see me, he just stayed in the basement drunk. He didn't come up for dinner any more, we never talked about it again and we all just sank into our own worlds. I quit school at sixteen, worked every job in the world and drank every single day.

"I never forgave my dad for being such a defining negative in my life, never moved past the hate. He kept the hate and never forgave either. I realize that the hate is what drove me to ruin my life, and if I can find a way to forgive, I can find a way to change my life. It really is the only chance I have. If I don't forgive him and I keep hating, I'll keep drinking and keep drugging. The way I've tried to look at it is, I have to forgive my parents for putting me in this cycle of hell. I have to forgive Mom for not doing more because she didn't know what else to do. My dad just drank—didn't feel, didn't think, didn't live, didn't do anything. He lived his life in the bottle. I have to forgive him for his addiction to alcohol because what else can I do? I have to find a way to move on.

"I have not seen my brother" –and at this point the man starts to cry–"in over twenty-eight years. He never did anything to me, but I just didn't want to see him. He has a wife, two kids, and I have never met any of them." He explains that he recently got his brother's number and called him. The man is crying openly, and wiping his nose as he continues, "He told me he missed me and he's going to pick me up from here. I am going to meet his wife and kids. I've not been this scared since I was a fourteen-year old kid in the kitchen. Leaving home at sixteen, drinking all day, living on the streets, none of that was scarier than that kitchen. And now, I have that feeling again. But, the one thing about this fear is that, for the first time in a long, long time, I actually feel something. Even if it's fear, it's a feeling. At the same time, I've never felt this kind of happiness, this kind of hope, this kind of reality, ever. It's the first time in my life where my decisions won't be driven by hate, revenge or despair. They'll be driven by clarity and honesty. I know how to do things in here, but I know it is going to be entirely different out there.

"I got here because a woman in a homeless shelter gave me a phone number to a church program. It changed my life. The twenty-five cents to make that phone call put me here, and I really don't know where I'll end up, but right now, at least I have a chance. I forgave and now I have a chance. It's like the world has been lifted off my shoulders and I can hold my head up for the first time in a long time. Thank you for letting me share."

People start to clap and nod, so I start and stop with everybody else. But the stories don't stop. Other people take the floor. They talk about being abused, being raped, stealing, beating people up. The stories are brutal in their honesty and uncomfortable in their content. I look around and wonder, *are they as damaged as me?* and a lot of them seem worse. I don't know how I'll ever tell any of these complete strangers anything about me. What does my story say about me, how fucked up am I compared to these people? Will they even believe me?

We sit for two hours. People cry openly in front of the whole room. I'm not ready to put myself out there right now and I don't know that I ever will be. When we end at eleven-thirty, William closes the session with a long reading from the Big Book.

Since lunch is at noon, I have thirty minutes to myself. I head out of the meeting to find room 210. I walk in, not knowing what to expect. It's like a hospital room–two beds, two chairs, but no TV. Somebody else's stuff is there, too. My bag is sitting on the chair on my side of the room, closest to the door. I sit on the bed as a big, dark-skinned black guy comes in the room. "Hey, man, I guess you're my new roommate," he says. "My name is Mike, but you can call me Scoop."

"Nice to meet you, Scoop, my name is–" as I look at my name tag – "Mark."

"I can read, man," he says as he smiles at me.

"Well, I– uh," I stammer.

"I'm just kidding, man," says Scoop, "Where you from?"

"I'm from Baltimore," I say.

"All right, I've been there before. Me and my boys used to go down there to party. My boy fought down there a few times," says Scoop. "You heard of Michael Spinks?"

"Yeah, I heard of him, he fought Mike Tyson," I say.

"Yeah, well, that's my boy," Scoop says. "Him and his brother Leon grew up in my neighborhood. We've been Boys since we were in first grade. They paid for me to be here. I got to do right by them."

"That's cool," I say, really because I don't know what else to say. Whatever I have to say wouldn't even be close to interesting.

"Yeah, Leon won the gold medal in the Olympics. Man, we partied when he got back from that. Michael was heavyweight champ, just like Leon. It was crazy, man," he says.

"I bet it was," I say.

"Boy, you don't even know. Strippers, clubs, all that shit, but I got on that coke and I couldn't stop. Started stealing, breaking into houses, robbing liquor stores. I got caught by the cops and it was either do two years or go to rehab. Here I am, thirty days in here is a lot better than two years in the can," he says.

I think, *My roommate should be in jail and instead is going to be sleeping in the bed next to mine.* This is definitely not some dorm room or frat house.

I try to play it cool and let the prison comment just go by. "Did you go to the Tyson fight?" I ask.

"No, man. I was fucking up at the time and Mike didn't want me in Vegas, he couldn't have no distractions. I was at the fight in Atlantic City when he beat Larry Holmes to win the title. Man, Jinx was killing it. Jinx is what we called him in the hood. Man, Larry Holmes couldn't touch him and Jinx wore him out. It was nothing but strippers and partying for three days after he won the title, didn't nobody think Jinx was going to do it."

"Wow, that's wild," I say. That's all I have. This guy is talking about jail like it's nothing, strippers for days, and partying with the heavyweight champ of the world. I think I'm just going to sit and listen. He doesn't need to hear about my world of station wagons and private schools. I have officially entered a different place.

|||||||||||||||||||||||||||||||||||||||||||||||||||||||||||

CHAPTER 25

|||||||||||||||||||||||||||||||||||||||||||||||||||||||||||||||||

By the time Sunday comes, I've found a way to be comfortable in my surroundings. I've been here since Tuesday, had individual meetings with my counselor Brendan, sat in small group meetings and contributed a little. I haven't had the courage to contribute in the large group meeting, but I know I will have to at some point.

The one change that I feel and even look at optimistically is my meeting with the psychiatrist, Andrew. These appointments are different from ones I had with any other psychiatrist. I'm not sure of the reason– possibly my outlook, possibly Andrew's demeanor– but I actually like this guy. He asks interesting questions, and I actually answer them honestly. Instead of hating him because he's a shrink, I talk to him like a guy who can unlock the questions I've never answered.

By now I've also met almost every person in the building from cafeteria people and custodians to doctors and nurses and counselors as well as patients. I actually feel better, probably because I have not filled my body with alcohol and my mind with drugs.

The only hesitancy that I have is that at eleven o'clock my parents are expected to visit, and I'm not sure how it will go. I haven't spoken with anyone from my family, mostly because I don't know what to say, and I don't want to give them false hope that I'm getting better because I don't know if it's true.

At 10:30 a.m. precisely, we finish our small group meetings and get ready for our families. We get to wear the clothes we walked in with and look like normal people for three hours. Since it's my first Sunday, I have no idea what to expect. At eleven o'clock people start to roll in and find their loved ones. I sit and watch little kids run to their moms, I watch wives hug their husbands. I also watch a young woman walk in, apprehensively, to an older man patient and he just starts apologizing. He grovels and starts to cry and she just stands in front of him expressionless and I wonder if she is even listening. *What did he do?*

I people-watch until I recognize my parents as they come through the front door, followed closely by Cleta, my grandmother. I have no idea what she's doing here, and I go from slightly nervous to butterflies in my stomach. Not once did I think she was going to be here today. I close my eyes and open them again to make sure that what I see is real. Yes, Cleta is definitely with them.

"Hey Mom and Dad, thanks for coming. Hi Cleta, how are you?" I ask.

"I'm fine, Mark," Cleta says as she hugs me. Then I turn to give Mom a hug and shake Dad's hand. Dad holds my right shoulder as he shakes my hand and gives me a long look. "You look better already," he says, "looks like you're getting some sleep."

He's right. The counselors keep us busy all day. We wake up early, go to meetings, have a half-hour in the morning and an hour in the afternoon to exercise. Otherwise, we're on the go to meetings, therapy, counseling. When lights go out at ten o'clock, there's not much to do. I close my eyes and get some good sleep, the best uninterrupted sleep I've had in years.

I look at Cleta. "You didn't need to come up here, I'm sure you have plenty of other things to do today," I say.

"Funny you should say that," she says, "because I can't think of anything else I should do today besides this. I told your parents I wanted to talk to you and now is the time. Let's go sit down."

I look at both my parents. Dad nods his head towards the door and Cleta and I head outside to a bench next to the lake. The sun is out and it's unusually warm, with no wind. It feels good in the sun as Cleta puts her hand right above my elbow as we walk. As we sit, I say, "Cleta, I have to say, it's a surprise seeing you walk in here."

"I don't know what I'm doing next Sunday or the Sunday after that. I'm seventy-nine years old and I don't even know if I'll be alive by the time you get out of here," she says.

"Of course you will, I'm only here for a month," I say.

"Nothing is guaranteed in this life. I know that I can be here right now, and I wasn't going to miss this chance. There are some things I have to tell you and I need you to listen." Cleta pauses and holds my eyes with hers. "Your parents have done all they can for you, and it's time that I tell you what I think. I've watched you since you were born, and over the last few years I've noticed a difference. You haven't been listening to your parents, you've gotten sloppy with your work and it's affected your family," she says.

I sit and listen. I know that this conversation is going somewhere but I don't know exactly where.

Cleta continues, "I know I've told you many stories but it's time I told you one that I've never shared with you. If you want to blame me for your problems with alcohol, go ahead, because I know it runs in my family. I told you about my father, Clark Franklin. He was a great businessman– he built Grayson, Saint Agnes Hospital, Notre Dame College. He was one of the most successful builders in Baltimore. If you were building with brick or stone, Franklin builders did the work.

"When I was growing up, we were wealthy. I had a driver take me to school. I never rode on a city bus because we had a driver. We had a country home and one in the city. Dad was successful, and that's all I really knew. Well, he died right around the time I met your grandfather. He died before our wedding. When it came to who would take over the business, my brother Charles was the one who got the job. Even though I was far smarter than my brother Charles, he took over because no one was going to let a woman run a big company, especially one in the construction field. Charles was paranoid, so he never wanted me or your grandfather Henry involved in the company.

"What you need to know is that my brother Charles was a terrible alcoholic. My father spent thirty years building an enormously successful business and Charles ran the company into the ground in less than three. He ruined the reputation of the company by not paying bills, lost customers by being rude, and ran every quality person in the company out the door. I was raising a family and Henry was traveling in sales, and, before I knew it, the company was bankrupt. Any stake I had was gone.

"My brother never recovered. He died, at the age of 51, from a failed liver. He was broke when he died. The bank repossessed everything we owned–every car, home, construction truck, piece of equipment, everything. Henry and I scraped together every penny we had to make payments on our house so the bank wouldn't take that, too. Mark, alcohol cost me everything I had, everything my father worked for, every luxury I ever knew. It cost me my family history and it cost me my brother.

"Now, I know you got dealt a bad hand when you were in that fire, but it's not the fact that you got a bad hand, it's how you play that hand. Make yourself better by believing in yourself. I lost everything I had except for Henry and my kids. You lost your innocence but you still have your parents and your brother and sisters. My brother Charles's alcoholism cost his family everything. Your alcoholism will cost your family if it keeps going. It affects other people whether you know it or not. I'm not here to tell you what to do, I just wanted to come here today to tell you what not to do. Don't mess up your family, don't be alone at fifty-one with nobody to care for you, don't put your parents through any more worry. We all want to see you do well, but we can't do it for you. Put simply, your actions affect other people. People who didn't do anything wrong are affected. Some already have been affected.

Today, your parents are here and they aren't with your brother or sisters. They're here because they love you, but they love the others just as much. Mark, I've seen you do so many good things, but it's been a while. I want to see you do good things again." At this point, Cleta puts her hand on mine. "Now that I've come here to say what I had to say, let's go get some lunch. Let's see if these people are feeding you well."

I stay still, letting what she said soak in. "Do you have anything to tell me?" she asks.

"No, no, not really. It's just that I never knew that about your brother. I never knew he did that," I say.

"He drank every day of his adult life. He drank until he got drunk, and then he drank some more. I drink two drinks and I don't want more. Some people can't get enough, and some people don't drink at all. It affects everyone differently. I think you drink until you get drunk and then drink some more. But you can get help, and you can change. You're young, you have your whole life in front of you. You'll be happier and healthier without alcohol than you ever will be with it, I promise you that," she says.

"Cleta, I'm going to try, that I can promise you. Thanks for coming up here, thanks for taking the time," I say.

"I wouldn't come up here if I didn't care about you. But I'm not coming back if you end up here a second time. This is it, this is your only shot at getting me up here, so come on, let's see what they're serving for lunch."

When we get to the cafeteria and pick up a tray, all the ladies behind the counter ask who my guests are. I introduce them, and they all talk like they're long-lost friends. I'm the subject of the conversation most of the time. At least nobody says I'm a deadbeat, so I just stand there, feeling stupid. One nice thing is they take care of Cleta, cooking her fresh grilled cheese and serving her a bowl of soup. We sit at our own table and for the first time I can remember, I'm happy to sit and eat with them, in no hurry to go anywhere and hoping that they're in no hurry to leave. We sit there until the clock reads 1:45. We are talking about family, cousins, lacrosse, my treatment, a little bit of everything.

At two o'clock, the end of visiting hours, Dad pulls the car up front. I walk with Mom and Cleta towards the front door. When we get there I give Mom a hug and turn to Cleta to hug her. She grabs my face with the palms of her hands and says, "Whether you like it or not, what you do, your actions, affect others, either good or bad. And you are the only one who can determine that. I know you can do it, but you have to know it, too. Get what you need here and I'll see you when you get home." She kisses me on my right cheek and walks away. Mom looks at me and smiles, gives me a second hug and says, "I love you" and walks out. Five days have passed since I got here and it feels like I've got a long way to go.

On Monday when I meet with Andrew, the psychiatrist, I let my guard down and open my mind to help. I've had at least twenty appointments with different shrinks since the fire and up until now, I've never told them the truth. What I offered was bullshit or what I thought they wanted to hear, but never the truth. Today, I tell Andrew, "Forget everything you've written down about me. Forget everything I've told you. From here forward, I'll give it to you straight. Go ahead, what do you want to ask me."

He says, "I'm not going to ask you anything. You just tell me something, without me asking."

"Okay," I say, and decide how to start. "The first time I got drunk, beer tasted like shit, but I loved how it made me feel. I love getting drunk and I think that, after listening and reading about it, I really am an alcoholic. I don't think I'm a drug addict, even though I did them. But I know I am an alcoholic."

"All right," he says, "at least that means you've been listening and you have an open mind. Tell me now, what do you think you can change that will help you with your realization?"

"That I really don't know," I say. "All my friends drink, that's what I've always done, so I'm not sure how I'll handle it. I know that I'm going to have to change some things but other than that, I'm not sure. I got twenty-three more days to figure it out."

"You're right, you do have more time to figure it out," he says, and we go back and forth like this for the whole hour. I don't glance at the clock every few minutes, I don't cross my arms and make up answers. I engage, I listen, I actually don't jump to quick conclusions, and I just think with an open mind. I know that people with addiction issues don't always see another perspective, but I work on it. I wouldn't say it's liberating, I would say it's interesting. I am literally finding a new way to think, a new way to see, a new way to believe. In the past, I pretty much believed that everything was either funny, cool, bullshit or dumb. School, sports, friends, family, work–everything fell into those categories. Now I'm trying to change the way I think and learn to let things actually be what they are. There are no categories, there are no set answers, just let things be what they are. In my mind, the freedom of independent thought begins to grow. I can allow things to be without judging or drawing up negative foregone conclusions. My thoughts feel real, meaningful.

How can words and thoughts become liberators of the soul? I recognize that I am flawed. I realize that my thought patterns have been a hindrance, if not a roadblock, to growth. When I am in addicted thought, it overpowers beliefs like hope and inspiration and replaces them with mindless routine and temporary relief. I, in my mind, can finally accept that if I can stay sober today, I won't completely fuck up tomorrow.

Over the next three weeks, I am honest. I live in truth, even when it hurts. I ask more questions than give opinions. I listen, really listen, to hear. While living with all different types of people from all different walks of life, I hear their stories and don't jump to quick conclusions. It makes me realize that none of us control who our parents are, what they do for a living, whether they even stayed together at all. Some of these people's parents were junkies. Some of these people's parents were company presidents, who had all the money they would ever need. Many people here had parents who neglected them, or even abused them, in one one way or another. I can't relate to that because my parents didn't neglect me. That's the thing. I wasn't neglected, abused or abandoned. I can't blame it on any of that. It was me, I kept fucking up. Sure, I had a weird, twisted fire story to tell, but that didn't do it, either. Yes, it was fucked, terrible, but I was headed in this direction the whole time. I drank to get drunk from the get-go, every time. I did this, and now I have to change. It is exposing to see myself as I am, all of my flaws, weaknesses and fears brought right in front of me. The truth doesn't always hurt, but it does hurt sometimes. And this time, it really hurts. My flaws include a willingness to dare to the point of danger. It has gotten me and others around me hurt, it has caused scars and scared or harmed innocent victims. Not everybody thinks my jokes are funny or humorous because people can get hurt and often do. I realize that a weakness of mine is self-discipline. Duh. Basically, I don't have any self-discipline. I will never stop feeding the beast. For me, the beast is booze, but it could be anything–food, cigarettes, laziness, anything. My weakness, my addiction so far is liquor, and I want to stop there. I see people transition to another addiction, and I don't want to get on that train. My fear is the same fear I had when I was twelve years old: growing up. I haven't wanted to grow up since I was twelve. I don't want a job or a wife or kids. I don't want any of those responsibilities and I never have. I haven't wanted to do anything but have a good time since I was in seventh grade. That is all that's mattered, right up until now. And, now that fear is real. It is now grow the fuck up time. The time for just growing up has passed, and now it's time to grow the F up.

I understand the positive qualities that I have, but although the counselors say we need to work on those, it's our negative qualities that we spend our time on the most. We find another weakness, dishonesty, and work on that. We find another flaw, irresponsibility, and make a change with that. I, first with my counselors and then with others, share my stories. People that were strangers two weeks ago and now are my friends, learn about my fears, like "What if I can't stop drinking?" I tell them about times that I had near-death experiences, getting away from the cops, some stories I had forgotten until I sobered up and recalled them. My new friends were stunned that an innocent-looking preppy kid from the suburbs crashed cars; bought drugs from dealers on street corners in the city; shot guns on farms, drunk; fell off boats at night in the bay, playing with toys and with people in dangerous situations. I realize I have cheated death on an ordinary Tuesday night at times because it was time to drink and eventually go all the way, whatever it was. Girls, beers, liquor, etc., all night. Sometimes it was a big night, sometimes it was any night. I remember the time right after I failed out of RMC, I went down to visit Art with Drew B and we did coke for seventy-two straight hours and came home. The time I drove with Bruce, Bouch and Art to Charlottesville and slid, with an 18-wheeler right next to us, down Route 64 going seventy-five miles an hour, drunk, and skirted away. Times I had gone into the city to buy coke from some brothers, a young white kid in a black bar, trying to pay some dealer for goods. Crashing Art's motorcycle, drunk, with no helmet because "who needs a helmet." I've gotten myself into dangerous spots, all in the name of getting wasted. Unfortunately, I don't have anything to show for it aside from a couple DUIs, some crashed cars, some debts to citizens and society. I have actually been paying for it for a while now. It really has cost me dearly, but that can be all over. I've got a chance. Because, who am I? A middle class kid from Towson, Maryland. A product of two full families, one Italian and one Irish. My lot in life, as I look around, is pretty good. I've had everything I've needed up until now. From here, it's what I do with it.

I am a sum of my days, wherever I came from, but one thing I know is, all I have is today. Who *I* can be right now, today. It's going to take a while to figure this out, but it has to happen. Work on my confidence, learn to think honestly, live in the moment, not in the past or the future. Sit in this seat, lie in this bed, walk in this hallway, and learn to be me, not an old me and not some new me, just learn to be me, who I am right now.

All of us here come from somewhere, different places all, and we realize we do have one thing in common. We have all done just enough, caused just enough problems, to be put in rehab, to need to clean up, to stop breaking the law, to live for a good today and a better tomorrow.

A funny thing happens to you when you realize that you had no control about where you came from. You can look at every other person without judgment. Skin color, age, sex, health, even their past, just becomes part of their story, their experiences. I do think that every person who learns to accept this looks at others differently and wants what is best for them. It is a collective benefit, a rising tide lifting all boats. We realize we came to this place, this rehabilitation facility as one person and can leave this place as one person of many. Our addiction to booze or drugs is replaced with our appreciation of diversity, our inner interests and our pursuit of a better way. My eyes are open, my mind is fresh. I know the world can be a cruel, harsh place. I have some advice for my new self: Don't get drunk today, and let's see how it can be a little bit better.

||||||||||||||||||||||||||||||||||||||||||||||||||||||||||

CHAPTER 26

||||||||||||||||||||||||||||||||||||||||||||||||||||||||||||||

My first thought as my mind rises from sleep to consciousness
is that I'm down to three more days in this place. It's early but I
notice Scoop is already awake and gone. Usually, we go to breakfast
together, so I sit around and read for about twenty minutes, seeing
if he is coming back or is down the hall talking to someone else. He
doesn't show up, so I head to breakfast by myself.

When I get back to the room, Scoop is there, but he is packing
his stuff in his bag and muttering under his breath. He doesn't
notice me at all.

"Scoop, where were you? I waited for you to go to breakfast."

"Fuck this place, man, I'm not playing their fuckin' bullshit
game," he says.

"What are you talking about?" I say. "Are you leaving?"

"Fuck, yeah, I'm leaving. I am not doing their bullshit," he says.

"Doing what?" What do they want you to do?" I ask.

"You listen to all these people spill their bullshit in the big
group?" He asks.

"Yeah, I listen," I say.

"Well, they want me to spill my shit in big group and I told
Brendan there ain't no fucking way. I ain't telling nobody shit," he
says.

"Scoop, who says you have to tell anybody?" I ask.

"Brendan wants me to tell everybody my story and what my
fuckin' plan is when I leave here," he says. "I got four fucking days,

and I am getting the fuck out of here, and I ain't telling shit."

"Then don't," I say.

"I ain't," he says as he starts putting his razor and shampoo in his bag.

"Are you leaving right now?"

"Motherfucker, you don't know how bad I want to get out of this fucking place," he says.

"I know, but are you leaving now?" I ask again.

"You know if I leave here without finishing this bullshit, that I got to do two years. Well, fuck it, I'll do two years then," he says.

"Don't leave, man, just don't leave," I say. "You don't want to go to jail for two years. I don't want to see you go to jail. I know your kids don't want to see you go."

"Fuck my kids, they don't give a shit about me," he says, mad. "Don't pull that guilt shit on me."

"Scoop, your kids come up here every weekend and they hold on for dear life when it's time to go," I say. "You know it, so you can bullshit me on some things, but I know you love your kids."

"You're right, okay, you're right, but I ain't saying shit in big group," he says.

"I don't give a shit about big group. I just don't want to have another roommate. People in here are fucked up," I say. I smile at him and cock my head, just like I do to defensemen I want to get a rise out of.

For the first time today, Scoop smiles. He looks at me, shakes his head, and says, "You are fucked up, you know that, you're the one that's fucked up."

"Scoop, I know I am fucked up, I just don't know how fucked up yet," I say and we both smile and laugh a little. It is a pretty intense morning and neither of us has even had a therapy session, big or small meeting, anything. Scoop had a conversation with his counselor, that's it. Tension is high and we just had breakfast.

||||||||||||||||||||||||||||||||||||||||||||||||||||||||||

CHAPTER 27

||||||||||||||||||||||||||||||||||||||||||||||||||||||||||||||

Later that morning I'm in a small group meeting when Brendan
knocks on the door and asks William if he can speak with me.
William gives the go-ahead, and Brendan and I head down the
hallway together. As we walk, Brendan turns and says, "I'm meeting
with Scoop and he wants you to be there with him."

"Okay. Do I need to do anything?" I ask.

"You need to listen, that's it. If you want to contribute, if you
want to say anything, that's your choice, but all you really need to
do is listen."

When we enter Brendan's office, Scoop is already sitting in a
chair and there are two other chairs so the three form a triangle.
Brendan sits down in one to the right of Scoop and leaves the other
for me. When I sit, Brendan addresses both of us.

"Michael and Mark, I think you know our last assignment. But
if you don't, I'll remind you. We feel it is very important for you to
share your story, your thoughts with your fellow patients, to open
up in order to heal. It's more difficult to to share with your peers,
as opposed to your counselors, but the acceptance and sense of
accomplishment you get as a result are great assets in your healing
process. We feel it helps to hear yourself say these things out loud,
and it helps to share them, so that they are no longer secrets. Mark,
Michael doesn't want to share his story in the big group setting. We
understand that; however, we want him to share his story with at
least one person, and he has chosen to share it with you. He hasn't

shared it with me, either, so we'll both be here for Michael and allow him the opportunity to open up to us and free himself of any difficult memories or personal struggles.

"Now, Michael, I'd like you to trust us and know that what you say is personal and private. Your feelings and your emotions are your own and they are not to be dismissed, by me and especially by you. These are all natural emotions, and once they are acknowledged, you can have healing and closure. Please feel free to share any of your thoughts, however they come to you. We feel that they are all of value and should be explored. I don't wish to direct the conversation; rather I hope, Michael, that you decide what is to be talked about and for how long. Anything that we discuss is kept between us as a matter of confidence with each other. Now if you would like, I'll ask you a few questions."

Scoop looks my way for the first time, and his eyes are different—they don't look scared, but they don't look proud either.

"All right," Scoop says, "what's your first question?" as he adjusts himself in his seat and looks back at Brendan.

"When did you try drugs or alcohol for the first time?" Brendan asks.

"You don't want to know," Scoop says as his whole demeanor changes and his eyes narrow.

"Why not, Michael?" Brendan says, "we all have used alcohol or drugs, it's okay–"

"You don't want to know because it was no drugs or alcohol that ruined my day. It wasn't some bullshit good time. My life changed that day and I never been the same since," says Scoop.

"Alcohol and drugs have a powerful pull, they change us as people," Brendan says.

"Liquor and weed didn't do shit to me. I wanted to get fucked up. That didn't bother me at all. I like to booze, I like the weed. I just don't like nobody fuckin' me in the ass, that's what I don't like," Scoop says.

Brendan stays calm, just tilting his head to the side, giving me the feeling that he felt compassion for Scoop. I just swallow and sit still. Brendan breaks the ice. "I don't understand what you mean by that, nobody here is trying to harm you."

"It's too late for that, Brendon. You asked me about the first time I used booze and drugs and that was the same day, the same motherfucking day, that a motherfucking junkie took me to an abandoned row house and tried to fuck me in my ass," Scoop says, anger rising in his voice. "So, you want me to stand up in front of the big group and tell everybody that the first time I got drunk, I was twelve years old and my reward for going to a crack house with a crackhead was to have to fight that motherfucker off from fucking me in the ass? Motherfucker, ain't nothing the same after that. A grown man grabs you, holds you down and tries to stick his dick in your ass. I didn't cry about it, I didn't call the cops, I couldn't do anything. He held me down and didn't let go, until I kicked him in his balls as hard as I could and took off running. You know what it is like to come that close to being raped? The only thing I could think of, the only thing I knew, was that this motherfucker was gonna die. All I thought about was what I was going to do to this motherfucker."

Scoop slows the cadence in his voice. "Is this what you wanted to hear, Brendan? Is this what you wanted me to share in your big group bullshit? That I got drunk, got high, and then a motherfucking junkie tried to fuck me? Is that what you want? Is that what you want?" he asks again, his voice is getting louder and more intense with each sentence. He is surprisingly calm, though, no crying or shaking voice. Just a steady increase in noise and intensity.

"Michael, I just want you to work through your grief, through your pain and begin your healing," Brendon says in his almost preprogrammed delivery.

"You want me to work through my pain, you want me to work through my grief. Motherfucker, where I come from, you don't feel pain. I ain't got time for grief, and I sure as shit ain't going to work on any healing. I took care of my problem. I took care of my shit when I was twelve years old. That mothefucker never bothered me again, I will tell you that much. So, there it is, Brendon, that is my shit, that is my story. A junkie tried to fuck me and then he didn't. There ain't much else to talk about," says Scoop.

"Are there any triggers that lead you to additional drug use or alcohol?" asks Brendan.

"What, somebody trying to rape me wasn't enough for you? No, there weren't any other triggers or whatever the fuck you wanna call it. I got fucked up with my boys, I got in trouble and I don't plan to come back. Now, Brendan, I told you my story, I told you what I ain't told anybody else, except my brother," Scoop says. *I didn't even know he had a brother, he never mentioned him once,* I think.

"Well, Michael, I want to thank you for sharing your story. Mark, I want to thank you for being here to support Michael. I would like you, Michael, to consider your recovery plan as an ongoing process. You've admitted today, to us, some of your early difficult moments, and by sharing those moments, you can begin to heal those emotional scars," Brendon says. "Now as we continue-" Scoop cuts him off.

"Brendan, I think we just done enough for right now," Scoop says.

"You're right, Michael, this has been a big step, let's allow this to be a wonderful opening to your road to recovery."

"You call it whatever the fuck you want," says Scoop as he shakes Brendan's hand. Brendan pulls him in for a hug and I see Scoop soften, just a little bit with Brendan, like talking wasn't as bad as he thought it might be. He seems just a bit less angry.

When they release their hug, I am standing there and Scoop goes to give me a bro hug, the kind where we both slap five and grab right hands about chest high, then take our left hands and put it behind each other's right shoulder. It kind of catches me off guard, because I wasn't expecting a hug, that's for sure. But what he says in my ear really surprises me.

"Don't say a fucking word to nobody." He moves in close, envelops me really, and holds me in a firm grip. Whether it is intimidation or love, I don't know, but this man told me something he does not want anyone to know and he trusted me. I think it's love. Heavy but healthy love. This place makes you feel like this, good and sad, heavy and hopeful, broken but healing.

"You know I won't," I answer and we both pull away. He looks at me, nods and smiles, and I think he knows he can trust me. We both head out of Brendan's office, me back to a small group meeting and Scoop, I don't know where. Neither of us says anything as we go in separate directions.

That night after dinner, after our night reading and group therapy, Scoop and I are lying in our beds, lights off and I speak up, "Scoop, I didn't know you had a brother."

"Yeah, man, his name was James, but we called him Scrap," says Scoop. "He was two years older than me."

"What do you mean 'was two years older'?" I ask.

"He died about four years ago," Scoop says.

"I'm sorry, man," I say. "I just didn't know you had a brother."

"Since we didn't have no father, Scrap was the man of the house. He took me everywhere, gave me clothes, helped my moms, did everything. Nobody fucked with me when Scraps was around," Scoop says.

"What did he do when you told him about the junkie?" I asked, almost surprised that I brought it back up. I hear Scoop shift in his bed and I see his silhouette leaning on his elbow in bed facing me.

"You sure you want to know?" Scoop asks.

"Yeah," I say.

"You can't tell nobody. Fuck, it's been so long I'm not sure it matters anyway," says Scoop.

"What do you mean?"

"Me and Scrap, we killed the motherfucker. Scrap went and

found him one night, about a week after it happened, and we went back to the same row house. We acted like we was drinking, but we would spit it out. We acted like we was smoking but we was faking. When the dude was good and fucked up, Scrap broke out his pipe. Scrap brought a metal pipe and I brought a hammer. Scrap hit that motherfucker in the head and I hit that motherfucker in the head and he was done. Scrap hit him a few more times, made sure he was dead and we left. Ain't no cops looking for kids when they find a dead junkie. We just laid low a couple days, nobody said nothing. That's what Scrap did when I told him," Scoop says.

I didn't know what to say but I muttered, "Damn, Scoop."

"He was my best friend, him and Jinx," says Scoop. "And before you ask me how he died, he got AIDS. He wasn't no homo, he used a dirty needle and got it. He died four years ago and I just couldn't get right. It fucked me up."

"You seem good now," I say, still searching for something to say.

"I will say this, I am better than I have been in a long time," he says and we both lie still, not saying anything and not moving, just thinking. I'm thinking about how two people can be so different yet see things the same way and as for him, I've got no idea what he's thinking.

When I wake up, I know I have two days left here. Today, I have to talk to a big group. Well, I don't have to, but Brendan, William and every other shrink, therapist and mentor tells me, "You should, you should tell everyone anything and everything that you can share. Every single one of us, every single one, has a story of addiction, of despair, or helplessness."

A wave of anxiety, of panic, hits my heart and my stomach. My heart races, my stomach churns and I haven't lifted my head off the pillow. I've been waiting for this day for awhile, twenty-eight days to be exact. Tomorrow, I get to wake up, eat breakfast and leave. Tomorrow doesn't even really count, but they count it as Day 30. Today is my last full day, my day of reckoning with this place, with my demons, with my truth.

When I lift my head, I see Scoop sleeping soundly, eyes closed. He has a short 'fro, same length all around. His hands are palms together, like he is praying with straight fingers, between his cheek and his pillow. He has a big head, big shoulders, big arms. He is so much bigger than I am, probably 6–2, 235 pounds and right now he looks delicate. His light breaths and what looks like soft skin give him an aura of peacefulness. He has taught me about himself, his lifestyle, his different and hard upbringing. His life is going to be so much different from mine every day. We'll never fully understand where the other comes from, but I have so much respect for his will, his strength.

As my heartbeat slows down and my stomach settles, I feel a wave of sympathy and safety. I certainly have felt safe with Scoop sleeping by my side. We came here to get right and get out. We both made it clear when we got here that we were going out together. Except for a couple touchy moments, we're going to make it. We have to get through today, and I think we can do it.

I want Scoop to have it as good as I will. I want him to get another chance at school, a safe place to live, to be in peace. I know he's going to move home with his mom and his family. He has a job lined up in one of the restaurants in Wilmington. Scoop isn't married to Wanda, just said they never bothered to. Never cheated on her, he told me and I said, "Then why the hell wouldn't you get married?" She is somehow related to Bob Marley, Rita Marley really. Scoop said she was Rita Marley's niece, moved to Wilmington from Jamaica when she was a baby. All I know is, she's in love with Scoop, this big teddy bear asleep right in front of me.

I put my feet on the floor from the side railing and make my way to the shower. The countdown begins, my second to last shower. I know when I step out of it, Scoop will be up and we can let this day begin.

At 10 a.m. precisely it will be my turn to stand in front of big group and speak. I take a pen and a small pad of Hidden Brook Recovery stationery and head to breakfast while Scoop is in the shower. I get my scrambled eggs, two sausage links, toast and OJ, the same thing I've eaten every day for the last twenty-nine days. I look forward to breakfast tomorrow, on the way out with a full stomach.

I put down my tray, slide it over in front of an empty seat and make notes. I write jumbled thoughts, what I've learned, what I can remember. By the time Scoop sits down with his tray, I've filled about ten pieces of paper. They're small sheets, so I have to write small.

"What have you got there, a love note?" says Scoop.

"No, man, but I should have grabbed some long pieces of paper," I say and put them away, folded and in my pocket. "Who's picking you up tomorrow?" I ask, already knowing the answer but trying to keep him from asking me what's on the paper.

"Wanda's coming by herself, is what she said," he says. "How about you?"

"My parents are coming, I think, both of them and that's going to be a long ride home. I'm happy to get out of here, but I don't know what to do next. I've got to live at home for a little while at least, that's going to be tough. I need to save some money and get back in school, but I don't know how I'm going to do it. Man, I don't know how I'm going to do it. My grades are terrible, I don't have a car—" and Scoop shuts me up.

"Man, what are you bullshitting about, you just do it. I didn't sit down for my breakfast to hear this bitchin'. Look at them notes I saw you writing. I can read. I saw the word 'content' and 'optimistic.' I saw you, we good, man, we good," Scoop says, holding his OJ high in his hand, looking for a cheers from me as he scans the room. "We are good, brother, real good," he says. I hold up my OJ and we toast with our plastic maroon juice cups and smile. I feel my shoulders lift. I found a guy that knows the meaning of a rough life and, if he can do it, so can I.

At ten o'clock I pull my ten white pieces of telephone note-sized stationery out of my pocket while I sit in my tan/yellowed steel folding chair. I know my turn is coming up and I don't even listen to William as he does his usual beginning of the meeting update speech. I run my story through my mind. When I hear him say, "Mark, final big group meeting," I come to and focus my eyes. I look at William and he is staring straight at me, arm extended. He looks so nice, smiling, about 5'10", thinning, wavy brown hair, straight white teeth, blue button-down shirt tucked into his khakis. He moves his arm again and I stand up and look around.

People are seated in chairs arranged in a kind of circle. "Hi, my name is Mark and I am an alcoholic," I say as I look around the room. I don't like to hear myself say that out loud, but it is both a requirement and the truth. "I'm from Towson, Maryland. I have grown up in a nice, two-parent, stable household. We weren't rich, we weren't poor. I went to private schools, but we didn't belong to the country club. My dad has always worked and we always have had food. I say this stuff because I've had my eyes opened while I've been in here. I realize that I'm fortunate, I am lucky. I don't know that I always felt that way when I was drinking. I thought I had it bad— like all of us—but I had no idea. I now realize that I've really lived a sheltered life. I saw only my little small world in Towson. We didn't travel much, just went to Ocean City because my family had four kids. So I thought that's what the whole country was like.

"You guys," I start, pause, and look around the room. I recognize almost all of the thirty-five patients. Those I know and those I don't know simply sit, waiting and listening. Some drink coffee and some shift in their seats. All the staff sits or stands around the outside of the circle. I spot Scoop on the far left, looking at me with his brow furrowed, listening. "You guys have taught me all the other upbringings, backgrounds, circumstances. I realize we all have our stories to tell. We're all different but alike in so many ways.

"My story really took off from others when I finished high school. Up until that point, I was like all my friends. I drank a lot all through high school—I actually had my first drink when I was in sixth grade. I learned how to get beer, get liquor and I drank to get drunk. It's just what we all did at the time, or at least that's what I thought. I didn't realize that I was setting myself up for tolerance. I learned to drink, I became experienced.

"When I finished high school, we had senior week in Ocean City, Maryland. We all went to the beach piled into cars, but I was the only one to come home in an ambulance." As I tell my story about the fire, I see people's faces change, I see them shift in their seats, some get a pained look on their faces—even Brendan makes a little noise with his mouth closed, "mmgh." I've told this story to psychiatrists, psychologists, doctors, William and others, so I can turn off the feelings and just talk about the medical side. Whenever anyone hears that your chest, arms, and back got burned enough to look like hamburger meat, they all give you the same look of sympathy. It's awkward to me now because it doesn't hurt anymore and I don't want them feeling sorry for me. But when I tell people that I got doused in rubbing alcohol and lit with a match, it still makes me feel sick to my stomach every time.

I continue. "I stayed in the hospital, transferred to the burn unit at Francis Scott Key Hospital and stayed there for recovery until, at last, they let me go home. It took a long time for my skin to heal. I took baths everyday and just laid around. I wasn't allowed to do anything, which meant I didn't drink, but as it turns out, I was just saving up. I drank every day of my freshman year, every day, played lacrosse, and came out with a 1.75 GPA and a DUI.

"When I went back for my sophomore year the following September, my drinking got worse. I got another DUI in Towson over fall break. Another mark on my record, another lawyer fee, another court date. The judge gave me two AA meetings a week for eighteen months. I kept drinking every night, kept doing drugs, kept going strong. Really, I drank to get drunk pretty much every day until I came here. I would sit in court-appointed AA meetings, get my note signed, get drunk, get fucked up and turn my two signatures a week into my probation officer. I didn't think I needed to quit drinking, I didn't think I was an alcoholic. I didn't think I had a drinking problem until I got here. I didn't think my problems with the law were because of my drinking, I didn't think my bad grades were because of my drinking. I thought I had it all figured out, except I didn't." I look down at my papers and start to recite some of the things I have learned since I have been here.

"I have learned that I've really been in denial. I have learned that I'm definitely an alcoholic. There is no doubt about that. Now I'm starting to understand the things that I have been hearing but not really listening to. First is the serenity prayer. 'God, grant me the serenity to accept the things I cannot change, the courage to change the things I can and the wisdom to know the difference.' I understand it now. If I can only focus on the things I can change, I have a chance. I know I will have to deal with paying fines and reporting to a probation officer, but mainly, I will just try not to drink, one day at a time. Make it through the day without taking a drink, just today."

I look down at my next two pages of notes. "I hope I can do it. Plus, this place has taught me that by living for today and only doing what I can control, I don't live in the past or get caught looking too far into the future. I hope I can do this when I get out of here." I look to my right and catch the eye of William. He just nods his head, never changing his expression. "Another thing I read in a book they have in the library was something that I can now just understand. The saying was, 'A rich man is not one who has the most, but is one that needs the least.' It hit me when I read that. I couldn't go any further in the book. It just struck me. I've been thinking about all these things, always wanting things, always chasing things. If I'm rich but an asshole, is that really what I want? And make no mistake,

I was an asshole when I got drunk. I was rude, obnoxious, flippant, crude, I managed to hit them all by the time the night was over." This last comment isn't in my notes, but if I'm going to be honest, I have to be brutally honest. "I'm hoping I can not only learn to live with less and be happy with what I have, but that I can also learn to appreciate what I do have. Instead of always looking out and at what other people have, I can look within. I want to learn how to not need anything—booze, anything. I don't want to need anything ever again. I probably won't be as much of an asshole, either."

I'm smirking now and I hear a couple people laugh out loud. I make eye contact with Peter, a middle-aged salesman, prematurely gray at forty-five but a nice guy. Got hooked on pills and lost his job and his house. His wife and kids always visit on Sundays, but they always look sad. I look down at the next two pages and each one has a phrase. "'Let go and let God.' I definitely didn't understand this one when I got here. I thought God dealt me a bad hand. I felt sorry for myself, thought other people caused my problems, thought my parents were a pain in my ass, I thought I never got any breaks. Now, I realize it isn't God's fault. I'm lucky. God doesn't want me to screw up, get DUIs, get arrested. It's funny because we don't go to church here, and I have grown up going to Mass most Sundays. I have thought more about God here in the last twenty-nine days than I have in ten years. And I think if I let go of my shit and let God help me, I'll be better off. It's a lot like the serenity prayer, but this one feels like it lightens the load even more. Let go of everything and do my own thing. I want to learn to do it on the outside. I know when I get out there, I'll feel some of the same feelings, but I don't want to take on other people's shit, other people's problems, their opinions, or their words. I just want to let them go, let bad thoughts go, let it all go, just let go.

"Another understanding I've come to is from the Twelve Promises of AA. Really, it's two promises. The feeling of uselessness and self-pity will disappear, and we will lose interest in selfish things and gain interest in our fellow beings. These hit me because I don't want any pity from myself or from anybody else. William told me when I got here that only about three in ten don't drink or use drugs again. I was hoping for better odds, but I also don't want to lie anymore. If three in ten is it, then that's it."

I look down at my last two pages then scan the room. "Thanks for listening, thanks for helping me, each one of you, and thank you to the counselors, the cafeteria people, everybody. You've given me all the tools and I can't use any lame excuse like I didn't know, if I screw up again. Thanks for your help, thanks for your care. And"—I look up at everybody because this one is easy to remember— "I read one other thing that I want to talk about. Walt Whitman wrote it and I am going to try and use it. He wrote 'Be curious, not judgmental.' I realized I judged everybody. I thought I could tell who people are by just looking at them or talking to them for a few minutes. All of you taught me that that is wrong. Each one of you taught me something I didn't expect from you. I want to be curious, to learn and put my judgment away. I want to live with an open mind. I'm twenty years old and I feel like this is a fresh start. I am, no doubt, scared of what it's going to be like out there. But I also know I am way different than I was a month ago. I have no idea what tomorrow holds, but I am not going to worry about that right now. I am going to stick with today for right now."

At this moment I realize I don't have anything else to say. It's a relief to stand in front of everyone, pour it all out. I know I'm flawed, damaged really, but so is everybody else. And we don't have to be damaged forever. I sit down in my steel folding chair. I look at my hands and lean forward in my chair. Nobody breaks the silence for at least a minute and then Brendan says, "Thank you, Mark, thanks for sharing your story." My fellow patients for one more day give me an obligatory round of applause but I don't look up. Brendan continues to talk and I don't hear a thing until I hear chairs being folded and put away. I follow suit, my head in the clouds, when

Scoop hits me with a grown man slap on my shoulder from behind. "Boy, you got some shit to you, don't you?" he says.

"Too much shit, Scoop, too much," I say. Time for lunch.

|||||||||||||||||||||||||||||||||||||||||||||||||||||||

CHAPTER 28

|||||||||||||||||||||||||||||||||||||||||||||||||||||||||||

I take three dollars' worth of quarters to the hall phone and test my memory on Allison's phone number on the phone in her dormitory. She told me the number the last night I saw her and I am going to give it a try. I drop three quarters into the slot and dial. It rings and rings but nobody answers. I hang up and my three quarters fall into the return slot. I slide my finger into the return slot and grab the quarters. This time I dial my house number. Mary picks up on the second ring, gives me a quick hi, then calls for Mom or Dad. I hear the phone click and Mom gets on the line. As soon as she says, "Hey Mark, how—" the phone clicks again and I hear Dad on the other one. "Hi Mark," he says, "how are you doing?"

"I'm doing fine, just wanted to call and say hi, I know I'll see you tomorrow but I just wanted to say hi." This isn't really true, I just want to have someone to talk to during phone call time and I figure they're home.

Dad says, "We'll be up in the morning. Brendan says we will have an appointment with him and then you'll be ready to come home."

"That sounds good. That sounds really good," I say as I think what going home means right now: no money, no job, and no school. I have to start over from scratch, it's real. I've been on my own for a year and a half. I've tasted freedom from my parents, their roof. Under their roof, it's all different. It's not true freedom. "I'm going to look for a job as soon as I get home, I know I need to get a job, probably two of them. It's been different in here. I've learned some good stuff, I have lost some of my other stuff. I don't mean lost it, I mean put it behind me. I want you to know also, Mom, Dad, there's a lot I don't know. I found out in here all of the things I don't know, and I thought I knew it all, I really did. So, thanks for all of your help. Thanks for all you've done already. Hopefully I can take it from here." The black payphone handle is pressed hard to my ear. My eyes water and I'm choking down a cry. Two things happened in the world outside of me, here in rehab: Michael Jordan hit a floating jumper over Craig Ehlo, and my sister Lauren graduated from college. I missed her graduation and I felt bad that day. Seconds elapse as I try to regain my voice. Dad fills the silence. "We look forward to seeing you," he says.

"I look forward to seeing you, too," I say. "I'm going to get going, someone wants to use the phone." I am looking down an empty hallway, the other payphone five yards away, on the hook, nobody in sight.

"Goodnight, Mom and Dad," I still whisper just loud enough for them to hear, even though nobody is within earshot.

"Goodnight, Mark, we love you," Mom says, speaking for both of them. I hang up and pull three quarters from my pocket and dial Allison's hall phone. It rings and rings. It stops ringing and the phone drops three quarters into the coin return, so I pick them out. One more try, I drop them in and dial 804-769-3819, and hope it's not busy. Sometimes girls purposely don't answer so they can use the hall phone. It rings and rings, and finally a girl picks up, "Hello Star," she says in an annoyed voice, her bare necessity confirmation that the caller has reached Star Hall Dormitory.

"Is Allison Robinson in her room, room 29, by any chance?"

"I don't know," she says, softening her voice. I hear some muffled voices as she covers the phone, some rustling, a knock on a door, music. "Hold on, she's here," she says, then silence. I envision the pay phone receiver dangling on its silver chain. I am wondering what I'm going to say when a soft voice says, "Hello?"

I haven't heard her pick up the phone and I cough out, "Allison, hey, sorry, Allison, this is Mark D'Antoni. I am sorry I haven't called you until now but I"—I'm stuttering— "I've been busy, I've been out of town."

I hear the phone move in her hand and she says, "I'm glad you called. I was hoping you would. How have you been?"

"I've been okay, well, I've been in rehab really," I say, matter of factly.

"I know, it's okay. I went to Baltimore with Sara Simpson a couple of weeks ago and her brother Brendan told us," she says. My heart sinks just a bit, knowing people know you are in rehab, talking about it. "Well, yeah, I went here right after we met. I've been here since, I wasn't sure you'd remember me. How have you been?"

"I've been good, school's been good and I am rushing into Alpha Beta. Are you going to be there much longer?" she says.

"I leave tomorrow," I say as I look around the long gray hallway from the cafeteria to the administrative offices. The floors are a blue cement, covered in a shine. Two patients walk through while I search for words. "I was wondering if I could see you sometime, maybe this summer."

"Sure, I would like that. How is it going there?"

"It's okay, I mean it's like a hospital, but the people are nice. I'm definitely ready to get out of here." I leave out the fact that I am not real thrilled about moving home with my parents. "How much longer are you in school?"

"I'm getting out May 23," Allison says. "Why don't we meet up this summer? You can come to Rehoboth if you want."

"Yeah, that would be cool. I'm kind of embarrassed to call you from here. I wanted to call you earlier but I really didn't know what to say. I had a really good time when we were together. I'm sorry you didn't go to Van Ripers Lake with us. It was a fun concert and based on the volume of your room when you opened the door, you probably would have like it."

"I'm sorry I didn't go, too, I just wasn't sure if you really wanted me to come with you guys," she says.

"Hopefully, Dave Matthews will have another concert in Charlottesville and we'll go together, how about that?" I say.

"I'll try to be available," she says in a playful voice and we talk, she asks about my roommate, my meetings. I tell her about the afternoon walks around the lake, the obsession with coffee and cigarettes. I ask her about classes and parties and she tells me about rushing her sorority and her upbringing. She talks about her parents and her family. She talks about the small beach town that she lives in, where everybody knows everybody. She tells me about sailing and swimming every day in the summer, working at the burger stand on the boardwalk. She talks about meeting her friends at the arcade, going to the pizza place and riding in jeeps on the beach sand. She tells me about her family friends who look after everyone in town. I listen and daydream, visualising her beautiful smile and kind manner, in a background of ocean seas and salt air.

I feed the phone quarters about every ten minutes and I realize I am about to run out of money and time on the phone. A nice, clearly-pronounced woman's voice comes on the line and says, "One minute remaining on call." Every time that voice has come on, I've put two quarters in and I am down to my last two. I want to know if I can see her soon, but I don't want to sound desperate. As I slide my last two quarters in the slot, I try to plot a time where we can be together. "Will you give me your home number so I can call you?" I ask.

"Call me here until May 20th and then, if you want, call me at home. My number there is 302-555-2272," she says. I write it on my hand with a pen that has been sitting on top of the phone case. Blue bic, no top. "Okay, I will. It was nice talking to you," I say, feeling emotion, different emotions: Embarrassment, in my scrubs, loose hospital clothes that I can lose tomorrow. Hope that Allison remembers me and wants to get together. Nervous because I don't know what I am going to do. School, job, sober, doesn't sound all that comforting. I don't want the phone time to run out on us. "I'll call you in the next couple weeks. Good luck with your exams. If you want to call me, my home number is 410-555-7172. Thanks for coming to the phone, I don't want to take you away from studying," I say.

"That's no problem. I'm really glad you called."

"Hope to see you soon," I say. "See you."

"Bye," she says and I hang up the receiver. I slide my hand back down the gray wall and sit on my butt, white Nikes with black swoosh on, my only allowance of individuality, our shoes. I have worn these shoes every day. I daydream about Allison, relieved to talk to her and hopeful, innocently hopeful that she won't judge me. She will give me a chance even if I am boring, sober, dull. I sit and think, not moving, leaning back on the wall. I will see Allison sometime, somewhere. She's different. She looks at me differently from other girls I know. The one thing I remember, from the night, from the light, she has that innocent, kind look in her eye. Plus, they are blue-green and soft. Her hair is blondish brown, her skin is soft, her heart seems open. Maybe this girl can teach me how to open mine. My heart has felt hurt, anger, despair, rejection, disappointment, panic, fear, struggle, self-deceit, self-loathing, shame, really not much joy, very little contentment and just about no hope. While this place has taught my mind many things, it has equally or even more helped to heal my heart. I believe that I have a good heart, I feel it, but it's been a long time since I led with it. While I know I need to keep my mind sharp, I must also let my heart decide the way.

I've been sitting here awhile in this sterile hall. I realize I'm shaking, not shivering, but shaking with energy, both nervous and excited. I blink my eyes into focus and stand. I know Scoop is back in the room, reading the Bible. It's nine-thirty and we have another hour until lights out. I'm not in a hurry to go back to my room, so I head to the cafeteria, uplifted that my time here is short.

II

CHAPTER 29

IIIIIIIIIIIIIIIIIIIIIIIIIIIIIIIIIIIIIIIIIIIIIIIIIIIIIIIIIIIIIII

Morning comes, departure day. I'm to meet first thing with Brendon, in his office. The familiarity of my surroundings is comforting but the uncertainty of the day keeps me on guard. We talk about my plan going forward, my approach to AA meetings, my desire to work and redeem myself in the eyes of all those I've done wrong. It is a steep hill to climb, a daunting task, and Brendan reminds me to approach everything one step at a time. Soon, we're interrupted by a woman poking her head into the office. "Brendan, the D'Antonis are here," she says.

"Thanks," he says as she closes the door. He looks at me, stands up from his chair and says, "No time like the present, right? Are you ready?"

I nod my head. "Yes, I'm ready."

He grabs the doorknob and pulls the door open. My parents are on the other side. "Good morning, Margaret and Daniel, it's good to see you."

They both nod their heads in agreement and say good morning as well.

As they walk into the office, I get up from the chair and feel a wave of excitement hit me. The thought that we were here four weeks ago, splintered and hurting, to where we are now is mind boggling. We have come a long way, but I know we have a long way to go.

Now come handshakes and hugs, signed papers and release

forms. My head spins as the list of services and treatments are recapped to my parents. Everyone keeps things positive. My bags are packed on the floor. I grab them and head out the door, determined to never return to this place again.

I get into the back seat, the same place I sat on the way up here. I look at the back of Mom and Dad as we head up the driveway to the main road. I lean my head on the glass window and, into my head pops the verse from the Jimmy Cliff song. "I can see clearly now, the rain is gone, I can see all the obstacles in my way, gone are the dark clouds that had me blind, it's gonna be a bright, bright, sunshiny day."

|||||||||||||||||||||||||||||||||||||||||||||||||||||||||

CHAPTER 30

|||||||||||||||||||||||||||||||||||||||||||||||||||||||||||

"Good morning, sir," says a young, brown-haired woman as I walk into Bacharach Rasin one bright morning—the first morning after rehab—just five minutes after the store has opened its doors for the day.

"Morning," I say as I walk past the counter.

"Let me know if you need any help," she says. Bacharach's is a store I've been in tons of times. It is the AI lacrosse store in Baltimore, actually pretty much the one and only lacrosse store in town. I'm here looking for cleats. I know that Mt. Washington Lacrosse Club is having practice tonight and I need a pair. Mom and Dad have given me thirty dollars and strict instructions: "You can buy some cleats and come home with a job." I know I can get a pair here, plus I don't mind taking a look at what new lacrosse products might have come out for this season. I heard Nike is making a pair of cleats called the Landsharks and I want to see if they've arrived. Plus, STX has put out a new stick called the Laser HI-wall, and I want to take a look at that. Right now I have a nice STX Sam and my backup is a Brine Super Light II. I don't think I want to get a new stick, but I definitely want to take a look. The young woman is doing paperwork behind the counter when I walk up and ask, "Do you have any Nike Landsharks in size nine?"

"Let me take a look. What color?" she asks.

"White with a black swoosh, please." I say and she walks through the curtain into the room behind the shoe wall. She comes back out in about two minutes with size nines. I sit down and unlace my navy blue Chuck Taylors to try them on. The Nikes are definitely nice, with black bottoms and molded cleats. The tag says $24.99, so I'll have enough money, even with the tax. I know that a five percent Maryland sales tax will only be $1.25 so I might have a couple dollars to get something to eat.

When I lace up my Chucks and head to the counter, I figure, *What the heck, I'll ask her for a job.*

"Would you like to see anything else or just the cleats?" she asks.

"That's it, just the cleats. Thanks. Also, are you hiring?" I ask just loud enough for her to hear me clearly.

"Are you looking for a job?"

"Yes, and I was wondering if you are hiring," I say again.

"Well, when could you start?"

"I could start today if you need me to," I say. "Otherwise, I can start whenever you say."

"What's your name?" she asks.

"Sorry. My name is Mark D'Antoni."

"Are you in school?" she continues.

"Not this semester," I say, "I plan on taking classes this summer and enrolling in the fall."

There's a pause. "Okay, how come you don't have a job right now?" she asks.

"Well," I begin. I've been told countless times recently to tell people the truth. They will give you a chance or a second chance if you are honest. They won't give you a third chance. "Well," I start again. "I just got out of rehab for alcohol and I need to get a job. I'm living at home right now and I need to save some money. I've always been around lacrosse and know all of your products. I have been coming here to buy my stuff since I was like seven years old. So, I figured I'd ask while I'm here." It just came out. I didn't plan on asking for a job here but it seems like a good idea now. Let's see what she says. "Otherwise, no big deal, I plan on going to five or six restaurants and see if I can get a job waiting on tables or cooking until I find something else. Just thought I'd ask."

She studies me from behind the counter. She's actually looking down at me because Bacharach Rasin has one of those counters that is raised two steps above floor level, and I have to look up at her to hear her answer.

"Why don't you start today? I'll get you to fill out the paperwork later. What time can you work to?"

"I can work until six if you want me to. I got these cleats because I plan on going to Mt. Washington at seven to play lacrosse."

"Okay, good. I want you to follow me and you can work with Brinkley. I know he has orders that he needs help with, so you can get started with that," she says as she walks me through the door in the back of the showroom, past a couple of offices and into the back, a tall- ceilinged, gray-walled warehouse. There, next to the oversized garage door, is a disheveled desk, with tools all strewn about. I suppose this is the shipping department. It's a lot to take in. It isn't very well lit, it's cluttered, but there are clean trash cans filled with lacrosse stuff. There is a can full of broken heads, one of broken metal and wood defense poles, one heaping can of helmets without masks, and another half-full. Everything I look at around this 25- by 25-foot space holds hanging, stacked or boxed lacrosse equipment and gear, new and old.

"Brinkley, this is Mark. He's on a trial run today as a new employee. Mark, this is Brinkley," she says. I'd seen this man a few minutes earlier when he entered the store, said 'Good morning, Miss Eileen,'and disappeared into the back room. Brinkley moves his head and looks over at us, glasses on the end of his nose looking at a yellow piece of printed paper. He seems to have an easy manner

"Nice to meet you," Brinkley says with a voice just as deep as I thought I heard the first time.

"Nice to meet you," I say as Eileen keeps talking. "Mark, please help Brinkley with anything he needs. Brinkley, I know we have

Army, Lafayette and Loyola College to get out by today because we have Towson and Princeton to get out by Friday."

"You're right, Miss Eileen, but I'll get them out. Mark here and I will get it done. You don't have to worry about that. Everything for Army and Loyola is done and ready to be packed." He looks down at the yellow paper and continues, "I just need eleven more helmets to finish with LaFayette and pack that up. It should be out of here by two o'clock."

"That's funny, Brinkley, I'll leave you guys to get started," says Eileen as she exits.

I look at Brinkley, a sixtyish-looking, stocky, African American man with short gray- specked hair, as he studies the yellow paper. A moment later he puts it down. "Let me show you how to make a helmet. We only have to make eleven to pack up Lafayette and that will be the last of it." He walks to a big gray shelf with helmet parts. He has the easy manner of a content man. His pace is measured and steady, not hurried in the slightest. The bottom row holds boxes of helmets labeled "white" and "black." The middle row is filled with masks and chin straps. The top row holds big boxes, unopened, unlabeled. We grab eleven white helmets. They feel odd in my hand without the masks, unbalanced. Next come eleven masks and eleven chin straps, which we place on a six-foot wooden work table. Brinkley pulls out four open boxes–one with screws, one with screw sleeves, one with washers and one with v-shaped metal pieces–and places them on the table in the middle. He takes a v-shaped piece on the face mask in one hand, and pliers in the other hand. "Mark, take this piece and set it all the way on the bottom and squeeze it until the ends touch. Then let go." He sets and squeezes, and the piece folds in half and separates just a bit. "Don't hold it closed, just let them touch and let go. It will open again, and you can slide it right over the plastic." He is demonstrating as he goes through it. "Do the same thing on the other side, same place. Now, the holes are pre-drilled so just take a washer and this screw. Now take another washer and this nut and put them right here." He slides the washer and the nut on the inside and spins the screw until it makes contact with the sleeve style nut, and the face mask tightens. "Same thing on this side," he says as he connects the other side. "Now take this smaller screw with a washer and slide it through this hole and the brim of the helmet and tighten it up." He smoothly pulls the face mask tighter with a Phillips head screwdriver, goes into another box and comes out with two snap screws. He puts the Phillips head inside the snap and screws it into the pre-drilled holes. "Go ahead and put the chinstrap on and she's done. Ten more to go."

I pick up a face mask, a set of pliers and two metal v-pieces and go to work. Brinkley does one right next to me, and I look over at him during each step just to make sure I'm doing it right. Once I finish mine, Brinkley says, "Go ahead and do the next nine and let me know when you're done." He turns to his desk, shuffles yellow papers, and picks one up. He heads over to the shelves in the warehouse with a big cardboard box and starts filling them. I stand at the workbench and knock out nine helmets. The face masks on these helmets are the three-bar type. I always played with a four-bar helmet as my face mask on my Bacharach helmet. I almost feel sorry for every guy with a three-bar. It doesn't have enough protection on your chin or your neck. I always used a four-bar helmet, two chin protectors. That way you can rest your helmet on your head with your chin on the top chin guard. Hang your two-snap chin straps under your throat, not touching anything. It's the way to wear your helmet. Of course, I'm going through this rating as I work, finish the helmet order for Lafayette College in short order and ask Brinkley what to do next.

"Grab one of the big boxes and one of those yellow sheets and meet me back here," he says. He shows me how to read the work order and I start packing Army's order. I begin with thirty black four-bar helmets, then grab some boxes and fill them quickly. I know the equipment. All the brand new arm pads from STX and

Brine. Army is an STX school, so I find thirty Sam heads, thirty string packets, everything. Army's order takes up nine boxes, and I drag them to the garage door. Brinkley says, "Don't tape anything. I need to see it before it goes out."

I grab another box and another yellow sheet and head to the back. When I turn the corner for twenty-four white, three-bar helmets, Brinkley is standing there, glasses on. "Slow down there, son," he says, "you got time to do it all." I'm not sure what that means but I slow down, grab helmets two at a time and stack them more neatly than before.

I got a job, it's in lacrosse, and I forgot to ask how much I am getting paid. Eileen didn't tell me, either, so I have to be sure I get that question answered before I leave for the day.

II

CHAPTER 31

IIIIIIIIIIIIIIIIIIIIIIIIIIIIIIIIIIIIIIIIIIIIIIIIIIIIIIIIIIIIIII

I pull up to the practice on Norris Field in a blue Chevrolet Delta 88, equipment in the trunk and new cleats on the seat next to me. I am nervous. I've been to this field hundreds of times and this is the first time I have been nervous here since I was seven years old. I played my first two years of lacrosse here, midget ball. I was nervous on that first day of practice, as a seven-year old until I realized I was one of the better players. Now I'm twenty and these guys are good. They're all twenty-five to thirty, a lot have made All-American. Every Tuesday and Thursday night they practice under the lights from 7 to 9 p.m. and play their games on Sunday afternoons. These are the guys I have watched play for Team USA, the guys who beat Long Island/Hofstra for the club championships. I don't think I'll get any game time but I came to practice. I know that and really, I need that. I know that in order to be as good as they are, these guys have practiced hard, and I am ready to do the same. I take the keys out of the ignition, drop them on the floor, pop the trunk, grab my new cleats and open the door. It is sixty-degrees with a nice early season chill in the air. I grab my equipment, shut the trunk and head to the field. By the time I have my cleats and socks on, some of the team is out on the field throwing the ball around. They are all good sized and most of them are working the facial hair. Some are clean cut and look professional, but the big guys have beards. As I grab my four-bar Bacharach helmet, white and sticker free, I see the coach, Skip Lichtfuss. He's the guy I have to talk to first–let him know my plan.

"Coach," I say to him, full equipment on and holding my stick and helmet in my left hand, extending my right to shake his hand, "my name is Mark D'Antoni. I understand you guys practice each Tuesday and Thursday, and I was hoping it would be okay with you if I just practice with you guys, try to give your guys a good look for their Sunday games. Would that be okay with you?"

"Are you Margaret's son?" Coach asks.

"Yes, sir."

"Okay, yeah, I think that will be fine, just introduce yourself to some of the guys and hop in line drills. We should be getting started in a few minutes."

"I will, sir, thanks," I say as I put on my helmet and put my right glove on my hand. I turn to a couple of the big bearded defensemen who are playing catch. "Hi, I'm Mark."

One says, "Hey, I'm Ronnie and that's Dave."

"Nice to meet you," I say as I put up my stick to catch a pass from Dave. He looks at me and throws it back to Dave, who goes back to Ronnie.

"Here's your help," I say to Ronnie and he finally passes me the ball. Both of these guys have really good stick work and I realize Dave is Dave McGinnis, the defenseman from JHU last year who was Defenseman of the Year in college lacrosse. He has his JHU helmet, but I didn't notice it until now. I must be out of practice.

While they're throwing the ball to each other mostly and me every once in a while, a guy comes over whom I've never seen, "What's up, guy?" he says and for some reason, he looks to me like a dog looking for a scratch. "What up, Clyde," says Ronnie as Clyde gets his equipment on. He has a long stick, too. Finally, when they throw it to me, I carry it from the top of the restraining line to goal line extended, roll and fire off a thirty-yard pass to Ronnie up top in the middle between the top of the box and the restraining line. He gets the message and carries it down the right angle and sticks a high overhand crank shot to the far top left corner. Damn, that was some heat. I jog over to pick up the ball up out of the net. It's funny with all the guys around, about twenty, there are only like five balls. I carry it along the wing, roll and throw to Dave, who doesn't take the message. Instead, he switches hands and throws a high lob pass to Clyde, who is stepping onto the field, fully equipped, chinstrap unbuckled. He catches it right- handed, switches to his left, dodges left, does a fake throw, switches back to his right, turns on some jets and slings a sidearm longstick bounce shot into the lower right corner. Damn, that dude is quick. When I get the ball this time, I throw to Ronnie, who throws right back, so I catch and dodge air, full speed and let one go, high overhand, and over the goal, into the far corner of the field, towards the building off the end line and the bleachers. I hear Dave say out loud sarcastically, "Nice shot." I don't want them standing around waiting on me, so I hustle over to the ball. When I turn to the field Ronnie and Clyde are talking to each other and Dave is standing up top. I get to the end line, make eye contact and loft a forty-yard lob, up over the top. This time he catches it in his left, goes left and sticks the top right. As he jogs by me he mutters, "Now that's how you shoot it." I just look down and nod. When I look up, Clyde is jogging over to me.

"Where did you go to high school?" he asks.

"St. Xavier," I say.

"When did you graduate?" he asks.

"Eighty-six."

"Did you start?" he asks.

"Yeah, why?" I counter.

"Just wondering," he says and walks away. Right about then Skip Lichtfuss yells, "All right, you guys, bring it up! Let's get ready to go!" I head over wondering why Clyde wanted to know about me.

After we start with line drills, we go right into one-on-ones. Every time it's my turn, Clyde is my defender. He's not big, but he is fast and he has an array of checks. He gets me with a wrap check and one time when I hang my stick on a shot, I get him on an inside roll and a couple of changes of direction, but I can't throw it past the goalies. These guys are good.

By the time we get five-on-fours, the ball is humming around. I move it a lot but get a ton of touches. I cut when I'm open. The ball is fast and I'm trying to handle it at their speed. *Just don't screw up.* I go through the whole drill and I haven't scored yet. I have a couple of assists, but mostly those are off really good shots by these six-foot one, 200- pound middies. At some point, Skip Lichtfuss yells "Everybody to the middle!" He explains the drill and the message: three-on-three groundballs to the goal, first team to pick it up is on offense. We have to win tough groundballs if we expect to win this league. This drill is a blood bath, each line is either a long stick or a short stick. Coach rolls the ball five yards in front of the middle two lines and the long sticks throw hard slap checks on every ground ball. When the short sticks win, we either try to fast break right away or, if nothing is there, we spread wide and go hard. Cut hard, carry hard, dodge hard. It's exhausting. I may be the worst one here. The defensemen chase you out everywhere, and every time I touch it, if Clyde is on me, he is bringing the kitchen sink. When the defenseman wins the groundball, I get another chance to see their shooting skills. They don't spread the field or take their time at all. They power through anybody covering them and shoot hard at the goal, chasing rebounds and causing chaos. Clyde has a slick stick, wth finishing skills. He chokes up on his long pole in the crease, and can shoot from range. He has more goals in this drill than I do.

The drill finally ends and we get water. I take a knee on the side and choke down a throw-up. This is harder than I thought and we are only halfway done. These guys don't look tired at all. When we bring it back up, the defense splits off to one side and split sides. The short sticks split up on the other side midfield. When we take our side I go blue and play attack. Clyde is, of course, white and guards me right away. While we wait for the faceoff, I say to him,

"Hey man, what's your name?"

"Jerry Kline," he says.

"Where'd you go to school?" I ask.

"Cartland State," he says.

"Okay," I say, nodding my head, wondering why some dude from Cartland State wants to guard me all over the field and taking it upon himself to be kind of a dick.

"But I only went there for one year, and then I failed out," he volunteers.

"Okay," I'm still kind of perplexed.

"But, I went to West Genny for high school and we always wanted to play you St. Xavier pricks."

"Uh-huh," I grunt and it all makes sense. "We felt the same way," I say. We always wanted to play West Genesee. They were the best high school team in New York and we were the best high school team in Maryland. We would look at New York papers and read all we could about them. The Syracuse school sent a bunch of players to college, but we could never get a game with them. We would beg our coach to get a game, volunteered to pay for the bus, volunteered to find a field halfway in between, but he never did it. We wanted to play them badly and as I am now finding out, they wanted to play us just as badly. That explains it, that explains everything, why this Clyde guy has a hard on since I met him. So, I hit him with this, "Did you start?" I ask, pretty sure of the answer, but just to fuck with him.

"Yeah, I fucking started. We would have kicked your ass," he says.

By now the faceoff has happened and my middie has picked up the ball.

"I don't think so," I say as I take off down the wing. I am surprised by the speed I have all of a sudden, but pride is at stake now and I am going to make this motherfucker work. I don't stop moving for the entire scrimmage, except when the ball is at the other end.

When it is at the other end, suddenly we don't have anything to say to each other.

We play for about forty-five minutes straight. I have a goal off of a rebound and an assist. He strips me once and clears the ball several times. He is an excellent ground ball player but I would never tell him so. We don't speak to each other the whole scrimmage. When it's over, the whole team meets in the middle of the field. I'm looking at Coach but not hearing anything. When we break, I say to Clyde, "See you next practice."

"You better fucking be here," he says.

I wasn't sure how this would go or who I would know, but I have found my motivation, a guy I have never met before, from a school I've never seen. Turns out I need this more than I realized. It has my blood pumping and gives me a reason to feel competitive.

The whole team heads to the locker room, defense guys together, Clyde tagging along. I remain standing where the huddle used to be, watching coaches walk away, talking, comparing, strategizing. I drip in sweat: arm pads soaked, chest burning, cold air on my face, helmet in my gloved hand. I have never been here before as a player. I'm not walking right into the locker room. I look around, under the lights, and wonder how I got here. What other person my age, is playing pick-up lacrosse with a bunch of twenty-five-year-old stars, fresh out of rehab and a year and a half bender. I shake my head at the absurdity of it all. I showed up to see how I would do and I got my ass kicked. I know these guys are good, but I didn't think I was this bad before I got here. I got my ass kicked and it turns out it was by a guy who is my age. The rest of them tore me up, too. Ronnie, when he would switch on me, chased me over the whole field. He's hard just to carry the ball against, much less take him to the goal. He throws every check in the book, and he tries them on you the whole time. Dave, when he switched onto me, didn't try that hard. I didn't try to take him to the goal out of respect for the fact that he is the best defenseman in the world. I didn't want to embarrass myself.

They seemed to beat me to every ground ball and they never missed the scoop. They were all bigger and faster than anyone I have ever played with and I realize I have a lot, I mean a whole lot of work to do to get better. The reality of it makes the walk to the car slower. I dump my sweaty gear haphazardly in the trunk of the Delta 88 that was passed down from Cleta.

By the time I start the car, three of the six lights are off on the now half-lit field. Leaving Norris Field, driving past Mt. Washington Ice Rink, I think out loud, "You might suck but at least you didn't get drunk as shit." I smell salt, dirt, sweat, store glove odor on my hands, serious armpit odor, but for the first time since high school, I don't smell like booze. I am not pickled this time, sweating off beer and vodka, beer and tequila, beer and bourbon, take your pick. I just smell like sweat. Small victories it is, then, because that's about the only victory there is tonight. I head home.

One month later, I wake up at precisely 8 a.m. on a Sunday morning. It's the end of May and I head to Cleta's to pick her up for 9 a.m. Mass. Mom told me yesterday, in no uncertain terms, that I was taking her to Mass today. Cleta is eighty-four years old and completely with it. Mom and my aunt and uncles took her keys to her car. Mom and Aunt Peggy each have a set in case someone is in town and needs to use a car. Cleta had a new set of keys made and still drives it, though. She told me once that she parks it in the same spot in the driveway every time. She tells each of us, the grandkids, not to say anything and as far as I know, it's still a secret. It's a nice, sunny spring morning when I drop Cleta off in front of Cathedral and find a spot in the parking lot. When I make it inside, the first hymn is starting and I slide into a pew near the front with Cleta and her friends from many years, her sister Marge, her crew. No one says a word the whole time. She whispers during the sign of peace part that she wants me to take her to breakfast.

We go to a place on Roland Avenue, Petite Louis. I have never been here before, driven by it a thousand times though. After I drop her at the door, park the car and come inside, I see Cleta at a round table with her church crew. When I walk up, I see one empty chair next to Cleta, and I have a seat. All women, old women and me. They talk about their grandkids, their husbands, the weather. We order, we eat and they talk. A couple of them question me. "Where do you go to school?"

I say, "I'm not in school right now, but I plan on taking summer classes." I'm embarrassed with my answer, while they don't skip a beat, talking about their grandson at North Carolina or their granddaughter at JHU. It is tough to listen to as I retreat into silence. After the check comes and the women split it up in cash, I lean over to Cleta. "I'll get the car."

"Hold on for right now, we're going to sit here for a few minutes," she says. I feel a wave of anxiety, similar to when I was sent to the principal's office. I tuck my hands under my thighs and look up at the ladies as they leave the table. They say goodbye, make plans to meet for bridge. I stand up to say goodbye to them. I shake their hands. I'm not a hugger with people I don't know too well and they look too fragile for that anyway. Almost all of them place their other hand on mine, look me in the eye, and say, "Good luck, be well, you look great," like they feel the need to give me some kind of consolation. My name did not come up one time today, but something tells me I have been a topic of conversation for these ladies.

Meanwhile, Cleta never gets up from the table. When I sit back down, the noise of the room seems to quiet down and Cleta starts talking. "Mark, I wanted a chance to talk to you alone without your mother and father around, so thank you for taking me to church."

"You're welcome," I say and start to tell her it was no problem, but she continues right over my words. "I know that you have gone through a lot lately, but I wanted to tell you some things that I didn't tell you when we talked at rehab. I had my own driver and went to a private school but my mother died when I was eight years old, during childbirth to my sister Margaret. I was raised by my father and a nanny until I was sixteen. By the time I was seventeen, my father had passed away and I was responsible for my younger sister Margaret, who was only eight years old. We lived in the custody of my Aunt Catherine while I finished school and it changed my plans to go to college.

"Margaret and I lived with Catherine until I met your grandfather. Henry was a great man and he took great care of Margaret. But we were married, we were broke with my little sister to care for, and to make matters worse, that's when the Depression hit. We didn't have anything. We lived in a little apartment on Charles Street and we made it work. Your grandfather hustled, he sold newspapers, he sold booze, he worked for any sales company that would give him a job. We made it work. I made curtains and bedspreads for the people in Roland Park and Guilford. Henry finished his college at the University of Baltimore, and eventually the jobs picked up with the war. It was a much different time back then. We brought your Uncle Jimmy home from the hospital to that little apartment. We didn't have any idea in the world how we were going to make it, but we did. Your grandfather believed that you can overcome anything if you just work for it. It might take a long time, it might take a lot of work, but it can be done. Now, I know what happened to you was wrong, what you had to go through was heinous, but you made it through. You don't have to feel that pain physically anymore, but the emotional pain can hurt just as much. I know you used alcohol to deal with it and it wasn't good. But, really Mark, I think you drank too much for a young man even before your accident. I told you a lot about my family when we talked at rehab. It's a blessing that you quit drinking now, instead of later."

I keep looking in her eyes and she hasn't broken my gaze since she started talking. She continues, "You have a chance to fix yourself earlier than a lot of other people. You'll understand that when you're older, but for now, you need to know that you can set yourself up to have all of your bad things behind you early in your life, at least as far as you're able to. If you can straighten yourself out now, you can live a long life and you can make yourself anybody you want to be."

I feel myself awash in melancholy. She continues, "Now I know you pretty well. Since you came home from the hospital as a baby, you and I have spent a lot of time together, at my house, at yours, every school, everywhere. I know you better than a lot of other people." I feel a tear in my left eye but I am not touching it. "And I know you so well, I know I can tell you anything that I want you to know. You are special, you always have been. You have a light that's always on. You have shined in your life for a long time. Unfortunately, it was extinguished for a while. You can change all that. These women at lunch think you're a very nice boy, you know that." I shake my head yes, feeling very small for some reason, like Cleta's a teacher. "But that does not mean a hill of beans. They might think you're nice but they aren't going to do anything for you to change your life. They all have their own worries and concerns. They are my best friends, but they wouldn't even do it for me. If you want anything to change, anything to go better, you have to do it yourself. You have to do it, nobody else, and it might take a long time and it might take a lot of work, but you can do it, whatever it is.

"Just when Henry and I thought life couldn't get any worse, it did. I've been through it. Your grandfather worked all day, every day. He came home late at night. All he wanted was to eat supper and go to sleep. He'd wake up early and do the same thing again the next day. Only when he was older and you knew him did he slow down. But up until then, he worked every day. And he never missed one of the boys' games. He didn't offer excuses, he just made it. He took buses, we had only one old car, he hitched rides to bus stops, whatever it took. And I think, because of that, your uncles learned to hustle. I will tell you this, I never saw a Corrigan get out hustled on a playing field. If they did, they heard it from Henry, so they didn't let that happen too often. You can do this, too. Go out there and outhustle people.

"You have good genes, know that. Don't depend on anybody to do anything for you, ever. Blind trust is for fools. Real trust is hard to earn and you don't suffer fools. Learn who you can trust and don't compromise. It's better this way. Do it all yourself, you won't get let down by anybody and you'll be happy when they do help. But don't count on it, just plan on doing it all yourself."

I sit in wonder, thinking about the differences and similarities in all our experiences. Cleta has been with me, around me, in charge of me on too many instances to count and one thing I know, she has been the one in control every time. She just speaks truths. "Now, I want to see you try, try really hard at your dream. You're not on the same path you were when you went to RMC, but you're on a different path. You are on a new path and you will make this path on your own. Okay?"

"Okay."

She says, "Okay, good. Now let's get going," as she lifts her wet-on-the-outside water glass and takes a small sip before she puts it down. "I'll walk with you to the car."

"Sounds good," I say as I stand up and hold her left elbow in my palm. On the way to the door, she says, "I can help you with some gas money on the way home."

I've gotten a check from Bacharach Raisin recently and the ladies wouldn't let me pay for breakfast, so I have like twenty-eight bucks in my pocket. I say, "No thanks, I don't think I'm going to need any help with that."

"Good," she says, "because I'm an eighty-year old woman who just ate brunch at a place that is way too expensive." She looks up at me and smiles and I know, right then, that Cleta is going to be one of the very few people in the world that I can trust.

‖‖‖

CHAPTER 32

‖‖‖

"Coach Faust, do you have a minute?" I ask as I knock on the open door and poke my head into his office. He looks up from the newspaper on his desk, glasses on the end of his nose and responds, "Yes, I have a minute."

I continue forward and stand between the two chairs in front of his desk. "Coach, my name is Mark D'Antoni," I say. "I enrolled here in the fall semester and am wondering if there's a chance that I can try out for the team this spring. I know it is late and the chances are slim, but I am hoping there is one."

"What did you say your name is?" he asks.

"Mark D'Antoni."

"Are you Margaret's son?"

"Yes, sir."

"Okay, you played at St. Xavier High School, didn't you?"

"Yes, sir."

"What brings you to Towson?" he asks.

I tell him about RMC, about playing for my cousin there, my academic disaster. Since then, I explain, I've finished summer school here at Towson, raised my GPA, and worked out with Mt. Washington to keep my lacrosse skills sharp. "I know it will be tough because it's the start of the spring semester after the break, and I know I won't have a lot of time to prove myself, but I would just like a chance."

"We have a two-day tryout February 10 and 11 that is open to all students. You're welcome to try out then," Coach Faust says.

"I would, Coach, thanks," I say. "Is there anything you want me to do before tryouts?"

"Show up in shape, that's what you can do," Coach says.

"Thanks coach, I will," I say and turn to head out the door.

"Mark," he says and I turn back to him, "tell your Mom and Dad I said hello. They're good people."

"I will, thanks again," I say as I turn and head out the door, light in my movements and emotions. I have an opportunity, that's all I can ask for. He didn't say no. The tryout is a long way off but it gives me something to look forward to. I head home to eat lunch after classes and before work at Bacharach's.

When I walk in the door at the house, Mom is sewing a set of drapes for a neighbor. My turnaround time is short, so I make a sandwich and change my clothes. As I get ready to leave, I poke my head into the TV room, where the sewing machine is. Navy blue draperies are all over the floor and over the sofa, over a chair, they are spread everywhere.

I'm not going to get into a long conversation, and at this point, I really don't even want to share my plans. I have talked about so much in my life and have done so little that I am not going to really talk to anyone about it, except maybe Allison. "I ran into Carl Faust today. He wanted me to say hi to you and Dad," I say.

She looks up from her seat, glasses on the end of her nose too, sewing needle between her lips and slurs, "Where did you see him?"

"I was in the gym and I introduced myself, he seems like a nice guy," I say.

"He's a great guy, he's been a friend of your father for a long time," she says. She takes the needle from her lips and slides it, with the thread attached, through a piece of the material and hand sews. "What did you talk about?"

"Nothing really, I just said hi. I've got to get to work so I'll see you later," I say as I take a bite out of my sandwich and head to the front door. "I close up tonight, so I won't be home until late."

I get to work on a typical weekday shift. The store closes at 9 p.m. and I am closing by myself. Stephen, my coworker, leaves at 8 p.m. and I spend the last hour reading the newspaper, watching the clock, and shooting baskets on the mini hoop that sits behind the register. Bacharach's, because of all the long distance calls it makes to colleges for sales, has something called unlimited long distance. It's not something I've heard of before but it works. At exactly 9 p.m. I lock the doors, turn out the lights in the showroom, head to the warehouse in the back and sit at Brinkley's desk. I pick up his phone, dial Allison's hallway and on the third ring, a female voice answers

"Is Allison there?" I ask tentatively. I'm thinking it's her but not sure.

"Hi Mark, it's me," she says.

"Hey, thanks for picking up, I wasn't sure you were going to remember."

"Last time we talked, you said you were going to call at nine on Wednesday, I remembered," she says and we both laugh. It's nice of her, but it also shows me that she cares. She remembers what I say, she thinks of things we can do, I can tell she spends time thinking about me. We talk on the phone for twenty minutes, laughing, joking, finding out about each other. Just before we hang up, I tell her I'll try to call sometime this weekend.

"Umm..." I can tell she is struggling to find words. "Can you call me on Monday? I have to go home this weekend, and I won't be home until late Sunday night."

"Sure, okay, what are you doing at home?"

"I just have to go home, I'll tell you about it next week. Thanks for calling," she says.

"Thanks for picking up. I always feel so stupid asking somebody to knock on your door," I say. "Have a good weekend and I'll try to call you on Monday at nine again."

"Thanks, you have a good weekend, too," she says.

"Bye, Allison," I say, knowing I have to hang up but reluctant nonetheless.

"Bye, Mark."

While I still have the phone to my ear, I reach out and push the phone release down, ending the call. I pick it up and dial another long distance number.

"Art, what's up?" I say when I hear my friend's voice.

"Mark, what's up man, what are you doing?" he asks.

"I'm just finishing work, making a couple calls, what's going on down there?" I ask.

"You know man, same shit, different day. I'm about to take some of these pledges and get them hammered, you know. Hey, every time I run into this Allison girl, she's asking me about you. You talk to her lately?"

"Yeah, man, I just talked to her a little while ago," I say as I hear the music begin to get louder in the background.

"Mark, I've got to get going, thanks for calling, though," he says.

"No problem," I say, and hesitate. "Art, I think I'm going to play some ball again."

"Mark, you need to. Get out and kick some ass again, shit we need you back here," he says.

"I think that door is closed, brother, but you never know. Don't get them too fucked up."

"You know I will," he says.

"Later," I say.

"Later," he says as I hear the phone click.

I turn off the light on Brinkley's desk and head to the front door. I stop in the doorway and change into gym shorts and a tee shirt. I put my dirty pants and shirt into a Bacharach's shopping bag and put on my hoodie. At the front door, I turn on the alarm, open the door and close it for the night. I drive home to my house, thinking about school, lacrosse, Allison and the old drunken days with Art. I take the keys out of the ignition, grab the shopping bag of work clothes, drop the keys into it and drop the bag onto the front porch. I turn around and lift the hood of my sweatshirt onto my head, put one foot in front of the other and run down the steps, up my road into the still night. My heartbeat races, my thoughts settle and my breathing steadies. I am on the road to recovery, to a comeback, to a brighter future, to where, I don't know, but I am on the road. Six weeks until February 10, tryout day one.

My body sweats and breathes in cold air while my mind wanders to my new life. The best way I've found to keep temptation and cravings for booze out of my life is to spend my day different from my friends' day. I love to see them and be around them, but I have to do it at times they're not drinking. I visit during the day. I stay away from bars and I leave any uncomfortable situation rather than be tempted. Tonight all my friends are already drinking, so I find something else to do that is not going to lead me down that road.

The best way to spend my day, I have found, is to stay busy and make sure I have something to go to. Tonight it's for a run. I always try to drag out the day and plan on exercise during dinner hours, pushing back my other responsibilities, and stay busy until around nine o'clock. Then I go home and take a shower. Most nights I eat dinner late and settle into some sports on TV or read a book and get ready for tomorrow. I go to an AA meeting every once in a while so I keep my alcoholic lessons in the front of my mind. Some of the time my situation can be confining since the people know so much about me, but it can also be liberating, not having to hide anything. I just want to move forward and leave the past in the past. The mantra of one day at a time really hits home for me because if I can make it through today and not drink, I don't worry about anything but not drinking. Simple. I don't think about not drinking at my wedding, not drinking at my buddy's twenty-first birthday party, my friend's graduation party. I just think about not drinking today and today only. It really is the only thing I can control fully, and while it is harder and lonelier than I thought it would be at times, I keep it that simple. Don't drink today and don't worry about tomorrow.

||||||||||||||||||||||||||||||||||||||||||||||||||||||

CHAPTER 33

||||||||||||||||||||||||||||||||||||||||||||||||||||||||||

I talk to Allison the next week and we catch up on the weekend. I just worked so I didn't have much to say.

"What did you do when you were at home?" I ask her right away.

"I went home to see my parents and my brother," she says, but she's from a divorced family and when she says her parents, she can be talking about two sets of people. Both of her parents remarried, so Allison's family is pretty different from mine. She has stepbrothers and a stepsister.

I feel like she's holding something back, but I don't want to pry. "Did you see your brother Cliff?" I ask. She has one full blood sibling, her brother Cliff.

"Yes, he was there," she says. "It wasn't much fun." I listen and wait for more. Without prompting, she continues. "You know how I have two stepbrothers on my dad's side that I told you about? Well before I met you, it used to be three stepbrothers."

I think, *What happened? He died? Did he get in a car wreck?* "What do you mean?" I ask.

"I had three stepbrothers, one who's twenty-five, one's twenty-three and one who was nineteen. The one who was nineteen took his own life in February, on the 27th actually. So, the town of Rehoboth, where I live, had a small ceremony to plant a tree to remember him. We—Dad, Debbie, Cliff, Evan, Jason and I—were there. Really, it was pretty sad and that's why I said it was not much fun."

That one hits me out of left field. Suicide, that's crazy. I want to ask how but I know it isn't appropriate. "Man, I am sorry to hear that," I say, and try not to pry.

"Thanks. It's just tough on my dad and Debbie. I know it's been really tough on them." She says.

"It has to be, man. You said he was 19?" I ask.

"Yeah, he was a sophomore at Maryland Art Institute. He was going through some stuff... I don't know." She says, kind of letting her words linger. I don't know what to say but she interjects.

"I don't want to bring you down with this stuff. What did you do?" she asks.

"Not much, worked and played some indoor. It's all right if you want to talk about it. It's okay. I mean, I talked to you about rehab."

"I know I can talk to you. It's just—I don't know what to say. He was a really cool guy. He was really talented as an artist. He was really funny. He had scoliosis, though, and it was a struggle for him. He was going to get surgery but it was too risky. I thought he was doing okay. I can't believe it, really."

I am thinking the whole time, *How did he do it? Did he hang himself? Carbon monoxide?* It's all surreal because I've never been impacted by suicide. I feel so sorry but helpless as well. The victims in suicide always seems to be the people they leave behind.

She volunteers, as if she knows what I want to know. "He was driving home from college and as he was crossing the Chesapeake Bay Bridge, he pulled to the shoulder of the road, got out and just jumped off. They haven't found him yet. They still haven't found him."

"Man, that has to be tough," I say. "It has to be hard."

"Yeah, it is. I just didn't know how to tell you. It's not like I can just say, 'Hey my stepbrother jumped off a bridge and died,' "she says.

"It's all right, my family is pretty messed up too," not knowing what else to say.

"I know, it does sound pretty messed up."

"I don't know, you just met me and I've been in a fire and gone to rehab. It's not like that is real normal," I say, knowing that that statement in itself, is messed up. We have found each other, two people who are not misfits, but unusual creatures, bound for each other. I know what she looks like, but I have only seen her one time, months ago. However, we've talked every week, sometimes a couple times a week. Her voice is soft and welcoming, her demeanor calm and understanding, her humor funny and contagious. She is sweet to talk to and mysterious in our separation. I have found a connection with someone away from me and not getting closer, at least in distance. We talk into the night, me on the upstairs phone, cord pulled into my room, her in the hall on a pay phone. I finally say good night and she replies, "Let's go to the beach this summer. I'm thinking about living in Nags Head with some friends."

"I'd love to go to Nags Head with you. That sounds good," I say.

After goodbyes, I hang up the phone and put it onto my dresser. It's after midnight and I crawl into bed, hopeful of an opportunity to see Allison and curious about the beach in North Carolina.

||||||||||||||||||||||||||||||||||||||||||||||||||||||||

CHAPTER 34

||||||||||||||||||||||||||||||||||||||||||||||||||||||||||

On the morning of February 10, I put my equipment on my stick: helmet first, shoulder pads, arm pads then gloves, cleats wrapped around once, with the laces tied together. I'm wearing plain blue Champion shorts, the only pair of gym shorts I own without a label or a logo, underneath plain gray sweatpants. I wear a tee shirt, a long sleeve shirt inside out, and a gray hoodie, also inside out. My shoes are tennis shoes for now, but I'm looking forward to putting cleats on.

The field is right behind the Towson Center, a basketball arena, and next to the TSU tennis courts, home to every regional youth tennis qualifying tournament. I'm not sure what you qualified for after the regional, because I could never get through it. Those kids took their tennis seriously, and I was just a lacrosse player playing tennis. Needless to say, it's a field I am familiar with. T. Burt, Beau O'Neil, Michael Frederick and I all met here on our bikes. There have been two goals, with creases sometimes, on this field since I can first remember.

Nobody is home when I leave the house, and I am glad of it. I flip my hoodie up, grab keys and head out the door to a green Beetle, stick. I park at the field, put my cleats on in the car. I get out, feel the cold of February 10, breathe it deeply into my lungs, and make a vow not to let the cold be a factor for the rest of the day. As I slip my four-bar, double chin pad old Bacharach on my head, I realize that for the first time in a while, I am playing to actually make a team.

Up until now, it's been an idea, now it is for real. Tryouts for the TSU lacrosse team start today and, although it is a day I have been looking forward to for a long time, I am as nervous as I have been in a long time. My stomach has butterflies and my heart is racing. The feeling of uncertainty is unmistakable, now it is time.

This has a very different feel, jogging out on the field for the first time at TSU, from my workouts with Mt. Washington. Those guys were veterans, all-stars, they were relaxed in their pre-practice. They talked and passed the ball around. Except for my one time with Dave Petriemala, everybody else loved to pass and catch. At TSU, nobody says anything to each other. Everybody is avoiding eye contact. I don't have a ball and only a couple guys brought one or two. They're in scarce supply. I see a guy working on his face offs with one, a guy doing ground balls with himself, not passing to anybody. There are about twenty guys in assorted equipment. Some wear another team's gear like Hampton and Towson High, a couple others have TSU jerseys. People try to prance in their named gear, which I've always found funny. Just because they have a "name school" jersey, they think they're better than they really are. I learned that a long time ago, beating posers in their fancy Grayson or St. John's gear. When I look down at the far side goal, I see a familiar figure. He's walking straight towards me, coming from the woods behind the goal, holding his stick like he has a few balls in it. It's Trevor, Trevor Boone, also known as the guy who tackled me with a sheet when I was on fire. I squint my eyes, to make sure it's Trevor, see that it is and jog over to him.

"Booner, what's up," I say, more statement than question.

"Mark, what are you doing, you trying out, too?" He asks.

"Yeah, I am, I figured what the hell, it's about time," I say.

"You trying out for attack?" He asks.

"Attack, midfield, I don't care. I just want to make plays," I say.

"Tell them you're trying out for attack. I know they're only looking for a couple of middies and I want to make this team," he says.

"All right, I'll tell them attack. When did you transfer in?" I ask.

"Just this semester. I played at Essex Community College last year and I was like screw it, my grades are good enough, I'll transfer in right now. I talked to Coach this week," he says. "What about you?"

I realize I have not stopped by Coach's office since six weeks ago. I hope he remembers that I'm coming out. Probably should have stopped by to remind him, too late now.

"I just got eligible," I say. "I took continuing ed classes, summer school, fifteen credits in the fall, got a 2.0 overall, and then enrolled as a full-time student this semester." I nod my head to Trevor and break out for a pass. Trevor drops the other two balls on the ground and throws me an outlet pass. I catch it over the shoulder and keep my feet moving. We pass it back and forth for a few until Trevor dodges from up top and shoots a sidearm high shot over the goal and into the woods. I see why I didn't see him at first when I came up to the field. At this point, I am closer to the two balls he dropped, so I pick up a lefty ground ball, and make a lefty—opposite- handed for me—long pass to Trevor. I always like to practice opposite-handed ground balls before a game because you have to get low for one of those. It helps me when I start picking them up right-handed. I do a give-and-go and as soon as Trevor catches it, he feeds me and I stick a bounce shot, no goalie. Let's get this thing started. I snag it out of the goal and toss it up to Trevor, he catches on the run, roll dodges and singes a side arm bounce shot to the side of the net, hip high.

"Dude, you have been working on your shooting!" I yell.

"Every day, Mark, every day," he says. Trevor is awesome, a saltwater farmer from the private school. Almost every party I have ever been to in Ocean City was attended by Trevor. He would get off a fishing boat—happy hour for him we would call it—and meet us out. He might come in late, come in drunk and smelling like fish, but he would never miss it. We have played summer league against each other with me at St. Xavier and him at Brice Academy, and hung out together through it all. He lives way out in Hartford County on a farm and can wake up early and stay out late. And now, over the next two days, we are going to rely on each other, once again.

About ten minutes later, Coach Faust and another coach, Coach Kauffman, come down the hill from the Towson Center and bring us into a huddle. They give us instructions, hand out reversibles, and make it clear about our chances of making the team. They are looking for two attackmen, three middies, two defensemen, and one goalie. I'm not sure if this is true; they just want to give us false hope.

Once everybody puts on his reversible, we are equals. The name on your hoodie or your helmet doesn't mean anything anymore. I purposely didn't wear one piece of equipment with a label.

We break up by position—I go with the attack—and start drills, passing, ground balls. By the time we get to one-on-ones and two-on-twos, I know that these guys are not as fast or as good as Mt. Washington. It's a welcome relief but I still have to play well, beat my man, score in traffic. When my teammates are trying to overdue their roles, it looks ugly and unorganized. Several times in team drills, like three-on-two ground balls to the goal, guys take bad shots and hog the ball. I want to say something, but I don't want to be a jerk. Often, I go back to the end of the shortest line after getting open and not getting a pass. It's frustrating at times, but at the water break, Coach Faust taps me on the shoulder and says, "I'm glad you made it out here, you look like you're in shape." He's a big man with broad shoulders in a big black TSU Lacrosse jacket with yellow writing on the front and back.

"Thanks, Coach," I say, "I think I am." I want to say something about the practice I'm having so I go with, "It's different out here, I've never played with some of these guys before."

"That's fine," he says, "It's a tryout, it's usually a little helter skelter, guys are nervous. Keep getting open, eventually they'll see you." He smiles. I nod my head. He puts his whistle in his mouth, turns, walks about five steps toward the middle of the field and blows it. "Bring it in!" he yells.

We huddle around him, and he picks teams for a scrimmage. It's a chance for all of us to show what we can do. Thankfully, Trevor and I are on the same team. For about the next hour, we play. No penalties are called, no pushes, and very few whistles. Guys rise to the top, guys sink to the bottom. You learn to pass only to guys who will pass back, pick up every missed shot off the end line. I get plenty of touches and so does Trevor. We each score, we each assist, we each ground ball. Trevor looks good and I shake off the rust. By the time it ends, I am still not ready for it to be done. It may be thirty-eight degrees, but it's sunny. There are goalies and this is fun.

Coaches send us on our way at the end of the session, and we must be back by 10 a.m. tomorrow, Sunday. I can't wait.

Sunday's practice goes the same way. When it ends, Coach Faust tells me to come to his office the following morning at ten. As I head to the car, Trevor walks with me.

"What do you think," he asks, "think we made the team?"

"I don't know, I think we are two of the better players here, but I don't know what they need for the team," I say. "Are you meeting with Coach tomorrow?"

"Yeah," he says, "he wants me to come by tomorrow at ten."

"Same here. I guess we'll find out tomorrow."

"What are you going to do tonight?" Trevor asks.

"I don't know, just take a shower and get some homework done, what about you?" I ask.

"I can't take this, I am going to get shitfaced," he says, "want to go out? Ah, shit man, I'm sorry, you don't get shitfaced anymore. Want to meet anyway?"

"I'm good, man, thanks. I am going to get warm and try to relax," I say, knowing that a few beers is not going to be the thing that makes me feel better.

By the time 10 a.m. Monday morning rolls around, I am nervous, my heart is beating fast and the butterflies are back. As I walk into the Towson Center, I feel lightheaded. I haven't been this nervous about anything since I took the SATs when I was hungover in high school. I turn the corner, walk down the hall and see Trevor, another guy I recognize as a defenseman from tryouts, and still another guy I do not recognize at all. They all look as nervous as I feel and seeing me does not relax them. Trevor always wears his heart on his sleeve and he looks like he is going to throw up.

"Booner, are you okay?" I ask.

Trevor whispers, "I'm hurting, bad. I barely went to sleep. Met up with Baxter and Cheese and we ended up at Schaeffer's until 2 a.m. Man, I hope he doesn't want us to work out."

"I hope not, my legs are killing me," I say, grabbing my calf and trying to be sympathetic, realizing yesterday was the first time I ran really hard since last May at Mt. Washington. However, my mind is clear and my thoughts are fresh, not polluted and clouded. I realize the benefits and effects of not drinking are invisible but felt throughout my whole body.

We're interrupted by Coach Faust opening his door. "Gentlemen, come on into my office."

We all look around at each other, lift ourselves out of our chairs, and walk in. The two other guys sit in chairs and Trevor and I stand behind them. Me because it is the only place available when I walk inside the room and Trevor because he doesn't want Coach to smell the booze on his breath.

"Gentlemen, thanks for being here and thank you for trying out for the team. You four are the players that we have decided to keep and put on the team for the spring season. You guys have shown that you have the skill to contribute to our program, but I want to tell you, this is just the first step. We begin practice February 24th, and that is when the real work starts. The level of play and level of intensity will be considerably higher than it was during tryouts. I am telling you this now so that you'll be prepared. So, congratulations on making it past the round of tryouts and I'm looking forward to seeing you guys with the rest of the team. Now, do any of you have any questions?"

We all look at each other and sort of shrug our shoulders, "No, sir," I say out loud, kind of speaking for all four of us.

"Well, okay, then. Thanks for coming by the office. Take a minute and stop in Coach Kauffman's office, give him your full name, your class schedule, your major, and I'm sure he will have some other questions for you," says Coach Faust.

We all thank him and file out, relieved and excited. We're on a journey that has just begun and it's about to start for real.

|||||||||||||||||||||||||||||||||||||||||||||||||||||||

CHAPTER 35

|||||||||||||||||||||||||||||||||||||||||||||||||||||||||||||

The first practice of the year starts with a meeting, equipment handouts and a full practice, outside in freezing temperatures. After the first full team meeting, in which we're given instructions, goals for the season and a healthy dose of discipline procedures, we head to the equipment room. Since I'm new to the team and want to blend in until we play, I stand in the back of the line while the excitement of new equipment and sweats turn some players giddy.

When I get to the front of the room, I see Coach Faust and the equipment man, Davey. Davey barely looks up. "Jersey number," he says as both a question and a statement.

"What numbers are left?" I ask.

"Seventeen, twenty-four, twenty-eight and thirty-four through thirty-nine," he says matter of factly.

"I'll take seventeen," I say.

"That's a good choice, D'Antoni, we have had some pretty good seventeens over the years. Hopefully you can fill the jersey yourself."

"I am going to try, Coach," I say. "Did we get this stuff from Bacharach's?"

"Yeah, been dealing with them for years," says Coach Faust.

"Did they deliver it here?" I ask.

"Yeah, they did, they had one of their guys drop it off yesterday," Coach says.

"Was it Brinkley?" I ask.

"Yeah, it was, how do you know him?"

"I worked there last spring, Brinkley is a good guy, he taught me a lot," I say.

"I didn't know that, D'Antoni. Now I know we got a guy that can fix some of this equipment when it breaks," he says to me with a sly smile on his face. "Who don't you know in lacrosse?" Coach asks sarcastically.

"Anybody from Syracuse, Coach, I really don't know anybody from Syracuse," I say, smiling myself.

I look around and realize that only the three of us remain in the equipment room. Everyone else has headed to the locker room to try on their new gear and get ready for practice. I hang my head a little and say, "I better get ready for practice," and turn to walk out.

I hear Coach say, "Yes, you should, it's going to be a tough one."

I get the message. The first practice of any season is always hard—lots of running, lots of drills, lots of yelling by the coaches. The best coaches I have ever had always set a standard that is almost unattainable, giving them a reason to yell and the players a high mark to achieve.

||||||||||||||||||||||||||||||||||||||||||||||||||||||||

CHAPTER 36

|||||||||||||||||||||||||||||||||||||||||||||||||||||||||||

Once the season ends with a loss to UVA in the first round of the NCAA playoffs, I am off to Nags Head, North Carolina to meet up with Allison. I drive the blue Delta 88 over the Wright Brothers Memorial Bridge spanning the Currituck Sound. The smell of salt air fills my car, as all the windows are down due to the non-working air conditioning. Docks and boats dot the horizon in all directions. The sun is high in the sky and the light glistens and reflects off the crystal blue water. While there's a slight chill in the air, the feeling of summer is in front of me. I can't wait to settle into a beach chair, ride waves and have bonfires on the beach. Allison gave me the address to the house and, as I glance at the map on the front seat, I decide to take the scenic route. I make a left once I get over the bridge, head towards the Atlantic Ocean and make a right on the beach road. It looks like a paradise. Small cottages are on the sandy shores of the North Carolina coast. Mom and Pop motels dot the road. People on bikes and in flip flops cruise slowly up and down the road. I drive slowly, soaking up the feelings, filling my senses, eyes wide open. By the time I pull into the driveway to the beach cottage just off the beach road on milepost 9, I can't wait to start my summer with Allison.

Lacrosse season is over, school is three months in the future, and all my worries and concerns are hundreds of miles away. I have no history here, no old memories, no reminders, everything is new. Allison must have heard my car pull up, because when I look up through the windshield, I see her coming out of the front screened porch, wide smile and arms outstretched. By the time I open the door, she is next to me and her hug feels like a warm blanket on a sunny day. She smells like Coppertone, feels like heaven, and neither of us let go of our hug. We stand, leaning against the car, and kiss and hug for as long as we can. At this point in my life, I don't know if I have ever felt like I belonged somewhere more than I do right now. The apprehension of living together for the summer that I felt on the ride down evaporates into the salt air.

"Let's walk up to the beach," I say, sliding my hand into hers and turning towards the east.

Allison smiles. "Sounds good," she says as we take our first steps together on this new journey, not quite full-scale adult style, but heading into a relationship that takes on a higher level.

III

CHAPTER 37

IIIIIIIIIIIIIIIIIIIIIIIIIIIIIIIIIIIIIIIIIIIIIIIIIIIIIIIIIIIII

Today is a day that I've been looking forward to since I got a call from Thomas last week to tell me he's coming down. Plus, there is a band tonight at the restaurant where Allison works. I have to work during the day, but I should be off by four and I'll get a chance to see Thomas. He's been at college since Christmas; we haven't seen each other for months.

I'm at work painting the Carolinian Hotel, an old, iconic beach hotel sitting on the sand of North Carolina's Outer Banks. As it gets near four o'clock, I clean up and keep an eye out for him. He shows up a few minutes later and we sit down on the deck overlooking the ocean and beach and enjoy a couple of ginger ales.

"What are you doing down here?" I ask.

"Beau said he was coming down to stay at his aunt's house for a couple of days and I told him I would take a ride, too. We got here last night about seven and went to someplace called Kelly's."

"You did?" I ask.

"Yeah, why?" He asks.

"That's where Allison works. She was there last night. I'm going there tonight to see the Violent Femmes. How long are you down for?" I ask.

"We're leaving tomorrow, I have to get back to work by Friday. Listen, I haven't seen you since Christmas. I want to make sure you are doing okay down here. I know none of your buddies are here and you're living with this girl, so I want to make sure you're okay," he says.

"I'm doing well. It's a beautiful area, the beach is never crowded, the people are nice, I like it here," I say.

"You like this girl don't you?" He asks.

"I do, Thomas. She is just different from the other girls."

He looks at me with his skeptical expression and says, "Since when have you liked girls that are different?"

"Ever since I met Allison, to tell you the truth," I say. "Instead of being one of those girls who want me to do everything, or acts all stuck up, we look out for each other, we hang out together. It seems like I can count on her and that hasn't always been the case with other girls. Plus, let's face it, I am not as much of an asshole as I used to be."

"That's probably true," he says.

"Do you want to meet us later?"

"I'll try, but we probably won't go back tonight," he says. "You staying sober?"

"So far, but I don't really go out much. Usually I work at night, too, but this is my night off."

"What are you going to do now?" he asks.

"I usually do the same thing when Allison is working. There's a basketball court near the elementary school down the road, so I ride my bike over there. If nobody's playing, I take a bike ride and run the dunes. By the time I'm done, it is usually about eight-thirty or nine o'clock, so I just take a shower, get something to eat and Allison is usually home by then. I find it's best to keep myself busy during the day, and then wait until dinner time and work out. That way, everybody is already out or headed out and I can just eat late, get cleaned up and the time to drink has already passed. I don't miss it too much, but there are times I'm tempted. Mostly it's only around happy hour on Fridays. For some reason, that's when I want a drink; otherwise, I don't really miss it."

"Well, you look like you're doing okay. I was worried that I was going to find you down here drinking again and getting fucked up.

You asked me what I'm doing here, I came down to check on you. I came down here to make sure you're okay. I wanted to see with my own eyes that you're doing okay. I know you've been through a lot, but that shit is over now," he says.

"I know it's over and, believe me, I am not trying to relive it anymore. I can't put Mom and Dad through it anymore, I can't keep waking up trying to remember what happened last night, hoping that my fuckups were just bad dreams. No matter what happens now, I can't fix yesterday, I know I can only try better today. The stuff I learned in rehab has really been helping. They tell you all sorts of stuff, but the living for today, let go and let God, only worry about the things you can control, it definitely helps. I find myself thinking about those things when I am alone, so I feel pretty good. Plus, I like not knowing anybody, I like meeting people for the first time. I definitely needed to get away."

"I understand, everybody in Baltimore knows everybody's business. All they do is gossip sometimes, so I definitely get why you want to get away. Just remember to call home, let Mom and Dad know you are doing okay. They worry about you, just like they worry about all of us. Don't forget to call them."

"I won't. It's not like I don't want to talk to them, it's just I have been working a bunch and when I am not working, Allison and I are riding bikes or driving to Hatteras or just staying busy. I feel like if I keep myself busy, I won't fuck up. And, right now, I just don't want to fuck up."

"Well, this has probably been the longest time in the last five years that you haven't gotten arrested for something," he says, laughing.

"Screw you," I say laughing back, knowing that there is some truth in what he is saying. Thomas probably knows me better than anyone else on this earth and, whether I like it or not, can cut right to the point anytime we talk.

"It's true though," he says.

"I know it is," I say, still smiling.

"All right, I'm going to get out of here. Beau and the other guys want to leave around six so I'm going to roll," he says.

"Thanks for coming down. You can tell Mom and Dad that things are good," I say.

"I will. I'll call you," he says.

"Sounds good," I say as we both stand up from the table and I reach out. He reaches out and instead of shaking hands, like we have done hundreds of times over the last ten years, we hug, we hug tightly, for the first time I can ever remember. My eyes water but I try to hold back the emotion. When we separate, I look away, and wipe my face with my forearm. We both look away and he heads to his car. I walk behind him, headed to my bike, both of us silent as I am unsure if he feels the same. When he gets to his car, he turns to me and says, "Tell Allison I look forward to meeting her. Enjoy the rest of the summer."

I turn and wave, afraid to yell 'I love you' but feeling it nonetheless. Instead I say, "Tell Beau and those guys I said hi." We head off in different directions, both heading into our immediate future and into the unknown.

When I get to the house, the usual end of the work day routine is already in place. Some make dinner, some have begun drinking and all seem to be on a buzz in anticipation of tonight's concert. I change out of my paint clothes and into gym shorts, tennis shoes and old gray tee shirt. Basketball is on my mind as I head out the downstairs door, no bothering to tell anyone where I am going.

When I get to Nags Head Elementary, there's a collection of guys and within fifteen minutes, we have a four-on-four game going on a smaller court, each team with a couple of subs. The game lasts for at least two hours and, as I pedal home, I swing by the sub shop and get a cheesesteak sub for dinner. When I get home, there is a full on pre-party going on and the house is full of people I haven't seen before. I've been in this situation many times before, so I head inside the first floor entrance, eat my sub and take a shower. Instead of going upstairs to the party, I head over to Kelly's to meet Allison.

I find her, still in her waitress uniform and ask, "When do you get off?"

"I only have about fifteen minutes of side work left and then I will be done. Let me introduce you to Samantha, she's finished, and I can meet you guys in a little bit. Follow me, I think she is back here," she says as we head towards a wait station outside the bar, where a blond, college-age girl is drinking a bottle of beer. Allison introduces us and says she'll meet us in the bar as soon as she closes out her checks.

Samantha and I find a place off to the right side of the stage. The band is still setting up and the crowd is kind of filling in and getting comfortable. It's a normal Nags Head crowd of twenty-somethings, beach kids with long hair and surf, college kids here for the summer in madras pants and tee shirts. The girls all look similar in their sundresses and long hair. The feel of summer is strong and the air is thick with anticipation for a band that we've all heard but never seen.

Samantha is a girl Allison has talked to me about, one of her co-workers whom she likes. I lean over to her and start the conversation. "So, Allison said you grew up around here, this has to be a pretty nice place to grow up."

"It's boring in the winter, just because there isn't anything to do, but it's great in the summer," she says. She has the easy demeanor of someone comfortable in her surroundings.

"She said you go to UNC, do you like it?" I ask, searching for other things to talk about.

"Yeah, I like it, it's a lot of fun. I'm not sure I like all the people but I love the school," she says.

"What do you mean about the people?" I ask.

"There are a lot of snobs there, so it gets annoying, but the school is great," she says.

"I know what you mean, some of the people I know who go there are kind of rude, but I do know a lot of really good guys there, too," I say.

"Allison said you play lacrosse," she says.

"Yeah, I do."

"Do you know any of the guys at UNC?" She asks.

"Yeah, I know a few of them," I say. "Most of them are good guys."

"I think most of them are cocky," she says.

"You're right, some of them are, but some are good guys." Instead of taking this any further, I change the topic. "How long have you worked here?"

"I've been here since high school. My parents know Mr. Kelly, so he gave me a job four years ago," she says.

"Seems like a good place to work, it's always busy," I say.

"Yeah, you can make good money here," she says, "I got to tell you, Allison is one of the coolest people I have ever worked with here. She does something nice for somebody every shift, she's always nice to the customers and she has guys staring at her all the time and she doesn't even notice. All she ever talks about is you. All innocent like. See that guy in the blue shirt over there?" she asks me, nodding her head towards a group of guys in the corner by the stage.

"Yeah, why?"

"His name is Steve and he's been working here for three years. He and his buddy Jay have picked up every waitress in this place. They are always working the girls in here and Allison doesn't even give them the time of day. They're obsessed with getting her attention and she just smiles at them and keeps working. It kills them. I think it is hysterical," she says. "These Southern boys are always trying to turn on the charm and it gets them nowhere."

"She's special, isn't she," I say.

"I don't know what's so special about you, but she sure thinks you are," she says.

"Well, thanks for looking out for her," I say.

"Shoot, she looks out for me every time we work together," she says.

We both stand in silence while I look at the crowd of guys in the corner, wondering if I should say something to Steve and if one of those guys is Jay. As I'm looking, I feel a body bump into me and look left. Allison is off work, dressed in a light blue sundress and flip flops. She has two bottles of Budweiser and a ginger ale. She hands one beer to Samantha, the ginger ale to me and we all cheers. The band is warming up, the crowd gets loud and I put my arm around her shoulder, more secure in my trust with Allison and hopeful in our future.

||||||||||||||||||||||||||||||||||||||||||||||||||||||||||

CHAPTER 38

||||||||||||||||||||||||||||||||||||||||||||||||||||||||||||||

It's August 11 and a warm breeze off the ocean covers the dark night with mist. The bar is open air, cement block building waist high with a wood canopy over the entire rectangular shape. It sits at the end of Avalon Pier, on the sand, with its front to the beach road and its back open to the ocean, nothing but sand between us. It may be the coolest music venue I have ever been in. Tonight it's Indecision with Dave Matthews and Tim Reynolds, and they are jamming. Allison has taken off work, I'm off, too, and some friends are here.

Halfway through the concert when the band takes a break, I step next door. This place is a sober concert goer's ideal. On the one side of the building is the bar and on the other side is an old school arcade with the same scenery: beach, pier, sand, cement block, neon lights. Inside the arcade, the lights come from pinball and PacMan. Budweiser and Red Stripe signs light up the bar side. Tonight I'm choosing the arcade neon. This is where I can be sober, play games and ignore the temptations of liquor that is right on the other side of the building. The place has Williams pinball machines–Galaga, Space Invaders, Deer Hunter–but the one I have been trying to beat is Missile Command. It features a ball that rolls in place and fires at the lines that come from the top of the screen. It's the best game in here and I seem to be the only one who plays it. I take on three games in a row while Allison has some drinks with her friends. When I hear the band start back and my game ends, I head back over and find a place to stand.

The night is full with people, music and fun. Beyond the salt air and drum beat, the place is filled with the faces of today, young, casual and free. I stand to the side of the stage and observe. With a sober view and an experienced eye, I watch the college age adults, too young to pay their own bills, but old enough to pay the ultimate price. They party, they dance and they sing. I recognize myself in the drunk ones, the ones by the bar, the ones in the middle of the beach scene mosh pit, the ones trying to pick up girls with slurred pickup lines too lame to work. My life, my day, is better, more fulfilled, with less. The music, the feel of the place, the joy is enough. I have learned in this slow beach town that I have enough. If I have love, if I have shelter, if I have fulfillment, I have enough. I want, I desire but I also accept. The life of a person should not be defined by possessions. It can be defined by my experiences, my hopes and my ambition. Dave Matthews sings, the air cools and the night gives mystery. I think when this is over I am going to take the beach home. The others can drive, but, tonight, under the moonlight and beside the shore, Allison and I can walk, where we belong, next to each other, into our future.

When we walk past the Avalon pier, I notice that one of the exit doors is open. They usually lock up the pier by nine or ten every night after the last fisherman has left. They leave the lights on, but they lock it up. Tonight, someone has left the door unlocked and open.

I say, "Allison, you see that door?"

"Yeah," she says, "do you want to go out there?"

"Yeah, let's go walk the pier."

We turn and walk across the sand to the wooden walkway. I slap down our flip flops that I've been carrying. We slide them on and walk through the door. It's open just wide enough for us, one at a time, to go through without touching the metal door or the frame. We hold hands and walk, straight out to the night, over the symphony of water, waves, wind and wood, some old and some new. We get to the end, alone in the world, and sit on a bench.

"What do you want to do, Mark, after this summer?" Allison asks as we look at the water around us.

"I don't know," I say, knowing she is asking about more than next week or next month. She is asking about me, my life, my plans. What am I going to do? "I know I have to finish this year in school, and then I don't know. Really, I have no idea. Do you know what you want to do?"

"I'm not sure, either. I like it in Rehoboth, but I don't really like it at home, so I don't know. I think I might want to be a nurse, but I don't think I want to live in Richmond."

"I know one thing, I'm not moving to Richmond. But I do like this, I like this summer. I definitely like waking up to you every day. I really do like that." Allison is blushing, she is looking down with her eyes. I know she wants to hear this but it's early. I know her but I don't really know her. I haven't met her parents or her brother. It's great now, but there's a lot I don't know. There's a lot she doesn't know about me either. But she certainly likes hearing this right now. "I hope you're having a good summer," I say.

"Yes, it's been great, I love waking up to you, too," she says.

"So, since neither of us knows what we're going to do, let's take a trip and find out," I say. "Next summer, before your senior year, we drive across country. When I finish lacrosse and school, next May, let's go on a trip. I think that would be fun, plus what else are we going to do? I don't feel like getting a real job right away."

"We can drive my car," she says immediately. Without hesitation, she's in. She's seen my old used car, and her car is much nicer than mine. I don't know if she really wants to take her car, or just not drive mine. Either way, I like the enthusiasm.

"Okay, we need to save some money between now and then," I say. Each of us is working two jobs right now. Allison waits tables at Kelly's and picks up catering shifts when she isn't waitressing. I'm cooking at Chardo's, the only Italian place in the Outer Banks, and painting the Carolinian Hotel during the day. We've been saving money and putting it away. Allison, I notice, earns her cash and keeps it organized, and I am trying to put every paycheck away for the school year. "I'll get a job waiting tables in Towson, so I should be able to save some more between now and then," I say.

Allison says, "I've already saved for school so I can put some money away for it too," again eager to help find a solution.

"Okay, well, let's look into it. I was supposed to go after my freshman year with Roy, but it fell through. Actually, I was in the middle of falling through, but either way, this will be better. It will be us." I say. I look at Allison, who now looks dejected. "No, this is meant to be, me and you," I say, trying to salvage the moment.

"If you want to go with Roy, that's okay," she says.

"No, I just mentioned it because it's true, but this sounds better. Like, it's meant to be. It was meant to fall through, so I can do it with you." I don't want to kill the mood. "I know it will be a lot of fun."

"I think it will be a lot of fun, too," she says and smiles. Her blue-green eyes sparkling in the moonlight and pier lights, looking up at me from my shoulder, with my arm around her shoulder, both of us leaning into each other, content in our togetherness, our bodies melted into one. We stay there in silence, listening, hearing the ocean and the "caw" of a hungry seagull in the distance, flying over the pier bait store.

As we walk back, we stop and look over the side, studying the waves, the in and out of the waves, the ebb and flow of the water. While we stand and stare, I say, "How high do you think we are?" The night, the alive makes me up for an adventure.

"I think we're about fifteen feet up, probably," she says.

"Have you ever gone off a high dive?" I ask. "Michael Frederick and I used to jump off the high dive at JHU all the time. He would do a flip sometimes, but I only tried it once and totally wiped out. But I have jumped off a lot, and this looks just a little higher than that."

"You're not thinking of jumping from here, are you?" she asks.

"Yeah. I am. Have you ever jumped off a high dive?"

"Yes, I have. As a matter of fact," she says, as she lifts her shoulders, separates and stares straight at me, "I've taken diving lessons. That doesn't mean I am diving off here, though."

"Don't dive, let's just jump," I say.

She looks over the railing and then back at me. "I don't like to go swimming at night. You don't mess with the ocean," she says.

"I'm not messing with the ocean. Look, look," I point as a wave moves forward in front of us. "We jump now and let the next wave push us in. Watch, after this third wave, the water will wash back out and then the next set will come in." The water continues to push in and in about thirty seconds, the white foam of broken waves pushes out toward the ocean. In another minute, a swell of water comes below us and rolls to the beach.

"You don't have to jump and I'll meet you on the beach," I say. "It's just that, since I don't drink and I don't party, I still want to do stuff. I'm young, and it's not like I suddenly look at stuff that might be fun and not want to do it. I see this jump right here—dark, eerie, quiet—and think to myself, we can make this something we will always remember. Now, I don't want to scare you, but I still want to live, I still want to seek joy even if there's a little fear. It's like the rush that you get from skiing down a slope and you're out of control. It's scary and fun and frightening and it makes you feel alive. I see this pier, I see the sea and I think, let's have some fun. I'm not drunk, I know how to do it, but it takes courage. I'm a guy so I don't ever want to lose my courage. You don't have to jump if you don't want to, but I'm going to do it."

"If you're jumping, I'm going too," she says.

"All right, let's do it. Let's put our flip flops on the beach, so we don't have to come back," I say.

We head down the pier, slide out the door and walk to the north side of the pier and put down our flip flops. I pull off my shirt and drop it in the sand right next to the flops. I don't see anyone on the beach in either direction. It feels very lonely. When I look back at Allison, she's standing in front of me, in her bra, her shirt in the sand next to mine. Her arms are in the form of an X across her chest.

"Okay, I see, is this what you learned in your diving lessons?" I say and laugh.

She smiles at me and says, "You haven't seen anything yet. I might do a gainer if you're lucky."

"I can't wait to see that," I say, my smile as wide as the dark starlit sky above us.

We hold hands and walk back to the spot on the pier. This is the only time we will get to do this. If we did it in the middle of the day, we'd get a ticket and a court date. We stop at our spot and look again over the railing, as the white water flows out to sea.

"Let's watch it again," I say, hoping not to show the nervousness that I feel. When I glance at Allison, she looks scared. "It's going to be okay, it's going to be fun and we are going to wake up together tomorrow," I say, trying to soothe her with a reminder of our usual routine.

"I know it will, but it still makes me nervous," she says.

"That's what makes you feel alive," I say. "We're right behind the waves we swim in every day. We're only about seventy-five feet off the beach, twenty-five yards, not even the length of one of your fancy Olympic swimming pools."

"An Olympic pool is fifty meters."

"Okay, a lap and a half, same difference. We can just jump between the first and second wave and get in front of the third wave. We can ride that one in." We watch the water build in front of us as we climb the railing and step on the other side. Both Allison and I watch the third wave go by and the white wash comes back.

"This is us, can you see it?" I ask.

"Yeah, I see it," she says, eyes down and east, to our right, watching the next swell roll in.

"All right, here it is. When I say 'three,' jump. Now make a cannon ball when you land, so you don't get too deep," I say. "Here we go," I grab her right hand with my left. "One...two...and three!" We both jump out, losing our grip as we fall. I hit the water harder that I thought I would, much harder than a high dive landing. I sink fast, lifting my knees and feet, trying to stay as close to the top of the water as I can. When I stop sinking, I kick up and it only takes three or four seconds to get to the top. I see the beach in the distance when I come up, so I turn around, looking for the next wave. It's cresting, but it's not going to break on me.

"Allison!" I yell, hearing nothing but waves and wind. "Allison!" I yell again. I still don't hear her. I spin around and yell again, "Allison!" louder than before, feeling panic.

"Mark," I hear her say, close and to my left. By now, the second wave is lifting us both higher and she sees me. We swim to each other and touch our hands.

"Let's go," I say as I swim sidestroke, like a distance swimmer trying to save my energy, away from the pier. "Let's catch this wave," It's hard to see how big it is but it looks like we're going to be able to catch it. "Are you okay?" I yell.

"Yeah, I got it!" she yells. I look left and see Allison in the moonlight, in a good spot to catch the third wave. I swim into it and feel it pick me up, I look over the edge and hold my breath. It puts me in the washing machine, head over heels, under the water, thrashed with the waves as I'm stuck, rolling and pinned under the surf. When I come up, I'm in the white wash. I look over and see Allison come up, hair all over her face. We're not out of danger, but we're closer to the beach.

"Are you okay?" I yell.

"Yeah!" she yells back as I swim sidestroke again, kicking and keeping my head above the water. Allison is swimming freestyle. In about thirty seconds, I start to feel the sand under my feet. We're inside the breakers, but caught in the white wash. I go under again and swim against the outgoing current. I feel it fighting me, but when I come up, I see Allison, next to me, still swimming straight ahead. When we can finally stand, I grab her hand as she swims. "We can stand," I say and she tilts straight. We're both on our feet and I feel a flush of relief. She still looks scared, so we rush to the water's edge. When we get out on the sand, we sit down, soaked and exhausted.

"That was scary," I say.

"I knew that wasn't a good idea," she says.

"I know, it was dumb as shit, but it was kind of fun, too," I say.

We stand and hug, our wet bodies together, streaks of sand between us. We find our shirts, put them on and walk, feeling the effects of the night of loud music, long walks, and midnight swims.

When we get home, I hear an after party going on upstairs in the living room and kitchen. Our bedroom is downstairs, so I quietly enter the downstairs and get two towels as Allison steps into the outside shower. We both stand naked under the cool water and the warm North Carolina summer air and clean the salt and sand off our bodies. We cover ourselves with towels and go inside to our bedroom. No one knows we're home as we close the door, drop our towels and lie together, under our covers, hoping not to uncover until we wake up.

||||||||||||||||||||||||||||||||||||||||||||||||||||||||

CHAPTER 39

||||||||||||||||||||||||||||||||||||||||||||||||||||||||||||

The first day of fall lacrosse brings many things. It brings exhaustion as I pick up the pace that cannot be duplicated in workouts or summer league. It brings togetherness, as we finally practice as a team, not as individuals preparing for the team. It brings a sense of urgency, as we get ready for fall intrasquad scrimmages and scrimmages against other outstanding Division One teams. Each day brings us closer to the spring, where games matter and playoffs are a real goal. The funny part is that fall brings my former nemesis from Mt. Washington, Clyde, onto my team, as a transfer from Essex Community College, just like Trevor. It brings my perspective full circle, as I see freshmen enter wide-eyed and ambitious. The pictures fall lacrosse brings to my mind make me appreciate the work, the grind, the behind the scenes play that makes our team and every team. We approach it with our heads down and our spirits up. We look to improve ourselves and our teammates, through sacrifice and hard work.

Coach Faust has given us a chance to make our own destiny by allowing us to have a say in our practice plans and weight room work.

After my first fall ball with Towson and my final fall ball in college lacrosse, I walk into the spring season a senior and a returning player. I understand the work involved in Division One lacrosse, the amount of weight room training, off-season running, academic requirements and social pressures. It's ironic, now that I understand and can adapt, the experience will be ending at the end of this season. My college career, my chance to wear a school jersey will be over, ending far more quickly than I ever thought possible. This spring season is an opportunity to put the work into one full season of lacrosse. I can feel this team, this group of guys have a sense of hunger. We have a desire, a camaraderie that did not exist last season. Our willingness to help each other, to stay after practice, to bring a level of seriousness and enjoyment to our practice routines verifies my feelings. We're going to be good this season, far better then anyone outside of this program believes we will be. I am confident in our team's leaders, our coaches and our schemes. Our players are good without being cocky. We share the ball, but rise to the occasion when our number is called. We are a team, each putting the collective over the individual. Does this sound ideal? Sure, but there is plenty of adversity. Coach Faust and Coach Kaufman kick our asses on a daily basis. We push each other to the point of exhaustion, challenge our leaders, encourage the freshmen. We understand the sacrifices that are going to have to be made in order to win the big games. Last season, we lost to every team that was ranked higher than we were. We let the moment overwhelm us and succumbed to its pressure. It is a tough pill to swallow, but we didn't come through when we needed to. As a result of the disappointment, every player and the coaches are determined to change the outlook, the output and the result. It all sounds cliche, but we want to do everything in our power to change the ending of this season.

As the schedule starts, we find a rhythm and trust in each other that continues to improve. Our skill and effort show that we are a legitimate team and we start to beat teams that we didn't beat last year. The sense of urgency that we had to start the season only increases and each guy realizes that we have a special opportunity to take this team as far as we can. The ride of the season continues into the NCAA playoffs and we avenge our loss to UVA in the semifinals and head to the finals against Carolina in, of all places, the Carrier Dome in Syracuse, New York.

|||||||||||||||||||||||||||||||||||||||||||||||||||||||||

CHAPTER 40

|||||||||||||||||||||||||||||||||||||||||||||||||||||||||||

When we walk onto the field at the Carrier Dome for warmups, the metal seats and hollow roof make for a vision in silver. The green AstroTurf field is empty but for two goals, one in each crease, facing each other and ready for use. We walk as a team, in two lines, to the midfield and separate into four lines for stretching. The echoes from our chants reverberate throughout the building, fueling our anticipation for the big game. There is no sight of Carolina, their players or their coaches. The only other people in the stadium are the grounds staff and two officials from the NCAA.

Once we huddle and get ready to break into our groups of attack, midfield and defense, with the goalies separating to take shots from Coach Kaufman, we hear Carolina come through the doors at the far end of the stadium. Their voices echo as we hear them hoot and holler upon their entrance onto the field. I don't look towards them but I can't help but crack a smile when I hear Clyde yell, loud enough for all of us to hear, "Fuck those bunch of private school pussies!" I look at JB and Glenn and smile, the private school in us hidden for the moment.

Carolina has several of my high school teammates on their team: Bresch and Greg, my nemesis, plus my cousin, John Walker. I love Bresch, he's a great guy and someone I see every summer. I have seen Greg one time since the fire, at a scrimmage day at Loyola College and he wouldn't look my way all day. He hid behind his teammates and avoided me during the handshake line. To be honest, I didn't have much interest in seeing him, but it was weird, seeing him avoid me at all costs.

By the time the captains—JB, Glenn and Rob— come back from the coin flip, the entire stadium is electric. While we are in the huddle, JB looks at me and says, "We are doing this" as he slaps me on the helmet.

I look at him and put a hand on his helmet, "You sure?"

"Never been more sure, brother, do your thing," JB says.

"All right, I will," I say.

When we break the huddle, I jog out to the middle of the field for pregame lineups. I look across at Bresch and he is all business. He stares at me, then Glenn, with his game face on the whole time. I look back at him, not trying to intimidate or pester, just looking. My eyes wander left, towards the middies and I look at Greg. He is looking away and, I can tell, purposely avoiding me. I start chirping, "Let's go, boys" just to see if Greg will look my way. A couple of the Carolina players look my way, but Greg won't. No surprise, he's got no balls anyway. I'm not even listening to the refs and their instructions, I am focused on this asshole right across from me. At this very moment, this game has become personal. It has always been about the win, but right now it's changed. It's about getting even, it's about revenge. I didn't know this was coming, but I can't change the feeling, I fucking hate this asshole.

The refs finally stop talking and we are supposed to walk to the person across from us and shake hands and wish good luck. Instead, I cut over on a forty-five degree angle and stick my face mask in Greg's face and say, loud enough for him to hear but not loud enough for the refs to hear, "I'm coming after you motherfucker, all day." He won't lift his eyes to meet mine and turns right, away from my end of the field. "I know you heard me, motherfucker," I say, making sure to keep it going. I know I am bothering him, and that is good enough for me. I turn right, towards the attack end and make sure to bump into Bresch in my way downfield. "Good luck, dude," I say as I turn to go to the right attack spot. I don't hear Bresch say anything, but I feel him hit the back of my head, a tap of acknowledgement.

While I am standing on the field getting ready for the first faceoff, Coach Faust turns to JB, our normal starter at right attack and says, "What are you doing right here?"

JB says, "Being a captain coach, being a captain."

Trevor and Greg go down for the first faceoff, with Rob on one wing and Clyde on the other. The ref places the ball down between their two sticks and backpedals as he blows the whistle to start the game. The ball squirts out behind Greg, and he turns and goes for it, with Trevor and Clyde chasing him. As Greg picks the ball up, the ref raises his hand in the air and yells "Release!" The timing could not have been any better for me, as I can see that Greg does not see me coming. I sprint out of the box and catch Greg looking over his shoulder for Clyde's stick check. I catch him clean, from the front and bury my right shoulder into his chest. The ball pops up in the air, out of his stick and, as Clyde goes after the ball, I stand over Greg and finally make eye contact, as he stares up at me from the ground, with the eyes of a scared dog, whites all around his bulging eyes. "Fuck you," I say as I stand over top of him and then turn and cut to the goal, looking for a pass. Clyde picks it up and moves it to Trevor. The building is buzzing as the fans have seen their first hit of the game in its first ten seconds. Trevor catches from Clyde, fakes a quick shot from fifteen yards and feeds a cutting Glenn, who scores. I hear the crowd go wild. I barely break stride as I slap Glenn on the helmet and head towards the sideline. I make eye contact with JB and he strides onto the field, headed towards his right-handed attack spot. We slap low fives on our way past each other.

When I get to the sideline, I walk past Coach Faust and say, "Thanks, Coach."

He looks at me and says, "Wasn't my idea, but I'll take credit for it," and smirks. JB and I gambled on that play and we ended up 1–0, eighteen seconds into the game. It's on and we are ready to play.

We take a two-goal lead into the second quarter 4–2. Carolina is playing well but our goalie, Rich Betcher, has made three unbelievable saves and JB has two assists to Glenn Smith. The pace of play is off the charts and the refs are letting us play, keeping their whistles in their pockets and letting us fight for every ground ball. Both teams are taking the opportunity to be physical when they can on ground balls and on defense, and, because of that, the game is intense. Our offense is getting good looks on the goal, and we're keeping the pressure on Carolina, something they're not used to, it seems. John Walker has both of Carolina's goals. Whether my pre-game cussing out has anything to do with it or not I don't know, but Greg is playing like shit.

At halftime, the score is tied and the crowd is fired up. We know we have to take care of the ball in the second half and keep it away from their offense. We have a great defense, but they are starting to pick us apart when we have to slide. Thank god Betcher's play is incredible; otherwise, we would be down by three or four goals.

When the second half starts, we win the opening faceoff. I hear Coach call for my midfield, so Trevor and I head out of the box. By the time the ball swings to Glenn, he steps in and shoots from the wing. The ball bounces off the pipe and as my man's head is turned, I see it bounce off the goalie's right side, scoop it up and put it in the lower near left corner before my man can find the ball. We take a one-goal lead. It happens so fast that I don't even have to think about it, and guys are hitting me on the helmet. I feel a wave of relief and exhilaration wash over me in one instant. One goal never felt so good in my whole life, and all I did was scoop it and throw it in the goal, one of the easiest goals I've ever scored.

By the time the fourth quarter starts, we're down by two and Carolina has grabbed the momentum, scoring the last three goals of the third quarter. We have to get the momentum back now. Coach sends Trevor out to take the faceoff and he wins it clean. JB and

Glenn have a nice give and go, getting us another goal and closing the gap to one goal.

However, Carolina wins the next two faceoffs and scores on each possession, one by John Walker on a nice high bouncer from the top of the box and another on an inside roll from Dennis Goldberg. Carolina is up by three goals again and the clock is ticking down, each minute shrinking our chances. I feel our sideline getting desperate as the groans get louder each time the ball bounces Carolina's way. Each possession steals more precious time off the clock until the clock hits 0:00, and we all watch Carolina throw their sticks, their helmets, their gloves in the air, and jump into a dogpile of happiness in front of their goal. We stand in silence, shuffling in different directions, towards our goalie, towards our coaches, waiting for the Carolina celebration to simmer down. The trophies need to be given to the runner up, us, and to the champion. The time moves slowly as we wait and wait, for what feels like forever.

We gather near our coach, in a huddle, and follow with the traditional post game handshake. I am happy for the Carolina players I like and keep my head up for Greg's hand in line. When he walks past me, his hand is out and his head is facing away, afraid to face me or not man enough to look me in the eye? Either way, I let his hand go by, untouched by me and shake the next hand in line, Bresch's. His smile is a mile wide and I can't resist a smile for him myself, one of the good guys.

‖‖‖‖‖‖‖‖‖‖‖‖‖‖‖‖‖‖‖‖‖‖‖‖‖‖‖‖‖‖‖‖‖‖‖‖‖‖

CHAPTER 41

‖‖

We're in the far corner of the Carrier Dome as parents and TSU administrators talk to the despondent players. Cleta comes down to the field.

"Thank you for coming, Cleta," I say.

"Mark, I wouldn't have missed it for the world," she answers.

"Sorry we lost."

"Oh Mark, that's okay. I'm sorry you lost, too, but you played great. Your team was in it until the end, you scored a goal. The last time a Corrigan scored a goal in the national championship was in 1958. Your Uncle Lee scored four, if I'm not mistaken, but they lost, too. To the damn JHU Blue Jays," she adds. "But, when you scored today, I said to myself, 'Well I'll be damned.' You did it, you scored." She leans her head back to look up at me, right into my eyes, and she says, "but you had more than one goal today Mark, I think you checked off a few goals."

I reach out to give her a half hug so I don't get her sweaty, but Cleta centers herself and squeezes hard. I return the hug, knowing that I'm getting her sweaty and knowing that she is okay with it.

She pulls away and says, "I'm proud of you Mark, and you know what, you should be proud of yourself." She turns to my mom and says, "Now let's get back to Baltimore."

I hug Mom, Dad, Lauren, Mary and Thomas. What a journey. I head to the locker room for a shower and the ride home. I've graduated, officially done on May 21. To me, graduation was a sidelight to the lacrosse ride, a necessary evil. Once I had turned in my senior papers and finished the exams, it was over— the school, the summer school, the night school, the labs, the study halls, the work groups, the teacher's assistant jobs, the work study, the meetings with my advisor, the cramming, over. From the first day at RMC, in Ashland, Virginia, hungover, sick with ulcers, demons in my thoughts, hurt in my heart, young in my years. It started in a place I had not heard of six months before I got there, and it ends in my hometown, at a place I have ridden my bike to since I was in fifth grade. Every journey begins in one place and ends in another, but this journey I never envisioned. On this trip, lacrosse carried me. It became the constant, the backup plan when I didn't have a plan A. I'm lucky for the opportunities it presented, the places it has taken me, the people I've been able to meet, the joy it has given me. Syracuse lacrosse team transformed my mind when I saw them for the first time at thirteen, and here I am now, in their house. Navy, JHU, Maryland, Virginia—everybody is the same on a lacrosse field. Names don't matter, pedigree doesn't matter, hype doesn't matter, it's a game that is played on a level playing field. And—I didn't know until I figured it out—life can be played on a level playing field, but it's up to us to make it level. Outworking, outthinking, outhustling—the same qualities that this game presents—all work in the game of life.

The things that I think are important now are completely different from the things I thought were important when I sat in my first English class at RMC. I even know now that lacrosse, the game, the big game won't define any of us. Being in it, being part of it, is what it's all about. Everyone wants to win, but you don't always win. Some might say, "Well, that's what a guy on the losing team would say," but I say, "The game is what it's all about. Playing the game, knowing there will be a winner and a loser. Playing the game, being all you can be, and seeing if that's good enough." Thousands of people watched today, I've played in thousands of games, I guarantee I will play in more games. That's the point, this is only one game. Win or lose, it's not going to define me. To come from where I have been and what I've learned, I only care about today and what's coming up in the future.

I don't care to look back. It's my story, my experiences. I just want to use them to manage today and prepare for the future. This moment is over, but this day isn't over. There's more to today that I can do. And, I know what I am doing in the immediate future. When the bus gets back to Towson, I am going to meet Allison, and we are driving across the US of A. So, I walk off this field, one of a thousand fields, and into the tunnel of the Carrier Dome. Today is the last time in a Towson jersey, but it's not a bad last day. It's like ending a job or finishing a test, the jersey gets turned in and you are graded. The only difference is, the game graders take on all shapes and sizes: little kids saying you did well, the coaches telling you that you could have done more, siblings and cousins telling you what you should have done. But the only real grader, the only one that matters, is me. I determine, I accept and I can change. Lacrosse, life, today and the future.

||||||||||||||||||||||||||||||||||||||||||||||||||||||||||

CHAPTER 42

||||||||||||||||||||||||||||||||||||||||||||||||||||||||||||

When we pull into the Sunset Cliffs Natural Park, and I view the Pacific Ocean for the first time in my life, I felt a sense of accomplishment and wonder. To travel all this way, see mountains and lakes, trails and desert, the great Pacific stretched farther than the eyes can see and mist in my face from a stiff eastern breeze has brought a sense of massiveness to my life: the massiveness of our country, the miles we have journeyed and the magnitude of change in my own life.

Allison and I drove straight to Colorado from Baltimore in two days and made it to Steamboat Springs. The beauty of Colorado in the summer is something I did not expect. The natural landscape is overwhelming to an East Coast guy who had never seen the Rocky Mountains. We experienced a rodeo, a hot air balloon festival, trail hiking and white water rafting. The outdoors in Steamboat presented challenges I hadn't encountered before and the lifestyle is something that I could get accustomed to.

From the Rocky Mountain National Park, Allison and I set off for the Grand Canyon for three days of hiking and camping, and from there to the West Coast.

The travel is soothing, the scenery breathtaking and the experience rewarding as we meet, talk to and enjoy the company of perfect strangers, fellow Americans and foreign visitors. Our minds are opened to the possibilities that this great country offers. Allison and I have become companions in our travels, learning more and more about each other with each day together. She has opened up about her family, her worries, her hopes. I have found in her a comfort that I have not found in anyone before.

We stand on the cliffs, climb down to the beach and jump into the chilly, early July Pacific water, surrounded by sea kelp and waves. The water is a deeper blue than the Atlantic and feels more salty. It washes off the sweat and dirt from days of travel. It refreshes and soothes sore muscles. It invigorates my mind. We are on the left coast, the opposite side of the country. We'll visit Kevin by July 20 in San Francisco, so we have two weeks to take ourselves up the coast of California. No agenda, no schedule and no expectations. Our trip so far has been as enjoyable as possible, living day to day, eating meal by meal, conserving our money and spending our energy.

We sit on the same towel staring out at the ocean, sun on our faces, cold Pacific Ocean water on our bodies. I turn to Allison and feel the need to tell her something important.

"When I was in rehab, my counselor told me a saying that stuck with me. It's not enough that we be forgiven by others, we must forgive ourselves. Sometimes I think that people never forgive themselves," I say. "So what about people whose lights don't go out, like they die before they are supposed to?" I ask.

"I think that stuff is just the sad parts of life, it's just not fair, but there is nothing we can do about it," she says. "I do think their spirit is still here, though. I know that sounds weird, but I feel like they are around us, they guide us. You know that church we went into in Taos? It had a big stained glass window that said, 'Love one another constantly.'"

"Yeah, I think I remember it," I say.

"Well, while I was sitting there I just thought, that's all we have. Love. And, it's all we can do, love one another. I mean what else is there?" she says.

"I think I know what you mean. I mean life is short, and it's hard, so what else can we do?" I say.

"Yeah, it's like there is this thin veil between life and death, so if we just live, just live with love, I think it will be the best way," she says.

"Two things I learned in rehab, things I want to do better, are honesty and animosity. If I can just be honest about everything, to myself, to you, to other people, life can keep getting better. I find that it's just easier—sometimes harder in the moment—but better in the long run because it makes you feel less guilty," I say. "And what I mean by animosity is that I want to live without it. Feelings like jealousy, but it's other things, too, like resentment, antagonism, bitterness. If I can live without those, life will be better. I learned that it is easier to live without some things than it is to live with them. So, I want to work on those right now. I know with you it's easy to be honest, but I have to work on being honest with everybody. And then, when it comes to other people, I want to not hold anything against them. It's hard not to fall back into that old thinking, but it doesn't get me anywhere. It's just negative and I don't want negative anymore, so, please, remind me when I get off track. Really, I want you to remind me, okay?" I say.

"All right, I will," she says. "I like those two, though, those are good."

I reach out and hold her hand, each of us lost in our own thoughts. The waves break in the distance, the sun shines overhead, the trees sing in the wind. Some things we will understand about each other right away, some things will take time and some things we may never come to fully know.

|||||||||||||||||||||||||||||||||||||||||||||||||||||

CHAPTER 43

|||||||||||||||||||||||||||||||||||||||||||||||||||||||||

When we get to Kevin's apartment in San Francisco, right on the edge of Chinatown, both Allison and I are ready for a shower, a bed and a good, home-cooked meal. We've been on the road, sleeping in a tent and traveling for the last eight days and I look forward to seeing Kevin and sleeping in a bed. We pull up out front and get out of the car. Kevin must've been looking out for us and when he comes outside to greet us, he pushes open the gate in front of the door and walks to us. When he reaches out and gives me a hug, I hear a "clunk" in the background. Kevin pulls away from me and, with his back to the door, says, "Did that gate just close?"

"Yeah," I say.

"Shit, I didn't bring my key with me," he says, "let me call the other apartments and get somebody to open it for us."

A half hour later, we are still sitting outside his apartment, cooler on the sidewalk while Kevin and Allison have a beer and I drink a club soda. It feels great to see Kevin, who is here in San Francisco working for a company selling construction equipment. He looks happy, telling us all about his adventures in northern California, his roommates and his journey across the country.

"Hey, Mark, by the way, your mom called and left a message on the answering machine a couple of days ago. She wants you to call her when you get to town."

"All right, I will. I'll call her once somebody comes by and opens the high tech security gate you don't know how to unlock," I say.

"Yeah, whatever, you dick," he says as we all laugh, enjoying the pleasant weather and, by now, the beautiful sunset over the neighbors' roofs and distant harbor. San Francisco has a pinkish, red glow at sunset as the light reflects off the water and the sky turns a multitude of colors.

"Is the sunset always like this?" I ask.

"Most days it is, man, it is beautiful out here," he says.

By this time, a young lady Kevin recognizes pulls up in her car and parks, Kevin walks over to her and she opens the gate. His apartment is a long, first floor, two-bedroom unit, with the TV room at the front and the kitchen in the back. Kevin tells Allison and me that we'll get the pull out couch in the TV room to sleep and we head outside, making sure to prop the door open and bring our bags, the cooler and other items inside. When we finish, I head back to the kitchen and grab the phone off the wall. I dial the number to my home phone on Anneslie Rd and wait for it to ring.

Two rings into the call, Mom picks up.

"Hey, Mom, it's Mark. We made it to Kevin's house. Everything is good. He said you called though, what's up?"

"Mark, there is no easy way to say this. Cleta died on Wednesday. She's been sick and we took her to St. Joe's Hospital, but she didn't make it. So, listen, her funeral is on Monday at Cathedral. I want you to be here, so we need to make some arrangements to get you home."

Before she keeps going, dismissing any shows of emotion, I interrupt her and say, "Mom, I am sorry about Cleta."

This is her mother, her rock, her sounding board. Instead of breaking down or crying at all, she plows forward with the details. "That's okay, Mark, she is in a better place." I think *Better place? She was surrounded by family and friends here, how can she be in a better place?*

She continues, "Now, your father and I looked into flights and I want you to fly home on Sunday. You'll be home for the funeral and then you can go back out to meet Kevin later next week."

"Okay," I say, trying to process the loss of Cleta, Mom's all business attitude and my uncertainty about Allison. I don't want to leave her out here. I feel weird leaving her with Kevin, who has a job and is leaving each work day, along with the fact that she doesn't know any of his roommates. "Do you want me to call an airline and get a ticket?" I ask.

"No, your Father already took care of it. I'll put him on the phone and he'll give you the details. In the meantime, make sure you have a haircut. You can wear one of your father's suits." I can't comprehend. Mom has lost her mother in the last couple of days, and she's concerned with me getting a haircut and making sure I look presentable.

"Mom, I'll take care of it. I'm really sorry about Cleta, I know you guys were close. Are you okay?" I ask.

"Mark, I am fine," she says in a defiant way, almost insulted that I check on her well being. "Cleta lived a full life, and she is in a much better place." I am not sure about that, but now is not the time to disagree. And right now, I just want to agree to get along. "Now listen, here's your Father. He'll give you the details and we'll see you on Sunday. I'll make sure someone is there to pick you up from the airport."

I start to say, "Okay, Mom, look forward to seeing—" but she has handed off the phone. I hear the rustle on the line as it's handed from one person to another.

"Mark, how are you? I guess you made it to Kevin in San Francisco. Please tell him we said hi," Dad says with his rapid question style of talking, rarely waiting for answers to questions he already knows the answer to. "Now listen, I got you on a flight from the San Francisco airport. Now get some paper and a pen so you can write this down. Let me know when you get a pen."

"All right, I'm looking for one. Dad, is Mom okay? She seems kind of short," I say.

"Mark," he says as he lowers his voice and jostles the phone. I am assuming he's covering it to keep quiet, "you know how your mother is, she's taking care of everybody and not even slowing down to take care of herself. She'll be fine."

"Okay, it's just...that it's Cleta, it's her mom and I know it has to be tough," I say. "Now, I have a pen, so what do you want me to write down?"

"Here you go," he says, "you are on American Airlines flight number 6739 out of San Francisco Airport. The flight leaves at 8:20 a.m., your time. It will arrive at BWI at 4:35 our time. We'll make sure Thomas or Lauren is there to pick you up. You can pick up your ticket at the counter when you get there. Just make sure you're at least an hour early and you can show them your license. You have your license, don't you?"

"Yeah, I got it."

"Good. Now listen, make sure you don't miss this flight."

"I'll be there. See you on Sunday," I say. "Hey, Dad, can you get Mom back on the phone? I want to tell you something and I know it will be pretty busy with family when I get home."

"Yeah," he says, "is everything all right?"

"Yeah, Dad, everything is fine, I just want to tell you and Mom something."

"Okay, hold on," he says as I hear him hold the receiver and yell a muffled, "Margaret, pick the phone back up."

I hear Mom say, "Mark?"

"Mom, Dad, everything is fine, there's nothing to worry about. It's just that, during this trip I've had a lot of time to think and a lot of time to talk with Allison. I want to say thanks, to both of you. You guys have put up with my bullshit, helped me in every way possible, believed in me when I didn't believe in myself." I stand in Kevin's kitchen, for the first time ever and have a conversation with my parents that I probably should have had a long time ago. "I know I was a pain in the ass, I know I kept you up at night, I know I drove you crazy. I am sorry. I'm sorry for all of it. From the age of fifteen until now, I shut you guys out of a lot of my thoughts. I blamed you guys for a lot of the problems I caused. I blamed you guys for things that you didn't have any part in. I was a jerk, and, I don't know why I want to tell you now, but I apologize. Who I was and what I was doing was all me, and it's taken me a long time to accept that. I apologize for freezing you out. You guys gave me everything I needed, gave me love whenever I needed it and helped me every step of the way. I took it for granted and I'm not going to do it anymore." I feel my eyes water and my voice shakes. Honesty brings emotion and I want to be done with holding back. "I love you both and I am sorry it took so long to really tell you from my heart. I am really, really grateful that I have you as parents. I'm sorry I put you through so much, but I want you to know that I love you and I want to make it right."

There is a bit of stunned silence for a moment on the other end until I hear Dad, in his calm, measured tone say, "We never stopped loving you. We've always known who you are, and we just wanted to see you take care of yourself." I am crying, looking out into an alley I have never seen. "It sounds like you're taking good care of yourself."

Mom picks up when Dad stops and says, "Thank you Mark, for letting us know how you feel. All we ever wanted for you is to be happy and, for a long time, you didn't seem very happy. For you to tell us all this, right now, means a lot and I just can't wait to see you and give you a hug. We both love you and we always will."

"I love you guys. I just have realized that there are a lot of things that I needed to say to you both and, well, no time like the present, right Mom?"

"Right," she says.

"I will make sure to be at the airport on time and see you guys in a couple days."

"We look forward to it," Mom says.

"See you guys," I say. I feel physically weaker than when I picked up the phone, but somehow relieved that I came clean, phone receiver in my hand, drying tears with my forearm.

When I hang up the phone and walk back to the living room, Kevin studies my face. "You good?"

"Yeah, man, I'm good," I say.

"How's everything with Margaret D?" Kevin asks.

"She's good, but my grandmother died on Wednesday. They want me to fly home on Sunday. The funeral is Monday."

"Cleta died?" Kevin has known her a long time. Cleta has taken the two of us out for lunch a few times and he's come over to our house enough over the years that Cleta and Kevin are friends. She always kept up with his lacrosse at Duke, told him about Uncle Jimmy and Francis. They had a funny bond, which I never thought would happen. "I'm sorry about that, Mark. I know you two were close."

"Yeah, I'm sorry, too. She came up to my game at the Carrier Dome, she seemed good. I'm really surprised," I say.

I look at Allison. I want to make sure she knows that we're in this together and I am not going to leave her in California. I want her to meet my family, my brother and sisters, my cousins, everybody. "I want you to come with me. We can leave our stuff here, is that okay Kevin?"

"Yeah man, that's no problem," he says.

"We can leave our stuff here, fly back on Wednesday and pick up where we left off. It'll be fine, plus if you want to get anything from home, we'll be close," I say.

"That's going to be expensive, are we going to have enough money?" she asks.

"We'll make it work," I say.

Kevin gets up from his chair and comes at me with his arms out. "I'm sorry about Cleta, she was a great lady," he says as he wraps me in a quick hug. "Now, I wanted to surprise you. I got tickets to the Giants game at Candlestick tonight. We would have been early if I didn't lock us out. Grab a jacket, let's go to the game," Kevin says as he grabs another beer out of the cooler.

"You got tickets for tonight?" I ask.

"Yeah, dude, let's go, you're driving. Nothing happens until the fifth inning anyway. We should be right on time."

I look at Allison and shrug my shoulders. "Let's go, we can call about a plane ticket in the morning." We rummage through a bag and get two light windbreakers for the game and head out the door. "Kevin, don't forget a front door key," I yell ahead to him with a laugh.

The beer is at his lips and I see him spit a little out. "I got the keys this time, all right, you prick."

I slap him on the back as I walk by and we head to the car, happy to see my good friend, with my girlfriend by my side, headed on another adventure, on to another place for the first time.

|||||||||||||||||||||||||||||||||||||||||||||||||||||||||||

CHAPTER 44

|||||||||||||||||||||||||||||||||||||||||||||||||||||||||||||||

We stand in front of Cathedral church, in suits. With Henry Corrigan, all the older male grandchildren walked the casket down the aisle. For Cleta, the younger male grandchildren have the responsibility. That means Hugh, Billy, Brian, Doug Radisson, Michael and me. At this funeral, I wasn't puking in the bushes the night before. I am awake, clearminded, happy, determined, aware, alive. The funeral director gives us our instructions and we all look at each other. The church is packed with Cleta's friends, family, family friends, lacrosse people from all over the East Coast. The air is humid, the sun high in the sky. Each of us is in black and we are sweating. At this funeral I don't feel nervous, I don't feel scared, I don't feel intimidated. I feel different—is this normal?— I don't know, but I feel confident. It's real confidence. It isn't false bravado or arrogance. I am not trying to impress anybody. It's the first time I have felt real confidence in my life. Why it is, I don't know. Sobriety, girlfriend, travel, awareness, I don't know but I really don't care. I feel real.

My right hand grabs the gold handle on the chestnut brown casket, and we lift it off the wheeled cart. Since I'm in front, with Brian to my right, we take our first step up the steps into the church, carrying the woman I trusted and who trusted me when I didn't deserve anyone's trust. My heart fills, not with sadness, but with gratitude for a person who never gave up on me but never pretended, either. I feel my eyes water and a tear or two run down my cheek. No sense in hiding it, I think I'm done hiding things. My shoulders lift, we balance at the top of the steps and start our walk down the aisle. I look at the handle and then at the casket. In a quiet voice I say four words that I haven't said since I was twelve years old but mean more today than ever before: "I love you, Cleta."

||||||||||||||||||||||||||||||||||||||||||||||||||||||||

CHAPTER 45

||||||||||||||||||||||||||||||||||||||||||||||||||||||||||||

I talk to Lauren on the phone from Lewes, a sea town off the coast of the Atlantic Ocean and the Delaware Bay and my home now for eight years. "The ceremony starts at 8 p.m., so Mom wants everybody there by 6 p.m., so I want to make sure you will be there on time," she says.

"I will be there at six, I promise," I say. I don't know why my family always thinks I won't be there on time, but I know I need to be there on time for this one. Mom is getting into the Baltimore Lacrosse Hall of Fame for her work with the little leagues for some twenty-five years. When she started, they didn't even have a girls' league and by the time she was finished, the league had hundreds of teams and thousands of players. She connected the Baltimore Area, the Annapolis Area and all the Eastern and Western Maryland teams into one league, the premier league in the country. The hot player of many a college championship team came through the MYLA, Maryland Youth Lacrosse Association. The funny thing is she did it all from the little living room and same telephone line, with a long cord and call waiting. I'm not going to be late to Mom's night. Plus, all the boys should be there. Uncles Jimmy, Francis, Gregory and Lee, Brian, Hugh, Leebird, the crew. It should be a good night. "You don't have to worry, I'll see you there around six. Where are you staying?"

"We're at Mom and Dad's, what about you?" she asks.

"We're at Thomas and Julie's, so I'll see you at the Hunt Valley

Lodge at six."

As I pull up to the Hunt Valley Mansion that is holding the US Lacrosse Hall of Fame dinner for Baltimore, I see Lauren outside the huge wooden doors, waving to the car. I slow down in front of the circle to drop off Allison, and Lauren leans in the car door after Allison gets out.

"You're not going to believe this, Greg's family is the caterer, can you believe it?" she says in a rapid fire voice, not pausing to let me answer. "Do you want to wait to come in?"

"Lauren, what are you talking about?" I ask, not even waiting for an answer. "I came here for Mom, so big freaking deal who the caterer is. "Allison, I'm going to park the car and I will meet you inside," I say over Lauren's shoulder, annoyed with her for making it a big deal. But if I am being honest, I'm also startled that I might see someone from my past who was nowhere on my radar before this second.

"I'll wait for you here," I hear Allison say. She is a small town girl in a big city setting, with people in tuxedos and dresses. Allison has a lot of class but not much experience around crowds of three or four hundred people in castle-like surroundings. Hell, I know I'll recognize a bunch of people and I'll have family all around, but this whole setup looks pretty intimidating for anybody. Now, throw the guy who lit me on fire into the middle of it all, and my stomach is turning before I get out of the car.

Lauren is still looking at me through the open passenger door. "Lauren, shut the door so I can park the car, okay, I will be in in a minute."

"Are you sure you're okay?"

"If you don't shut the door, I'm going to run over your foot, and then you definitely won't be okay," I say, staring at her with cold eyes. "Shut the fucking door."

"Okay, I just wanted you to know," she says as she slams the door.

I push the window down on the passenger side and yell out, "See you inside, Lis!" as sarcastically as possible. I know deep inside I am just giving her shit because she's the one that gave me this shitty news.

By the time I pull into a parking spot a hundred yards from the front door, my hands are shaking and I feel a weird taste in my mouth. I have not seen this motherfucker in I don't know how long, but my rage shoots along my nerves. I sit in the driver's seat, car turned off, lights off, in the dark and wonder *why, why now, why here.* I am here to see my mother get inducted into the Baltimore Lacrosse Hall of Fame for all she has done for lacrosse and all she has done for kids that are not her own, and my worry right now is whether I can get out of this seat, get out of this car and walk into this place. Suddenly my plans to meet Brian, Billy and Hugh don't mean shit. My plans to see Uncles Francis and Jimmy, Lee and Gregory are tossed aside. I don't know what's going to happen next.

By the time I get to the front door, the cool October night air has hit my face and it feels good, brisk. Whatever happens, happens. I realize now that I don't have to do anything. I am not in the wrong. No matter what the circumstances, I didn't do anything wrong that night and I don't plan on doing anything wrong tonight.

Allison has a wide smile and sympathetic eyes as she stands waiting to go in with me. We put our arms around each other's waist and walk through the two big doors, open to the cold air. The interior is huge: high vaulted ceilings in a big foyer, a big banquet hall through the doors in the distance. I look to the right as we enter and see Uncle Francis, Billy and Hugh. We walk over to them and share hugs. Allison looks beautiful and takes on the shenanigans.

I see Bob Scott from JHU, the nicest man in the world, and Buddy Beardmore from Maryland right next to each other. The biggest people in lacrosse are here and I get lost in the talk, the people, the game.

Spook Riley is talking to me. "Mark, your mother took the MYLA from 800 kids to 20,000 kids throughout the state. She did it all, came up with a plan, she got it all together. She should be really proud of herself," he says, as I look past him and across the foyer.

"Wow, twenty thousand, huh," I repeat but I'm not listening.

It's Greg in a black bow tie and white shirt. He looks thin and pretty pale. He needs a haircut, but it is definitely Greg. I think Mr. Riley sees me staring. He knows Greg and the whole thing, so he stops talking. I stare a few seconds longer and turn to him. "Spook, I'm going to go see Mare and say hello. She is the star of the show tonight and I want to make sure she knows it. Please tell Brian I say hello," I say. His son is Brian, an old friend.

Spook just looks me in the eye and says, "Mark, I'm glad for your mom and I'm glad to see you doing well, too." He gives me a knowing look, a wink and a heavy pat on my left shoulder.

I turn and look for Mom or Dad, not because I need them right now but more because I want to see them, make sure they're doing well. When I walk through a door to the banquet hall, I see Mom, Uncle Francis, his wife Lena, Aunt Mary, Gregory's wife, and head over for the round of hellos.

Mom makes eye contact and steps away from her crowd. She walks toward me with a look of concern and tilts her head to the side. "Did you hear who was the caterer?" she asks.

"Yeah, Mom, it's fine, okay, it's no big deal. This is your night, and nothing is going to get in the way of that tonight, okay," I say and come in for an uninvited hug. I'm not asking. She hugs me back and instantly, I know it's okay. I feel Mom relax and and I feel my body ease and we separate. A mother's hug is the answer to a whole lot of questions.

Together, we ease back into the conversation about the night and move on. Nobody talks about it, I don't say anything to Brian or Hugh. Allison comes by every once in a while, and gives me a squeeze but she is talking to Kristin, Brian's wife, and Jen, Billy's wife.

By the time people start to make speeches, the crowd has

been here for a couple of hours of good time, people are drunk, laughing at the jokes. Mom's speech is great. She touches on the kids' perspective, the new players, the lessons the game teaches. She talks about the sportsmanship, the fairness and the fact that the results of each game don't matter as much as the people in the game. Everybody who has played the game has won some and everyone who has played the game has lost some. The game teaches humility to those who will listen. The game teaches respect to those who can sense it. The game teaches heart to those who will open theirs.

I sit through another speaker and get up to get a drink at the bar in the foyer. When I walk out the door and into the foyer, I hear a man say, "Sorry sir, the bar is closed."

"I just want a glass of water," I say to the voice on my left and he insists, "Sorry sir, we're closed."

"Okay, I just wanted a glass of water, that's all," I say and hear a voice from the side say, "It's okay, Bill, I got him." It's Mr. Simonson. He grabs a glass, turns it right side up and fills it with water from a half-filled pitcher. "Here you go," he says as he appears earnest, helpful. I look at him as I take the glass out of his hand.

I ask, "Is Greg here?" No reason for small talk.

"Yeah, he is, he's in the kitchen," he says.

"Can I see him?"

He appears startled. "Yeah, let me get him for you." And he turns toward the kitchen.

I stand at the bar, me and Bill, the bartender who doesn't pour water when the bar is closed, and take a sip of water with no ice. Not very cold but it eases my throat. I don't know exactly what I am going to say, but I am going to make my point.

Greg emerges from two industrial kitchen doors with his head down and looks up when he gets to the foyer. I'm standing ten feet away. He breaks eye contact and I start to speak. There is no reason for me to wait for him to tell me anything.

"Hey, I don't know what you've been doing but I know what I've been doing. I moved on. I can't live in that past anymore. I don't think about it, I don't dwell on it. It is shit that happened. It's over. It doesn't hurt anymore. I don't know what you're carrying around or what you're dealing with, but I moved on. If it helps to hear it, I forgive you. All right, I forgive you. It sucked, it hurt, but motherfucker, it is over. I've moved past it." I feel an instinct to reach out my right hand to shake his, but my sweaty water glass is in my hand and I don't think I want to touch this motherfucker anyway, so I just stand there.

He looks at me, kind of gaunt, kind of bewildered and says, meekly and with his eyes downward, "Thanks, thanks for saying that. I'm sorry about all of it. I really am."

"So am I," I say nodding my head in agreement, fairly certain there is nothing else to talk about. I turn and head back into the banquet. My sides tingle as I walk away, unsure if the feeling is panic or relief. My glass shakes in my hand as water spills out. My eyes water from what, I don't know, but I make sure Greg doesn't see. I don't look back and I don't say anything, just open the door to the banquet hall with my left hand and walk back in, drink in hand, and no one needs to know anything else.

Allison looks at me when I sit down and I smile back at her. She mouths, "You okay?"

I look back and say out loud, "Never better." On the stage a woman named Lindsey Sheehan Bradley is talking about her career at St. John's and University of Virginia. I concentrate on her words and try to listen, but my thoughts drift to Greg's eyes, his demeanor, his skin tone. He was big and strong and physical the last time I saw him, and now he is thin, looks weak and feeble. He seems unsteady, but I have no sympathy. He looks like he is fighting demons of some kind, but I don't care. He looks tired, but I feel refreshed. I don't know if there is anything else to do, but I don't plan on making any more amends. My days of carrying this shit around with me are over. I came to see my mother get in the Hall of Fame and I got a gift as well. The gift of forgiveness and the gift of a clearer conscience. The Lord does work in mysterious ways.

And then it hits me, I guess because I have not thought about it for so long or because I had buried it so deep. "How am I ever going to explain it to my kids?" Luke is five, Hank is three and Lindsay is one year old, precious little kids. They don't want to hear about that from their dad, they don't want to hear that *about* their dad. It would be incredibly scary to hear that about anyone, much less me. This story has so many layers I didn't know even existed. When you carry things for a long time, they become either a story in your life or become the story of your life. I've come to know this: life is a long, interesting, winding, funny, hopeful, loving, nostalgic story that is ever changing. My story has more chapters.

While there are many people who have played a critical role in any undertaking, I would like to especially thank those who have helped me in this one.

Thank you to Tim Corrigan and John Walsh, for listening, guiding and instructing me.

Thank you to Liza Dolan and Susan Frederick, for making a discombobulated endeavor into a streamlined experience.

Thank you to Mom, for giving me words of wisdom, tough love and a gentle touch, all at the time I needed them most.

Most especially, I want to thank Alysia, for being an inspiration, a beacon of light and a believer in us.

CPSIA information can be obtained
at www.ICGtesting.com
Printed in the USA
BVHW041456070421
604413BV00012B/276